Great Lakes Chronicle

*Funded by the Wisconsin Coastal Management Program and the
National Oceanic and Atmospheric Administration, Office for
Coastal Management under the Coastal Zone Management Act,
Grant # NA17NOS4190035.*

GREAT LAKES CHRONICLE

Essays on Coastal Wisconsin

FOREWORD BY SCOTT WALKER

GOVERNOR,

STATE OF WISCONSIN

Compiled and Edited by

JAMES M. LANGDON

WISCONSIN HISTORICAL SOCIETY PRESS

Published by the Wisconsin Historical Society Press
Publishers since 1855

The Wisconsin Historical Society helps people connect to the past by collecting, preserving, and sharing stories. Founded in 1846, the Society is one of the nation's finest historical institutions.
Join the Wisconsin Historical Society: wisconsinhistory.org/membership

Front cover image Cave Point, Jon Jarosh/Door County Visitor Bureau; back cover image Big Bay Town Park, Travis Olson
Printed in Canada
Designed by Mayfly Design
22 21 20 19 18   1 2 3 4 5

Library of Congress Cataloging-in-Publication Data
Names: Wisconsin Coastal Management Program, issuing body. | Walker, Scott (Scott
    Kevin), 1967– writer of foreword.
Title: Great Lakes chronicle : essays on coastal Wisconsin / Wisconsin Coastal
    Management Program ; foreword by Scott Walker, Governor, State of Wisconsin.
Description: Madison, Wisconsin : Wisconsin Historical Society Press, [2018] | Includes
    index. |
Identifiers: LCCN 2018028382 (print) | LCCN 2018030168 (ebook) | ISBN
    9780870209192 | ISBN 9780870209178 (case : alk. paper) | ISBN 9780870209185
    (pbk. : alk. paper)
Subjects: LCSH: Wisconsin Coastal Management Program. | Great Lakes (North
    America)—Management. | Coastal zone management—Wisconsin. | Conservation
    of natural resource--Great Lakes (North America) | Michigan, Lake—Environmental
    conditions. | Superior, Lake—Environmental conditions.
Classification: LCC HT392.5.G7 (ebook) | LCC HT392.5.G7 W568 2018 (print) | DDC
    333.91/709775—dc23
LC record available at https://lccn.loc.gov/2018028382

Contents

INTRODUCTION

Mike Friis

On the occasion of the Wisconsin Coastal Management Program's 40th anniversary, it is a great pleasure to present this publication to the people of Wisconsin. This compendium of essays first published in *Wisconsin Great Lakes Chronicle* from 2002 to 2018 presents successful projects and thoughtful analyses of issues impacting the health and vitality of Wisconsin's Lake Michigan and Lake Superior coasts from the past two decades.

Many of the essays that follow describe initiatives that were supported with financial and technical assistance from the Wisconsin Coastal Management Program (WCMP). The WCMP balances community development and economic growth in the areas of community planning, Great Lakes public access infrastructure, recreation and tourism, education, and resource protection and restoration.

The WCMP is part of a system of coastal management programs within every Great Lakes and oceanic state and territory. The structure that provides for the development and implementation of state-specific programs is the Coastal Zone Management Act (CZMA), a federal program that addresses local priorities within the construct of national programmatic priorities focused on the collective health our nation's coastal communities.

The CZMA was passed in 1972 and is funded through the National Oceanic and Atmospheric Administration and administered by its Office for Coastal Management. Wisconsin's program was among the first ten state programs created nationally and first in the Great Lakes. The WCMP was formally approved in 1978.

The WCMP sits as it always has in the Wisconsin Department of Administration where it has a strong connection to the state's executive branch and is networked with the various other state agencies and programs that deal with the diverse coastal management issues—transportation, tourism, economic development, education and resource protection. It is administered within the broader guidelines of the CZMA with implementation that is specific to the needs and issues of Wisconsin.

Wisconsin Great Lakes Chronicle—distributed each September—coincides with an annual proclamation by the Governor of Coastal Awareness Month. The intention of the *Chronicle* is to highlight the work of coastal managers and policy leaders, provide context to the importance of our coastal resources to the entire state, share information on emerging issues and feature the funded work of the WCMP.

At its inception, the *Chronicle* was a communication tool and report card on the activities of the WCMP. It has since documented the work of the WCMP and scores of our partners in coastal management. The *Chronicle* is also an educational piece that supports the public and local, state and federally-elected officials in growing their Great Lakes coastal literacy and the role of the WCMP.

Each edition of the *Chronicle* is printed in full color and contains at least two images per article that illustrate the content of story. The authors and their contact information at the time of publication are cited and projects approved for funding though the WCMP's grant program for that year are documented. All past issues are available online at the WCMP's website at www.coastal.wisconsin.gov.

This publication, *Great Lakes Chronicle: Essays on Coastal Wisconsin*, is a collection of 120 essays and articles by coastal management practitioners whose work is significant to the well-being of our Wisconsin's coasts. Authors in the compendium and each edition of the *Chronicle* represent a mix of coastal managers and policy leaders including local, state and federal government officials, researchers, community nonprofit leaders, elected officials and WCMP staff. The *Chronicle* strives for a balance of geographic representation and focuses on emerging and critical issues of the day.

Each *Chronicle* also includes a list of Wisconsin Coastal Management Council members serving at the time of publication. The Governor-appointed Council represents the diverse constituency for coastal resources and provides a strong voice to guide WCMP policy for the benefit of all areas of our coasts.

The *Chronicle* also recognizes WCMP staff who strive to efficiently and effectively implement the program. WCMP staff have grown the program by building networks and relationships within the state, region and nation, and their passionate work from Superior to Kenosha is well documented.

A name you will see in each original edition of *Wisconsin Great Lakes*

Chronicle is that of our editor, James Langdon. What is evident in the *Chronicle* is the vison required to see the importance of sharing these messages. His devotion to these messages and attention to detail is admirable.

While this compilation focuses on only seventeen years of essays, in a broader sense it illustrates the expansive work of the WCMP over the past forty years. The WCMP and its hundreds of partners in communities across Wisconsin's coasts have for decades dedicated themselves to creating a balanced approach to coastal management. These articles reflect changing stresses on our coastal regions and represent a long-standing community of people devoted to preserving and protecting our Lake Michigan and Lake Superior shores.

Like original editions of the *Chronicle*, this compendium is a reference material for future students, policy leaders and coastal managers. We offer it as a syllabus of projects, places and people who strove to better our Great Lakes resources and the quality of life in our state.

Mike Friis is the Director of the Wisconsin Coastal Management Program.

FOREWORD

Governor Scott Walker

For seventeen years, *Wisconsin Great Lakes Chronicle* has provided a forum for community leaders and coastal managers to write about issues of importance to Wisconsin's Lake Superior and Lake Michigan coasts. During this time the Chronicle has presented over 120 articles on topics such as economic development, community planning, transportation, recreation and stewardship.

This compendium of *Chronicle* essays from 2002 to 2018 is presented to school and public libraries across Wisconsin in commemoration of the fortieth anniversary of the Wisconsin Coastal Management Program (WCMP). The WCMP works with federal, regional and local partners in support of community planning, port and economic development, public access, water quality, hazard mitigation and other projects along our Lake Michigan and Lake Superior coasts.

This anniversary year is an appropriate time to recognize and celebrate the many people dedicated to the stewardship of Wisconsin's Great Lakes coasts because Lake Michigan and Lake Superior are among the most precious of our natural resources. These vast inland seas have for centuries provided clean water, transportation and economic development for Wisconsin residents.

Wisconsin Great Lakes Chronicle has told the stories of many who have gone beyond the call to ensure the health and prosperity of Wisconsin coasts. For example, in 2015 we learned about the restoration of the Cat Islands in Green Bay. This important project led by Brown County and the US Army Corps of Engineers used dredge material to restore a chain of islands damaged by waves in the 1970s. The result is a new line of islands that provide wave protection for the bay and habitat for waterfowl, fisheries and other wildlife.

The 2017 *Chronicle* described work to recover Saxon Harbor on the shores of Lake Superior. This important harbor of refuge was damaged in severe storms and flooding that swept northern Wisconsin in 2016.

Through the leadership of Iron County and other local officials, work is underway to restore Saxon Harbor as an economic, recreational and marine resource for the area.

In 2013, the *Chronicle* highlighted the work of several communities dedicated to providing clean beaches for residents and visitors. Projects in Racine, Milwaukee and Door County were acknowledged for implementing best practices to improve and maintain the beaches health. The article noted that clean beaches attract visitors to coastal counties and have a positive impact on the state's economy.

Wisconsin's ports were featured in a 2011 *Chronicle* article that underscored the importance of this infrastructure to Wisconsin coastal communities. Ports across our Lake Superior and Lake Michigan coasts support billions of dollars of economic activity and thousands of jobs for Wisconsin families. Local officials and port-related industries are working together to ensure these economic assets continue to serve as Wisconsin's gateways to world markets.

It is my privilege to thank the thousands of women and men who are devoting their time and talents to Wisconsin Great Lakes. I welcome readers of this compendium of their stories to draw knowledge and inspiration to undertake new initiatives that will ensure Wisconsin's Lake Michigan and Lake Superior coasts continue to be destinations and economic drivers for generations to come.

Scott Walker was elected Wisconsin's 45th Governor in 2010.

2002

Foreword

Governor Scott McCallum

Water is an integral part of the lives of Wisconsinites. Our history, culture, ecology and economy are rooted in our lakes, rivers and streams. No water bodies are more significant to our well-being than the Great Lakes.

Welcome to the inaugural *Wisconsin Great Lakes Chronicle*. This and future editions are intended to promote public awareness of Wisconsin Great Lakes issues, provide a vehicle for experts to educate public policy and opinion leaders, and create a historical record of Great Lakes events and perspectives.

The importance of the Great Lakes cannot be overstated. They are diverse ecosystems that provide habitat for aquatic animals and clean water for millions of persons. They connect Wisconsin farmers and manufacturers with global markets, and citizens and visitors alike with unique recreational opportunities.

It is for these reasons that I place a high priority on protecting the Great Lakes for this and succeeding generations. I am pleased to report that we are making significant progress on several fronts.

In May 2001, I signed into law a landmark wetland protection bill. Wisconsin was the first state to respond to a United States Supreme Court decision that narrowed the water and wetland areas subject to federal regulation. Today, Wisconsin protects precious isolated wetlands—including many in coastal areas—from being dredged or filled.

In June 2001, I added my signature to the Great Lakes Charter Annex. This agreement between Great Lakes states and provinces strengthens our ability to manage water resources and sets a framework for water diversion standards.

In August 2001, I signed legislation banning oil and gas drilling on the Great Lakes. While adequate energy resources are crucial, we must not pursue opportunities at the expense of the largest surface fresh water source in the world. Invasive plants and aquatic animals pose a significant risk to the Great Lakes and our inland waters. For that reason, I appointed Lt. Gov. Margaret Farrow to lead a Governor's Advisory Task Force on Invasive

Species. It evaluated the severity of invasives in Wisconsin and developed a plan to combat the introduction and spread of non-indigenous species.

In March 2002, my administration provided local and state agencies with nearly $7 million of federal coastal management funds to protect our Great Lakes shoreline.

I invite all Wisconsinites to join me in pressing forward with a full Great Lakes agenda. Together, we will restore fragile coastal areas, enhance water quality, improve the environmental and economic well-being of the coasts and meet future challenges to the prosperity of the Great Lakes.

Enjoy *Wisconsin Great Lakes Chronicle*, and thank you for your commitment to the Great Lakes and Wisconsin.

Scott McCallum served as Wisconsin's 43rd Governor from 2001 to 2003.

Why Coastal Management?

James M. Langdon

Coastal communities attract complex concentrations of commerce and foreign trade, intermodal transportation systems and population. They are home to sensitive and diverse terrestrial and aquatic ecosystems and marine-centered recreation. In addition, their special place exposes these communities to shoreline and maritime hazards not typically found inland.

The federal government recognized these unique characteristics when it established the Coastal Zone Management Act of 1972 (CZMA). Congress declared it was in the national interest to preserve, protect, develop, and where possible, to restore or enhance, the resources of the nation's coastal zone for this and succeeding generations.[1]

The National Oceanic and Atmospheric Administration (NOAA) supports state coastal management programs through financial assistance, technical services and information. This unique state-federal partnership leaves day-to-day management decisions to the 33 states and territories with federally approved programs.

Wisconsin established its Coastal Management Program (WCMP) in 1978. The program leverages the abilities of state agencies, regional planners, universities and local governments for the management of resources along the state's 820 miles of Lake Michigan and Lake Superior shoreline.

The fifteen Wisconsin counties along Lakes Superior and Michigan comprise 19% of the state's total area and 37% of its population.[2] If left unmanaged, pressures from coastal population growth would degrade water quality and wetlands, reduce sensitive habitats and limit opportunities for access to public waters. Coastal management fosters balance between development and natural resource protection through various means.

Financial Assistance. Coastal management grants encourage the protection and wise use of shoreline resources and increase the public's opportunity to enjoy the Great Lakes. The program emphasizes wetland protection and habitat restoration, nonpoint source pollution control and coastal land acquisition. It also promotes education, public access, historic preservation and community planning.

Wisconsin's coastal communities received a significant boost in 2001 when Congress provided $5.7 million on a one-time basis for restoration initiatives. Looking ahead to 2003 and beyond, the WCMP expects to allocate $1.3 million annually for local projects in the coastal zone.

Regulation. The CZMA provides state coastal management programs with authority to review proposed federal government activities in the coastal zone. These reviews ensure federal actions along Wisconsin's coasts take place in harmony with state law and policies. The program also develops a sound base of information used by state and local officials to guide resource management decisions.

Research. The University of Wisconsin System is a national leader in the study of critical coastal issues. Recent research addressed shoreline erosion, invasive species, coastal restoration and water quality. Coastal management connects local government with academic research to improve the Great Lakes environment.

Education. Great Lakes protection and preservation require the involvement of an enlightened citizenry. Coastal management informs the public of coastal issues and increases opportunities for citizen participation in decisions affecting Lakes Superior and Michigan.

Coastal Network. As a networked program in the Wisconsin Department of Administration, the WCMP acts as a facilitator among state agencies, local governments, regional planning commissions and others in the management of shoreline resources. This method of organization maximizes CZMA dollars for project work—not administrative overhead—and ensures the program balances environmental and economic development objectives.

Performance Indicators. In 2001, NOAA selected the WCMP as one of five state programs to develop recommended performance indicators for CZMA programs nationwide. Aided by this experience, the WCMP will monitor the health of Wisconsin's coastal zone by tracking wetland acreage, slope recession rates and other critical measures.

Diverse Coastal Leadership. A multidisciplinary council representing local governments, the Legislature, academia, state agencies, Indian tribes and the public plays an active role in coastal management issues. The Wisconsin Coastal Management Council (WCMC)—a Governor-appointed body—sets WCMP policies and direction, establishes annual funding priorities and recommends grants to state and local projects. The WCMC provides coastal stakeholders a forum for discussion of emerging and critical issues.

Outlook. The need for effective coastal management continues. Nationally, some large coastal metropolitan areas are consuming land ten times as fast as they are adding new residents. If today's land consumption trends continue, more than one quarter of the coast's acreage will be developed by 2025—up from 14 percent in 1997.[3]

Policy leaders are paying close attention to such projections. Congress is poised to reauthorize the CZMA in 2002, thus reaffirming its commitment to the nation's coastal resources. In addition, the US Commission on Ocean Policy will recommend a national policy on oceanic and coastal issues by 2003.

Wisconsin must blend the expertise of state and local stakeholders with federal funding and technical assistance to maintain equilibrium between ecosystem protection and anticipated development. Coastal management will continue to play an important role in preserving the resources of our Great Lakes.

In 2002, James M. Langdon was Director of the Bureau of Intergovernmental Relations, Wisconsin Department of Administration.

---

1. Coastal Zone Management Act of 1972.
2. Demographic Services Center, Wisconsin Department of Administration. 2001. 2001 Official Population Estimates.
3. Beach, D. 2002. Coastal Sprawl: The Effects of Urban Design on Aquatic Ecosystems in the United States. Pew Oceans Commission, Arlington, Virginia.

COASTAL HAZARDS

Alberto Vargas, Ph.D., and David Hart, Ph.D.

People are strongly attracted to the coast as a place to work, relax and live. Coastal areas were historically settled because of their role in the transportation of goods, military protection and the production of food and energy. In recent decades, coastal areas have attracted development for their aesthetic characteristics—as a scenic location to live and recreate. Unfortunately, development along the coast is also subject to a variety of natural hazards. The major natural hazards associated with Wisconsin's Great Lakes shoreline are erosion and flooding.

Coastal Erosion. Coastal erosion occurs naturally when land is lost due to wave action and surface runoff. As waves strike the shore and return to the lake, they carry sediment along the shore in a process known as littoral drift. High water levels and strong winds and waves expose new land surfaces to wave action and erosion. Erosion at the toe of vulnerable slopes destabilizes them and results in massive slumps of soil farther up the slope.

Surface and ground water flow resulting from heavy rainfall and the freezing and thawing of ice also cause slope erosion. In general, the erodible sections of the Lake Michigan shore occur from the Illinois state line to the Sturgeon Bay Canal, northeastern Brown County and smaller segments of bays and clay banks. On Lake Superior, erosive high clay bluffs stretch from Bark Point in Bayfield County to Wisconsin Point in Douglas County and from the eastern border of Iron County to the White River in Ashland County.[1]

Lake Levels. Coastal flooding along low-lying sections of the Great Lakes results from long-term increases in water levels or short-term storm surges and wind set-up. Water levels in the Great Lakes fluctuate on both a seasonal and long-term basis. Seasonally, the lowest levels occur during the winter—following evaporative losses in the fall and winter—when much of the precipitation is held on land as snow and ice. The highest seasonal levels are usually during the summer.

Long-term variation of lake levels depends on precipitation and evaporation trends in the Great Lakes watershed. The water volume of the Great

Lakes is large and outflow from natural outlets is limited. Flow regulation structures exist at the outlets from Lakes Ontario and Superior. However, structure size and the need to regulate water levels for multiple interests, including shipping, limit their influence.

Recent periods of high lake levels on Lake Michigan include 1972–76, 1983–87 and 1996–98. Since 1999, water levels on Lakes Michigan and Superior have been low. Areas on Lake Michigan vulnerable to coastal flooding include southern Kenosha County, northern Ozaukee and southern Sheboygan Counties, the western shore of Green Bay, and low-lying river mouths in urban areas. Vulnerable Lake Superior areas include sections of the City of Superior and coastal estuaries. Shoreland and riverine power, sewage treatment, water pumping and industrial plants, grain elevators, communication tunnels, storm sewer outlets and other infrastructure are also vulnerable when lake levels exceed the levels for which these facilities were designed.

Impact of Coastal Erosion. Coastal erosion and flooding cause millions of dollars of damage to coastal property and structures. Storms and high lake levels in 1987 resulted in $16 million of documented damage to public facilities alone. Experts speculate, however, that future damage may be even higher due to increased coastal development.

Most of the highly assessed land in Door County is along the coast. The assessed value of land and improvements that intersect the 1,000-foot shoreland zoning jurisdiction of Lake Michigan in Door County totaled over $1.9 billion in 1999.[2] In addition, smaller homes along the coast are being replaced with much larger homes.

Finally, urban infrastructure may be vulnerable to damage from high lake levels. Public works facilities and industrial plants sited many years ago incorporated design standards that are no longer adequate. Another illustration of the vulnerability of public infrastructure to bluff erosion is County Trunk Highway LS in northern Sheboygan County. A one-mile stretch of the highway is in jeopardy of being lost, and one segment is only six feet from the edge of the bluff.

Managing for Hazards. Managing for hazards is a priority of many coastal stakeholders. The Wisconsin Coastal Management Program (WCMP), University of Wisconsin Sea Grant Institute, State Cartographer's

Office, Wisconsin Department of Natural Resources (WDNR) and Wisconsin Emergency Management (WEM) formed a Coastal Hazards Work Group to provide technical assistance and coordinate state resources.

The Work Group determined that improved information was the most important factor in managing for coastal hazards. To that end, a multi-year strategy is being implemented to assist in developing the coastal hazards policy:

- Update and integrate information and methods in a geographic information system (GIS) compatible format.

- Develop a comprehensive education program regarding erosion rates and flood-prone areas directed at the public, government officials and the private sector.

- Develop an institutional framework to improve regulatory mechanisms and local mitigation efforts.

Since the mid-1970s, the WCMP and its partners have sought ways to address the issue of coastal hazards. An important legacy of this early work is the publication of a model ordinance and a state plan to deal with coastal erosion. About half of Wisconsin's coastal counties and a handful of municipalities have adopted some type of provision to regulate construction near the shoreline.

The official state policy for all shoreline development in Wisconsin specifies a 75-foot setback from the ordinary high water mark set primarily for environmental and scenic beauty protection. However, this setback is not always appropriate to prevent damage from coastal erosion in the Great Lakes. One priority for the Work Group is to assist coastal municipalities and regional planning commissions to agree upon appropriate shoreline development provisions that minimize potential damages due to coastal erosion.

Hazards Mitigation. The Work Group also contributed to the inclusion of coastal hazards in the State Hazards Mitigation Plan coordinated by WEM. This plan, which is in the process of receiving Federal Emergency Management Agency (FEMA) approval, sets the framework for the development and implementation of mitigation measures aimed at preventing—rather than responding to—natural hazards in the state. The WCMP and its partners are doing their part to support local mitigation plans that include coastal hazards as an important element.

In addition, a long-term project to assess the economic impact of fluctuating water levels in the Great Lakes is being coordinated by the Army Corps of Engineers, Detroit District. In cooperation with the University of Wisconsin, WCMP, WDNR, private consultants and State of Michigan agencies, the Corps has organized the Lake Michigan Potential Damages Study (LMPDS).

The objective of the LMPDS is to create a modeling procedure and engineering-management tool for estimating economic effects of lake level changes and related social, environmental and cultural impacts. The LMPDS modeling approaches are expected to be the framework for economic assessments for each of the other Great Lakes. It is also intended to be a forum for concerted information system development between international, federal, state and local governance about the resource base that is commonly shared.[3]

Several state and local benefits should result from the LMPDS project, including better tools to predict lakeshore erosion and improved availability of erosion data. Nature has the greatest role in determining lake levels, although regulation of outflows at Superior and Ontario has some influence. However, reducing economic and environmental losses from variable lake levels must involve improved local land use planning to minimize erosion risks to lakeshore development.

Wisconsin's Great Lakes coast is a privileged area of extreme natural beauty that ought to be protected for the enjoyment of this and future generations.

In 2002, David Hart was a GIS Specialist for the University of Wisconsin-Madison Sea Grant Institute. Alberto Vargas was the Natural Hazards Coordinator for the Wisconsin Coastal Management Program. The authors thanked Phillip J. Keillor, UW Sea Grant Institute, and Marie Strum, US Army Corps of Engineers, for their assistance.

1. Springman, Roger, and Stephen M. Born. 1979. Wisconsin's Shore Erosion Plan: An Appraisal of Options and Strategies. Madison, WI: Wisconsin Geological and Natural History Survey. Pp. 6–11.
2. Hart, David. 2000. Building a Horizontally and Vertically Integrated Coastal GIS Using Local Governmental Spatial Data: The Case of Coastal Erosion Hazards on the Lake Michigan Coast of Wisconsin. Ph.D. Dissertation. University of Wisconsin-Madison.
3. US Army Corps of Engineers, Detroit District; (www.huron.lre.usace.army.mil/ coastal/ LMPDS/index.html)

Wisconsin Commercial Ports

Dean R. Haen

Wisconsin accesses world markets through fifteen commercial ports located along Lake Superior, Lake Michigan and the Mississippi River. The ports of Wisconsin transport over 40 million metric tons of cargo annually. The cargo consists of coal, grain, cement, steel, iron ore, liquid asphalt, limestone, pig iron, salt, fuel oil, wood pulp and many other important commodities that are valued at over $7 billion each year. The larger ports of Superior, Milwaukee and Green Bay have an annual economic impact of over $200 million within their local economies.

Wisconsin ports are critical to our state's transportation system and serve as multi-modal links that move cargo throughout the state. Wisconsin as a whole benefits from the port industry. Commodities moved through ports are essential for our state's power plants, paper mills, manufacturers, farmers, governments and consumers.

Waterborne transportation is the safest and most environmentally friendly means of transporting cargo. Fuel consumption and emissions are substantially reduced when cargoes are transported by ship rather than rail or truck. A modal shift from water to trucks or railcars would alter our quality of life in Wisconsin.

For example, at least 16 million tons of coal per year are loaded onto ships at Superior for transport to eastern Great Lakes ports. This avoids many trainloads of coal destined for Detroit Edison facilities that would otherwise travel rail routes through Wisconsin. Transporting via water avoids the consumption of an estimated 32 million gallons of fuel and the release of 5,120 tons of exhaust emissions annually. Additionally, waterborne transportation reduces the number of at-grade railroad crossing events with cars and trucks.

Even though ports support an economical and environmentally responsible mode of transportation, there is an immediate need for long-range sustainability planning. Land use surrounding existing ports has shifted from predominately industrial and commercial uses to conflicting residential and recreational uses that threaten or impede the operation of port facilities. As a result, many coastal communities no longer serve as operating commercial ports.

The overall loss of commercial ports increases Wisconsin's dependency on our remaining ports. These ports must be commercially active if our state is to maintain its economic stability.

In 2002, Dean R. Haen was Port Manager of the Brown County Port & Solid Waste Department (Port of Green Bay) and President of the Wisconsin Commercial Ports Association.

GREAT LAKES CHALLENGES

Secretary Darrell Bazzell

Many homeowners are following a trend of installing backyard ponds to enjoy the benefits of water. As they care for their ponds, they soon learn the importance of maintaining the miniecosystem they have created. If a particular element of the system gets out of balance, it affects everything from water quality to the survival of plants and fish. The job of managing the system is one that never ends.

The same lessons apply to the Great Lakes ecosystems. Despite major success in cleaning and restoring the Great Lakes over the past few decades, there remains the need for continuing attention and care. Remediation of contaminated sediment and the problems associated with invasive species represent two major areas of current effort.

Contaminated Sediments. Contaminated sediment is part of the legacy of past discharges that deposited harmful chemicals such as polychlorinated biphenyls (PCBs) in the Great Lakes and their tributaries. Of the 42 Great Lakes Areas of Concern, 40 areas—including the Fox, Sheboygan, Menominee, St. Louis and Milwaukee Rivers in Wisconsin—have problems associated with contaminated sediment. Wisconsin has seen tremendous improvements in water quality by eliminating pollution sources. However, contaminated bottom sediments continue to release harmful chemicals, and fish consumption advisories are still issued for portions of the Great Lakes and some tributaries.

The State of Wisconsin has made it a priority to clean up contaminated sediments. Several actions from completing cleanup plans to active remediation are underway along Wisconsin's coasts. Experience tells us that the job of cleanup is costly, difficult and more expensive than prevention measures. Progress is being made and we are confident of further improvement to the Great Lakes as more implementation occurs.

Invasive Species. Since 1810, more than 140 species of fish, plants, invertebrates, algae and pathogens have been introduced into the Great Lakes. The spread and impacts of invasive species—especially aquatic exotics—pose a second challenge to the Great Lakes.

Many exotic species threaten the diversity or abundance of native species, the ecological stability of aquatic habitats and recreational activities. Invaders take over new waters because their natural predators are not present, and native species are not able to hide from them, compete with them or fight back. Once in Lakes Michigan and Superior, many of these species can be inadvertently transported into Wisconsin's inland waters.

Several aquatic invasive species were initially introduced to the Great Lakes through the ballast water of ships and by migrating from the ocean via man-made canals. Additionally, recreational boating, sport fish stocking and accidental releases associated with the aquaculture industry, aquarium trade, bait businesses and horticultural practices continue the introduction and spread of aquatic exotics.

Once aquatic invasive species become established in a water body, they are difficult to manage and nearly impossible to eliminate. For these reasons, the Wisconsin Department of Natural Resources focuses on teaching people to prevent the spread of exotic species. The goal is to change boaters' behavior by educating them on their role in maintaining clean waters. The Department's message is "Clean Boats, Clean Waters."

There are many reasons to care about aquatic exotics and support efforts to stop their spread. Even the smallest aquatic invasive species can have big economic impacts. Zebra mussels attach to virtually any available surface—including boats—and have been known to clog water intake pipes. Large water users in the Great Lakes, including municipalities and industries, spent about $120 million from 1989 to 1994 to combat the spread of zebra mussels. As this species continues to spread, the cost to raw water users will continue to increase. Zebra mussels also illustrate the ecological impacts of aquatic exotics. These invaders reproduce and spread rapidly, consume microscopic plants and animals, affect the food web and decimate native clam/mussel populations.

Aquatic exotics can also affect the recreational uses of a water body. Eurasian water milfoil displaces native aquatic plants and forms thick mats that interfere with boating, swimming and fishing.

In response to problems caused by aquatic invasive species, Governor McCallum established a Task Force on Invasive Species in July 2001 to address the invasive species problem in Wisconsin and create guidelines for future efforts. In its final report to the Governor in January 2002, the Task Force recommended:

- The statutory creation of a statewide invasive species program to combat the introduction and spread of invasive species.

- The creation of an Invasive Species Council to oversee the state program and communicate and coordinate activities among state agencies.

- The establishment of a program director that would serve as Wisconsin's point person on invasive species.

- The implementation of regional ballast water regulations and promotion of a Great Lakes regional invasive species strategy.

The Wisconsin Legislature enacted regulations aimed at reducing their spread. These new rules—which took effect in May 2002—prohibit launching a boat, trailer or boating equipment in navigable waters if aquatic plants are attached or if a law enforcement officer has reason to believe that zebra mussels are attached. The Department received $300,000 funding from the state for initiatives including a watercraft inspection program and a campaign to inform boaters of the new regulations and instruct them on how to clean their boats properly.

As part of the next budget cycle, the Department seeks additional funding to implement the recommendations of the Governor's Task Force.

In 2002, Darrell Bazzell was Secretary of the Wisconsin Department of Natural Resources.

MANAGING THE BAD RIVER
OF LAKE SUPERIOR

Rae Ann Maday

The Treaty of September 30, 1854, between the United States Government and the Bad River Band of Lake Superior Chippewa Indians established the original boundaries of the Bad River Indian Reservation. The 125,000-acre Reservation is located in parts of Ashland and Iron Counties in northern Wisconsin. Approximately 77% of the Reservation is forested, 11% consists of wetlands and sloughs, and the remainder is covered by farmland, residential communities and roads.

The Reservation has approximately 40 miles of Lake Superior shoreline and over 100 miles of navigable rivers and streams flowing into Lake Superior via the Bad, White, Marengo and Kakagon Rivers. Approximately 200 acres of Reservation land are on Madeline Island, the only Apostle Island not included in the Apostle Islands National Lakeshore. At the mouth of the Kakagon and Bad Rivers is the most extensive, least disturbed, fully functioning estuary on the south shore of Lake Superior. The Kakagon and Bad River Sloughs are hosts to the largest wild rice beds in the state, long considered an asset by the tribe.

The Bad River Band has a Natural Resources Department that consists of 16 fulltime and 15 seasonal employees. The fulltime staff includes a Natural Resources Manager, Fisheries Specialist, Lake Superior Fishery Specialist, Wildlife Specialist, Forestry Technician, Watershed Coordinator, Air Quality Specialist, Wetlands Specialist, Water Resources Specialist, Water Resources Technician, GIS Specialist and two Conservation Wardens. The Department staff are involved in many projects within their respective disciplines.

Water Resources. The Water Resources Office is responsible for developing the qualitative and quantitative standards for water resources on the Reservation. Once these projects are complete, the Bad River Tribe will have a complete picture of the water resources on the Reservation.

The following projects are an example of the type of research necessary to accomplish this goal.

- Baseline water quality monitoring began in 1997 with the five-year baseline completed in July, 2002. Sampling is done at 22 different sites on Reservation waters. The parameters monitored in the field are temperature, dissolved oxygen, conductivity and pH. Additional tests are conducted in the tribal water lab to determine hardness, dissolved solids, total solids, turbidity, phosphate, nitrate, fecal coliform and E. coli. Although the preliminary results show fairly clean water, there is concern about elevated levels of fecal coliform.

- Macroinvertebrate monitoring was begun in 1998. Analytical metrics used include Hilsenhoff Biotic Index (HBI), taxa richness, Ephemeroptera/ Plecoptera/Tricoptera (EPT) richness, percent EPT, percent dominance and percent chironomids. The five-year baseline of invertebrate data will be reached in 2003. The indicator species so far suggest that the waters on the Reservation are healthy.

- A wetland nutrient investigation just completed the first year of a five-year study.

- A five-year sloughs flow study began in 2000. No results are yet available.

Fish Hatchery. The Bad River Tribe owns and operates a fish hatchery established in 1975. The fishery is a highly valued resource to tribal members for cultural, social, subsistence and recreational purposes. Although Reservation waters are hosts to many species of fish, the walleye is the one most valued by the membership. Therefore, the fish hatchery focuses on raising walleye for restocking into the Kakagon and Bad Rivers.

In 2001, the fish hatchery received a grant to replace worn and outdated equipment. The grant also allowed for the purchase and installation of 40 solar panels and a wind generator. The improvements greatly enhance the economic efficiency of the hatchery, and will help to replenish a resource used heavily by both members and nonmembers. Another fish that is significant to the Bad River is the lake sturgeon. Only three rivers in United States waters of Lake Superior support a self-sustaining population of lake sturgeon. In 2001, an intense monitoring program was begun to estimate the population of this species.

Integrated Resources Management Plan. In April 2001, the Bad River Tribal Council formally adopted an Integrated Resources Management Plan (IRMP). The goal of the IRMP is to maintain a diversity of forest types within the Reservation while protecting and improving water quality. The management principles promote sustainability of the resource while establishing a buffer along riparian areas. Timber harvesting has a long history on the Reservation and has promoted extensive aspen regeneration. In order to maintain biodiversity on the Reservation, the Tribe has made a priority of promoting old growth and reseeding of white pines in areas that have recently been harvested.

A number of wildlife resources are monitored annually on the Bad River Reservation, and many are related to coastal issues. Presently monitored are wetland and riparian raptors—bald eagle, merlin and northern harriers. Also monitored are many other wetland and riparian avian species including colonial birds (e.g., great blue herons, black tern), piping plover, trumpeter swan and other waterfowl.

Important near shore mammals related to the aquatic food chain or those that exhibit aquatic terrestrial food chain linkages—such as river otter, mink, beaver and muskrat—are monitored on a periodic basis. Many of the Tribe's monitoring programs were initiated through Wisconsin Coastal Management Program funding.

Air Quality. The latest program added to the Natural Resources Department is the Air Quality Program. Initiated in November 2000, monitoring is done on an arduous six-day schedule using a PM10 monitor. A five-year baseline study will be completed in 2005.

The Bad River Tribe has made great strides in protecting resources for today and seven generations hence.

In 2002, Rae Ann Maday was Watershed Coordinator for the Natural Resources Department of the Bad River Band of Lake Superior Chippewa Indians.

PROTECTING COASTAL WETLANDS ON THE DOOR PENINSULA

Cate Harrington

Caressed by the waters of Lake Michigan to the east and Green Bay to the west, the Door Peninsula is a slender piece of land than juts 80 miles into Lake Michigan. Its nearly 250 miles of shoreline, sheltered bays, sand beaches, towering bluffs and inland lakes attract thousands of visitors each year.

The Nature Conservancy was drawn to the peninsula 40 years ago to protect the natural features of this special place that is home to the greatest number of rare plants and animals in Wisconsin.

Stand on Toft Point and one can see or hear nine different warblers singing. In the deep shade of the white cedars, one will find wild orchids—with names like ram's head, showy lady, dragon mouth and Hooker's—growing in sunlit patches. The dwarf lake iris and dune thistle are found only in the Great Lakes area. Moreover, the world's largest remaining population of the endangered Hine's emerald dragonfly depends on marshes and sedge meadows fed by the calcium-rich waters of the peninsula.

Focus on Coastal Wetlands. In 1962, the Conservancy made a loan to The Ridges Sanctuary to preserve a critical parcel of coastal wetland. Today, we continue work with multiple partners and communities to protect this special place. As a result of planning in April 2000 by Conservancy staff, other conservation organizations, the academic community and state and federal agencies, we focus the majority of our time and resources on protecting wetlands along the Lake Michigan coast.

The places where the Conservancy works include the Mink River Estuary on Rowley's Bay, the area around Mud Lake, The Ridges Sanctuary and North Bay, the north end of Kangaroo Lake, and the diverse complex of wetlands between Cave Point and the Sturgeon Bay ship canal.

Unique Geology Affects Water Flow. Because of the peninsula's unique geology, it is a fragile place and wetlands are particularly vulnerable. The Door Peninsula is underlain by a portion of the Niagara Escarpment, a rock formation that arcs around the northern shores of Lakes Michigan and Huron from West Union, Iowa, to Albany, New York.

Much of the escarpment is underground, but rises above the surface at certain locations including very prominently along the Green Bay side of the peninsula. Because this side of the peninsula tends to be higher than the Lake Michigan side, surface water also tends to drain from the peninsula toward the lakeside. The rock that forms the escarpment is dolomite—it is hard, brittle and very porous due to the many holes and cracks within the rock.

When snow melts or rain hits the ground on the peninsula, some of the water runs off the surface and into nearby streams to be carried to the lake. Another portion of the water is captured by soil and vegetation. Where soils are thin, as they are in northern Door County, more of the water travels through the soil and down into bedrock. Because the rock tends to be porous, water travels quickly to the lake or into wetlands via springs.

Effect of Pollution on Wetlands. Where water goes, pollution follows. Oil, salt and other chemicals on roads, driveways and other impervious surfaces end up in the water. Water is at risk from pesticides, herbicides and fertilizers applied to lawns, golf courses and roadsides. Acid pollutants in the air from automobiles and manufacturing plants and waste from failed septic systems threaten water. That water flows into streams, the bedrock, underground aquifers, wetlands and the lake.

Migratory birds that use the wetlands as stopover feeding sites during migration are impacted by pollution, as are frogs, turtles and fish that feed and breed there. Additional nutrients added to the wetlands can change the type of vegetation found there. What was once a wetland dominated by sedges and bulrushes may eventually become a cattail marsh, a plant community not unique to the area. While we know that the federally endangered Hine's emerald dragonfly uses the wetlands unique to the Door Peninsula, we do not know how it will respond if those wetlands change.

Strength in Numbers. Many conservation organizations and public agencies are working to conserve the wetlands and other natural features of the Door Peninsula. Groups including The Nature Conservancy, the Door County Land Trust (DCLT), The Ridges Sanctuary, Door County, the US Fish & Wildlife Service and the Wisconsin Department of Natural Resources (WDNR) collaborate to address threats to the peninsula's wetlands and other natural features. Land acquisition, conservation easements, education and outreach, and research are some of the methods employed.

Together and separately, The Nature Conservancy, DCLT, The Ridges Sanctuary and the WDNR have received a North American Wetlands Conservation Act grant and four Coastal Wetlands Planning, Protection and Restoration Act grants from the federal government totaling $2.62 million. The partners will use this money and match raised through private fundraising to buy and protect wetlands along the Lake Michigan shoreline of Door County and in the Grand Traverse Islands located at the end of the peninsula.

Wisconsin Coastal Management Program grants fund other partner efforts to communicate the importance of protecting wetlands in Door County to local government officials and private landowners and address threats that non-native invasive plants like purple loosestrife pose to wetlands and other native plant communities on the peninsula.

To maintain the health and diversity of the peninsula's wetlands and restore those that have been degraded, more information is needed. The Conservancy is funding a research study by a University of Wisconsin-Green Bay graduate student at the Shivering Sands Preserve east of Sturgeon Bay that will provide vital information.

When the study is completed in December 2003, we plan to make this information available to Door County conservation and planning departments, local township governments, the WDNR and other interested parties. The Ridges Sanctuary also conducts studies to gather baseline information about water flow at the sanctuary.

In 2002, Cate Harrington was Director of Communications & Outreach for The Nature Conservancy-Wisconsin Chapter.

WISCONSIN COASTAL POPULATION TRENDS

Donald R. Harrier

The rates of population growth in Wisconsin coastal counties varied by location since 1970. This article examines population trends in Wisconsin's coastal zone during the preceding three decades and factors that led to growth and contraction.

Most Coastal Counties Gain. Between 1970 and 2000, Wisconsin's total population grew by 945,854 persons, or 21.4 percent. The 15 Wisconsin coastal counties collectively gained 78,000 persons, or 4.1 percent, from 1970 to 2000.

Ozaukee County grew fastest during the period at 51.1 percent. Brown County added the most population with 68,000 new residents. Milwaukee County both declined most rapidly (10.8 percent) and lost the most residents (114,000). Only Milwaukee and Douglas Counties lost population during the thirty-year period.

The Bay-Lake counties (Marinette, Oconto, Brown, Door, Kewaunee, Manitowoc and Sheboygan) grew fastest from 1970–2000 at 112,000 persons and 25.6 percent. Lake Superior counties (Douglas, Bayfield, Ashland and Iron) grew at a modest 3.0 percent and 2,400 residents. The Southeastern counties (Ozaukee, Milwaukee, Racine and Kenosha) declined by 2.6 percent and 37,000 persons.

Milwaukee County's experience tends to skew overall coastal population trends. Coastal counties exclusive of Milwaukee grew by 192,000 persons, or 22.3 percent, over the thirty-year period. That rate of growth outpaced the statewide trend.

Mixed Migration Trends During 1970s. During the 1970s, Wisconsin experienced a population increase of 6.51 percent. Natural increase (births minus deaths) during this decade was 277,693 persons and net in-migration was only 10,128 persons. In addition, Wisconsin followed a national trend called the "rural renaissance" when growth in smaller communities outpaced more urban areas.

Wisconsin's coastal counties decreased by nearly 33,000 persons or 1.71 percent during the same period. Milwaukee County led the decline with a migration loss of nearly 155,000 persons. The remaining coastal counties experienced net in-migration of about 7,000 persons.

The seventies saw population change vary widely between the three coastal areas. The Lake Superior region showed an increase of 2.69 percent. The population of the Bay-Lake region outpaced the state average with a 7.85 percent increase. These were in contrast to a decline of 4.95 percent in the Southeastern region.

Out-Migration in Much of the 1980s. During the 1980s, state population grew by only 3.96 percent. Although natural increase was 313,123, net migration showed a loss of nearly 127,000 persons. Most of the state's out-migration occurred during the deep recession of the early and mid 1980s.

Milwaukee County alone experienced net outmigration of over 75,000 for the period. Only three of the 15 coastal counties (Brown, Marinette and Ozaukee) experienced net in-migration during the eighties. However, natural increase was significant enough that the coastal counties gained nearly 26,000 persons during the decade.

Again, population change differed among the three regions. The Lake Superior region lost 4.32 percent of its population from 1980–1990, while the Bay-Lake region increased by 4.72 percent. The Southeastern region experienced only a marginal gain of 0.53 percent. Each region experienced natural increase and out-migration.

Rebound of Migration in the 1990s. During the 1990s, Wisconsin's population increased by a robust 9.65 percent. The decade experienced the smallest natural increase of the 30-year period because of fewer births and a larger number of deaths. However, the most significant trend during the 1990s was a turnaround in migration with 228,219 more people moving into the state than moving out.

The impact of natural increase and positive net migration yielded the greatest increase of the three decades. In fact, the 1990s were the second fastest growing decade in the state's history, only trailing the 1950s.

All three regions experienced population growth during the decade. The Bay-Lake region set the pace at 11.18 percent, the Lake Superior region increased by 4.86 percent and the Southeastern region grew at a modest

1.91 percent in spite of a nearly 9 percent decline in Milwaukee County population.

Although population growth was slower in the coastal counties than for the state, the increase was still significant. The coastal counties added nearly 85,000 persons or 4.44 percent during the nineties. They collectively suffered out-migration of more than 25,000 persons, again led by Milwaukee County.

Conclusion. Wisconsin's population increased by 21.4 percent between 1970 and 2000, but Wisconsin's coastal counties increased by only 4.1 percent. Slower growth in the coastal counties reduced their share of the state's total population from 43.3 percent in 1970 to just over 37 percent in 2000.

Much of the lower population increase of the coastal area resulted from the decline of Milwaukee County's population during 30-year period. Without Milwaukee County's figures, Wisconsin's coastal counties grew by a more robust 22.3 percent from 1970 to 2000.

Today, over two-thirds of Wisconsin's coastal counties' population resides in the Southeastern region, 28 percent in the Bay-Lake region and just 4 percent in the Lake Superior region. The Southeastern region, and Milwaukee County in particular, remains the most significant driver of population trends in Wisconsin's coastal counties.

In 2002, Donald R. Harrier was Section Chief of the Demographic Services Center, Wisconsin Department of Administration.

2003

FOREWORD

Governor Jim Doyle

Dear Friend of Wisconsin's Great Lakes:

In 2003—Wisconsin's Year of Water and the 25th anniversary of the Wisconsin Coastal Management Program—I am pleased to join citizens from around the state in celebrating and safeguarding our greatest natural resource, the Great Lakes.

Lake Michigan and Lake Superior have profoundly influenced Wisconsin's history. Today, Wisconsinites continue to rely upon these major waterways for leisure, clean water, unique wildlife and international commerce.

While our Great Lakes and their coastlines remain particularly vulnerable to environmental degradation, I am pleased to report that we are making significant progress toward a cleaner, healthier Great Lakes system. Here are examples to date:

- The Wisconsin Department of Natural Resources and the US Environmental Protection Agency recently released the Record of Decision on the plan for cleaning PCB-contaminated sediment from a 13-mile portion of the Lower Fox River. After decades of study, discussion and debate spanning several administrations, we are finally poised to move forward with the cleanup of the Fox River.

- The Wisconsin Coastal Management Program and its partners together provided $13 million for the acquisition, cleanup and restoration of lands along Lakes Michigan and Superior. Cleaner, more vibrant Great Lakes benefit all Wisconsinites. These projects protect wetlands, restore critical habitat and enhance public access to our state's coasts.

- In 1990, Congress required coastal states to create nonpoint pollution control programs. After more than a decade of effort,

Wisconsin's coastal nonpoint program gained approval from the National Oceanic & Atmospheric Administration and the US Environmental Protection Agency. Today, Wisconsin's program serves as a national model that addresses nonpoint source pollution from urban impacts, marinas, forestry, agriculture, and hydromodification.

The coasts and water we protect today will benefit our children for years to come. However, we must also help our children build a foundation of knowledge that enables them to continue our work. To that end, the Wisconsin Coastal Management Program celebrated its 25th anniversary by giving a special version of the classic children's book *Paddle-to-the-Sea* to the state's elementary school and public libraries. The book inspires our children—and their parents—to enjoy and protect Wisconsin's Great Lakes.

Wisconsin's Great Lakes shaped our history and will sustain us in the future. Working together, we will ensure that the waters of Lakes Michigan and Superior will be clean and accessible in the decades to come.

Enjoy this year's edition of *Wisconsin Great Lakes Chronicle*.

Jim Doyle served as Wisconsin's 44th Governor from 2003 to 2011.

WISCONSIN LOVES ITS GREAT LAKES

Jane Elder

In 2002, a public opinion research project commissioned by the Biodiversity Project examined public attitudes about the Great Lakes. The Great Lakes study included focus groups in Milwaukee, Grand Rapids, Michigan, and Columbus, Ohio. It also included interviews with policy makers and a 1,500-sample telephone survey across Illinois, Indiana, Michigan, Minnesota, Ohio, Wisconsin, and portions of New York and Pennsylvania.

What have we learned?

Wisconsinites love their Great Lakes. Although Michigan leads the pack in public fervor for this amazing resource, Wisconsin is not far behind in regional appreciation for the Great Lakes. More importantly, state residents feel a sense of responsibility to care for them.

A Source of State Pride. Wisconsin residents take pride in the breathtaking beauty and mystique of their natural resources, particularly the Great Lakes.

Roughly one quarter of Wisconsinites say the Great Lakes are "one of the reasons I live here," and 77 percent acknowledge that the Lakes are "vital to the economy of the region." This tells us that people who live near the Great Lakes recognize the recreational and economic importance of the resource. Not surprisingly, those who live closest to the Lakes and those who visit them frequently were among the most concerned about their fate.

Great Lakes beaches and parks are popular destinations for Wisconsin residents. Across the region, 57 percent of adults said they had been to a beach or park on one of the Great Lakes within the last year. Whether hiking along the Lake Superior shoreline, boating on Lake Michigan or just strolling on a beach, residents take advantage of Wisconsin's access to these magnificent bodies of water.

Of particular interest, Wisconsin citizens trust their leaders and neighbors to be good stewards of the Lakes. During a Wisconsin focus group in a separate study last summer, a woman responded to a question about beach closings in this way: "Well, you'd expect something like that in Illinois, but not around here!" People recognize that the state has special places that families return to from one generation to the next and the commitment to take care of Wisconsin's natural beauty and resources helps make them special.

A Sense of Responsibility. Not surprisingly, this deep appreciation for the state's natural resources leads Wisconsin residents to regard the Great Lakes and other water resources as cherished treasures, not commodities.

Wisconsinites sense that these treasures belong to everyone, and therefore all share a responsibility to protect them. The notion that water could be commercialized or privately owned, or that Great Lakes protection is someone else's problem, is antithetical to Wisconsin values. Instead, a sense of the common good and protecting their children's future overrides personal privilege and private interests.

Can Something so "Great" be so Vulnerable? It is heartening to know that people appreciate the remarkable Great Lakes, but many residents do not grasp that there are serious threats to the ecosystem—threats that go well beyond pollution.

The survey showed that Great Lakes residents, including Wisconsin respondents, understand some threats to the Great Lakes. Toxic pollution leads the list with zebra mussels and invasive species not far behind. However, other dangers to the Lakes are poorly understood.

For example, people in the focus groups were largely unaware of the relationship between groundwater and surface water in the region. People who depend on well water understand concepts such as the water table better than people who drink city water. However, the impact of groundwater depletion on the Great Lakes—especially on near-shore or upstream habitat—simply is not yet on the radar screen. This is a particular challenge in Wisconsin where many communities just beyond the Great Lakes basin consume groundwater at rates that may pull water out of underground sources that supply the Great Lakes. This can affect everything from temperatures and water flow in trout streams to water supply for shoreline marshes and other important nesting and breeding areas.

Without the knowledge that a serious problem exists, many citizens will not see the need to act. However, research in the last several months indicates that a substantial portion of Wisconsin residents understand that groundwater shortages cause more communities to look for ways to tap directly into the Great Lakes.

What Next? To protect the Great Lakes they love, Wisconsin residents must gain a better understanding of the threats to these natural wonders.

In January 2002, the Joyce Foundation announced plans to invest $16 million over the next three years to support efforts to protect Great Lakes water resources. As a key component of this investment, the Biodiversity Project initiated an 18-month public education campaign in the region to improve Great Lakes ecological literacy.

During the campaign, the Biodiversity Project will target a few key topics and messages to help close critical gaps in public understanding regarding Great Lakes ecological issues, such as the role that groundwater plays in keeping the Lakes healthy. We will first test our public outreach campaign in Wisconsin. Then we hope to incorporate it in a broader campaign across the Great Lakes region.

The goals are ambitious, but the stakes for the Lakes are high. After all, unlike beach closings, having Wisconsin residents informed, engaged and active in Great Lakes protection is something you'd expect around here.

In 2003, Jane Elder was Executive Director of the Biodiversity Project.

RESTORING COASTAL RESOURCES
IN WISCONSIN

Travis Olson

The Great Lakes have been subject to intense human use for the past two centuries. Several restoration efforts underway in Wisconsin address the legacy of industrial pollution and the conversion of natural ecosystems to agricultural and urban uses. The Wisconsin Coastal Management Program (WCMP)—guided by the Wisconsin Coastal Management Council—leads efforts to improve the state's coasts. The program encourages and supports acquisition, planning, education, remediation and ecological restoration initiatives taken by many state and local organizations.

Protecting Wisconsin's Coastal Legacy. Public acquisition permanently protects coastal resources and provides an opportunity to reduce further habitat degradation. It increases access to unique coastal ecosystems and provides future opportunities for resource management and ecological restoration. The WCMP has provided grants to acquire several significant coastal properties.

The Lion's Den Gorge Nature Preserve in Ozaukee County provides access to nearly a mile of the Lake Michigan coast. The preserve now occupies one of the last undeveloped lakeshore parcels between Port Washington and the Illinois state line. The high bluffs and spectacular gorge leading to the lake provide important natural habitats that benefit southeastern Wisconsin. Ozaukee County will soon restore a wetland on the site using additional WCMP funds.

Critical coastal wetlands on the west shore of Green Bay protect water quality and provide bird and wildlife habitat. The fisheries of Green Bay depend on these wetlands and adjacent streams. As part of a larger effort to restore fisheries and water quality, the Department of Natural Resources (DNR) acquired several Green Bay wetlands and streamside properties with WCMP grants. These acquisitions complement the intensive clean up and restoration of the Fox River and its estuary at Green Bay.

Community Involvement. Coastal communities and residents face special challenges and opportunities due to their proximity to the Great Lakes. The WCMP encourages communities to prepare for their future and actively participate in coastal management through comprehensive planning, education and other coastal conservation activities.

Lake Superior is a point of pride for the City of Bayfield. Community members recently adopted a comprehensive plan to guide the city's future. The plan recommends maintaining the small town character and natural features that attract visitors and residents. It promotes development of an integrated economy with diverse housing opportunities. The plan establishes a framework that will enable Bayfield to thrive as a place in which to live, work and visit.

The entire Lake Michigan coast receives the attention of an ever-growing number of private conservation organizations. The Lake Michigan Shorelands Alliance—a project of Gathering Waters Conservancy—collaborates with land trusts that develop priorities for land conservation in coastal areas. One of these trusts, the Ozaukee Washington Land Trust, recently joined the DNR and the WCMP to restore Huiras Lake in Ozaukee County.

Restoring Urban Coasts. Our Great Lakes cities boast a long history of economic development that depends on a coastal location. The legacy of this history unfortunately includes intense contamination of land and water from industrial and other urban facilities. The WCMP works in conjunction with several local, state and federal agencies that clean up brownfields and polluted waterways.

The Menomonee River Valley in central Milwaukee will soon begin a large-scale rehabilitation of areas that once served as the industrial heart of the city. Land use planning, innovative designs for stormwater management, development of the Hank Aaron State Trail and the Milwaukee Riverwalk combined with an historic resources inventory will facilitate private redevelopment and revitalize the city while improving the health of coastal resources.

Restoring Coastal Natural Areas. Wisconsin's Great Lakes coasts contain unique and rare natural communities found nowhere else. However, polluted runoff, encroaching development and the introduction of exotic species of plants and animals threaten the health of these ecosystems.

The Town of Mount Pleasant in Racine County is restoring the Pike River from a channelized drainage ditch to a meandering river with wetlands on its fringes. The restored river will slow the flow of runoff from surrounding developments, reduce the threat of flooding and improve water quality. Key to the health of the river are the restored floodplain wetlands that will filter runoff, hold floodwaters, and become home to native wetland plants and animals.

The DNR, local governments and nonprofit organizations are restoring coastal wetlands in ten State Natural Areas. Invasive plants are being removed from 332 acres of wetlands that have been preserved because of their significant natural and scientific features. Removal of invasive plants, such as common reed and Eurasian buckthorn, helps native plant species that depend on these unique coastal habitats to flourish.

Whether protecting existing natural areas or rescuing degraded industrial waterfronts, many organizations employ restoration as a useful tool in their efforts to manage coastal resources effectively for the benefit of Wisconsin's Great Lakes communities. The complex nature of restoration requires neighbors and diverse organizations to work together to accomplish their mutual objectives. The WCMP continues to support partnerships that tackle the difficult task of restoring our Great Lakes.

In 2003, Travis Olson was Wetland Protection and Land Use Planning Coordinator for the Wisconsin Coastal Management Program.

A String of Pearls: The Estuaries of Chequamegon Bay

Cathy Techtmann

es•tu•ar•y (ĕs' chōō-ĕ r´ē) noun. An arm of the sea that extends inland to meet the mouth of a river.[1]

Along Lake Superior's southern shore, rivers draining the land flow into the cold blue waters of the world's largest freshwater sea. These places, on the edge of water and soil, have been shaped through time by nature and man. Like their saltwater cousins, the shallow coastal wetlands formed where the waters from the land and inland sea mix and mingle are estuaries.[2]

Like a string of pearls, fresh water estuaries grace the sweeping curve of Lake Superior's Chequamegon Bay. Each estuary is a unique treasure connected by the waters they share.

Just as the Lake shapes these coastal wetlands, the estuaries in turn influence the Lake. In a dynamic relationship the quality of water sent out through the estuaries affects the people, wildlife, plants and even the future of the Lake Superior region. Each has a story to tell that is best shared by the people who cherish and protect them.

A 20-minute video, *"A String of Pearls,"* captures the stories of estuaries of Chequamegon Bay. The University of Wisconsin-Extension and Wisconsin Coastal Management Program (WCMP) produced the video with help from tribal elders, natural resource managers and concerned citizens. Shot on location on Lake Superior, the program takes viewers on a virtual tour of each estuary and allows them to experience their rich diversity—without getting their feet wet! Viewers gain personal insights from the people who manage and care for these resources. From historic photos and on-the-water scenes, they learn about the issues and opportunities concerning protection of the estuaries.

The video is organized into five vignettes featuring the traditional Native American flute music of Frank *Anakwad* Montano. Each vignette reveals a different perspective on how each estuary has shaped the region's culture, history and ecology, and the challenges of preserving them.

- Kakagon-Bad River Estuary . . . protecting the 16,000 acre "Everglades of the North" and what is sacred to the Ojibwe people.

- Fish Creek Estuary . . . discovering how natural events and human activities have made change a constant.

- Whittlesey Creek Estuary . . . restoring a damaged watershed and the native Coaster Brook Trout through a new National Wildlife Refuge.

- Sioux and Onion River Estuaries . . . citizen volunteers taking leadership for preservation and protection through land use planning.

- Raspberry Bay Estuary . . . sustainability through tribal leadership to prevent erosion and preserve water quality for wild rice, fish and traditional uses.

The freshwater estuaries of Chequamegon Bay have experienced many changes. Only now are we beginning to appreciate the function of these unique coastal wetlands and recognize their cultural and biological importance. "*A String of Pearls*" explains how citizens, agencies and tribes work together to preserve these rare treasures. The stories of these estuaries remind us of how much our past and future are linked to the water and how, in turn, they are linked to each other.

The creation of "*A String of Pearls*" builds on a partnership between the WCMP and the University of Wisconsin-Extension through the Northern Great Lakes Visitor Center in Ashland. The video raises the awareness of visitors to the region, citizens, students and local decision-makers of the importance of Chequamegon Bay's freshwater estuaries and coastal wetlands. The Northern Great Lakes Visitor Center distributed the video to schools and libraries throughout the Lake Superior region and features it in estuary education programs. It is available in VHS or CD format or via webstreaming at www.uwex.edu/ces/nglvc.

Organizations providing technical expertise in the creation of "*A String of Pearls*" include the Bad River Band of the Lake Superior Chippewa, US

Fish and Wildlife Service, Wisconsin Department of Natural Resources, the Inland Sea Society, the Red Cliff Band of the Lake Superior Chippewa and the University of Wisconsin-Superior Videography Department.

Lake Superior's Chequamegon Bay estuaries shaped the character of the region for centuries. Educational projects such as "A String of Pearls" help to ensure that these irreplaceable resources prosper in the decades to follow.

In 2003, Cathy Techtmann was the Education Coordinator for the Northern Great Lakes Visitor Center's University of Wisconsin-Extension Office. She was a Professor of Community Resource Development and the producer of "A String of Pearls."

---

1. The American Heritage Dictionary. Second College Edition. Copyright 1982.
2. U.S.C. §1453(7) Coastal Zone Management Act of 1972 (as amended 1996).

River Restoration through Selective Dam Removal in the Lake Michigan Basin

Helen Sarakinos

Wisconsin has prospered because of the abundance of natural resources contained within the state. Our prosperity has been built on our forest, water and mineral resources. Among these natural treasures are over 44,000 miles of freshwater streams winding through the landscape. Since the mid-1800s, Wisconsinites harnessed the power of these flowing waters to move timber, irrigate crops, operate mills, generate power and accomplish a myriad of other purposes.

Yet progress comes with a price. Over the last 150 years, more than 3,800 dams have been built across Wisconsin rivers. Each dam produced a perceived benefit, but each also contributed to extensive cumulative impacts. Along with polluted runoff, dams constitute one of the greatest threats to rivers in the state. Dams alter the flow of water and prevent the natural movement of sediment in the river channel. They also block fish and mussel passage, limit access to habitat, fragment river ecosystems and impair water quality both in the reservoir and downstream.

Many Dams Are Old, Obsolete and Uneconomical. According to the Wisconsin Department of Natural Resources (DNR), there are over 700 permitted dams in Wisconsin's Lake Michigan Basin. While it is difficult to pinpoint the exact age of each dam, recent studies show that of the dams with a documented age, 60 percent are between 50 and 100 years old. Another 10 percent are older than 100 years. The national Association of State Dam Safety Officials states that the engineering life of a typical dam is 50 years. Beyond that age, dams require repair and maintenance to keep them safe and functioning properly. In Wisconsin's Lake Michigan Basin, municipalities or private individuals own 42 percent of the dams. The expensive repairs that aging dams require can place a heavy burden on these owners.

As we face the growing crisis of aging dams in our waters, the River Alliance of Wisconsin is working with multiple partners—including dam owners, municipalities and the DNR—to examine available options. One of those options is selective dam removal. With funding from the Charles Stewart Mott Foundation, the River Alliance initiated a three-year project to examine the impact of dams at a basin level rather than on a case-by-case basis. We also educate interested dam owners about their financial and legal responsibility to maintain the dam and minimize harm to people and the natural ecosystem.

Not All Dams Are Created Equal. Just as some dams provide a greater economic benefit than others, some do more harm to rivers than others. The amount of harm dams may cause varies due to their size, location, proximity to species of concern or their role in exacerbating other river problems (e.g. nutrients, invasive species). The River Alliance's Lake Michigan Basin Project seeks to evaluate the relative impacts of these dams on river ecosystems and determine where to gain maximum restoration benefits through selective dam removal.

Using Both Quantitative Data and Local Expertise to Understand Impacts. The Lake Michigan Basin Project also has as a goal the development of a more inclusive decision-making framework to help dam owners and public administrators decide when dam removal is a desirable option. Using Geographic Information System technology, we can spatially link ecological, engineering and logistical information to existing dams in the Lake Michigan Basin. Such a framework can apply to other regions or eventually statewide.

Some of the variables under consideration include species of concern, commercially valuable fisheries, proximity to headwaters, connectivity and special designations (e.g., Outstanding and Exceptional Resource Waters). Additional factors include dams considered by DNR as priorities for removal (basin reports, fisheries management plans, interviews with field staff) and dams that are neglected or ownerless.

Dam Removal Is About People, Not Just Rivers. While a solid, science-based approach to assessing the impact of dams is a priority, this work fits within a larger social framework. The River Alliance of Wisconsin works cooperatively with dam owners and the public to promote informed decision-making. We encourage consideration of the financial and legal obligations of dam ownership, the ecological impacts of dams and the benefits of selective dam removal. Wisconsin is a national leader in demonstrating how dam removal can be as much a community revitalization opportunity as an effective river restoration tool. Dam removals in Milwaukee, West Bend and Baraboo provide a few of the many examples of how dam removal led to new economic development opportunities and brought people and investment back to the waterfront and river communities.

The River Alliance passionately believes that a healthy river is good for the community and the economy. With over 108 dams removed in the last 50 years, Wisconsin leads the nation in dam removal. Just as natural resource use and extraction built our history, a vibrant and economically stable future relies on protecting our rivers and the recreational and tourist economies that depend on them.

In 2003, Helen Sarakinos was Dams Program Manager of the River Alliance of Wisconsin.

Beach Monitoring In Milwaukee

Mary Ellen Bruesch and Sandra McLellan, Ph.D.

The City of Milwaukee Health Department (MHD) has monitored Lake Michigan beaches (Bradford, McKinley and South Shore) in Milwaukee for several decades, testing for *E. coli* or fecal coliform organisms. *E. coli* and fecal coliform bacteria are always present in bird and animal waste, including human waste. The number of *E. coli* in a 100 milliliter (mL) volume of water currently serves as an indicator of the extent of fecal material in the water and the likelihood that pathogens (harmful bacteria, virus and protozoa) might be present in the swimming water sampled.

E. coli levels in natural waters can vary widely from day to day. Because no rapid tests are available to measure the amount of *E. coli* in the water, MHD recently focused efforts on estimating current water quality at Bradford and South Shore beaches through the use of predictive models. These models employ a number of environmental variables—other than *E. coli*—measured at the time a water sample is collected. In the past, MHD used a "Rainfall Model" to predict *E. coli* levels at South Shore Beach. The environmental models currently piloted use rainfall data as well as other measurements to predict water quality.

Based on values of environmental parameters measured at the time of sampling, the models assess current water quality by estimating the levels of *E. coli* in a water sample. Environmental variables measured at Bradford Beach include algae, turbidity, wind vector, recent combined sewer overflows and water temperature. All measurements at Bradford Beach are taken manually at the same time water samples are collected. Measurements at South Shore are obtained by an in-water automated monitoring station that measures pH, conductivity, water temperature, rainfall, wind vector and turbidity. In addition, records of recent combined sewer overflows are plugged into the model.

The results of recent research demonstrate that not all pollution sources contribute the same type or concentration (if at all) of pathogens to swimming waters such as those at Lake Michigan beaches. Each beach has its own unique set of environmental influences and point- and nonpoint-pollution (*E. coli* and pathogen) sources. Sewage effluent—as well as overflows that may enter the rivers and harbors during combined sewer overflows or sewage treatment diversions—is more likely to contain human pathogens than the feces from various types of birds. Certain types of bird feces, however, can contain human pathogens. A beach impacted by human sewage would be of immediate public health concern. The MHD works with the research community to determine sources of *E. coli* at Milwaukee beaches to provide improved risk assessment and subsequently better health advice to persons using the beaches.

Research Efforts to Determine Sources of E. coli Contamination. Investigating sources of fecal pollution is important not only for estimating potential health risk, but also for focusing remediation efforts so major sources of contamination can be minimized. One critical step in determining sources is to characterize spatial distribution. Research into the sources of *E. coli* found that water quality in swimming areas is influenced by both local and regional factors. At one beach site in Milwaukee runoff from the beach area and adjacent parking lot contributed to the degraded water quality. *E. coli* levels at the beach were not necessarily a reflection of overall water quality in Lake Michigan. Local inputs of fecal pollution include urban storm water runoff and roosting waterfowl. Both may deliver high levels of *E. coli* to surface waters.

Algae accumulation—such as the *Cladophora* that washes up on several Lake Michigan beaches—may further confound the problem by offering nutrients and a protected environment that may prolong the survival of *E. coli*. Additionally, algae may attract waterfowl to the shoreline with the food source of invertebrates that are intertwined with the algae. Management strategies that may improve local contamination problems include treating storm water before discharge to the lake, closed garbage receptacles and public education to discourage feeding waterfowl.

River discharges to Lake Michigan influence regional water quality and may simultaneously impact water quality at beach sites. Combined sewage overflows, urban storm water runoff from impervious surfaces, failing infrastructure in sewer systems and upstream inputs from agricultural lands may all contribute to elevated *E. coli* levels in rivers.

Various approaches have been recently developed to distinguish human vs. nonhuman sources of contamination. One methodology evaluates the frequencies of antibiotic resistance traits in *E. coli* isolates in contaminated waters. This approach is based on the hypothesis that *E. coli* strains from humans are exposed to antibiotics, and therefore will more often display the resistance trait than will *E. coli* strains from wildlife, which are not exposed to antibiotics.

One current study in the Milwaukee area combines spatial mapping of contamination with an evaluation of the antibiotic resistance found in sources. This methodology allows researchers to characterize the sources, transport and fate of bacterial contamination in the Milwaukee Harbor. These studies, combined with an assessment of pathogens carried with difference sources of contamination, will provide insight into potential health risks of recreational waters.

In 2003, Mary Ellen Bruesch was an Environmental and Communicable Disease Scientist with the City of Milwaukee Health Department. Sandra McLellan, Ph.D., was an Assistant Scientist at the Great Lakes WATER Institute.

Clean Boating

Mike Friis

Nearly 45 percent of Wisconsin residents participate in recreational boating.[1] More than 575,000 boats are registered in Wisconsin[2] (sixth nationally) with one boat per every ten residents (tenth nationally). Water-based recreation along Wisconsin's 1,000 miles of shoreline[3] provides enjoyment to the state's population and contributed to the estimated $4.1 billion[4] spent by travelers in the state's coastal counties during 2002.

Appropriate boating practices can protect Wisconsin's Great Lakes coastal resources. This article summarizes four areas of best management practice for marina operators and boaters, and discusses recent federal and state action on coastal nonpoint source pollution.

Petroleum Control. Petroleum spilled during fueling or engine servicing can be harmful or even fatal in an aquatic system. A large film of floating fuel reduces light penetration, limits the availability of oxygen and may be toxic to aquatic life.

- Wise fueling practices prevent contamination of water and shore areas. When filling a gas tank avoid spilling, topping off or overfilling the tank.

- Wipe up all gasoline and oil spills. Take waste oil to a used oil recycling center.

Sewage. Improper disposal of sewage causes degradation of water quality. Human and pet wastes pose a serious health risk. Waterborne diseases from fecal waste may pass directly to water users and aquatic animals. Microorganisms within sewage use oxygen and any effluent discharged to waterways reduces the amount of oxygen available to fish and other forms of aquatic life. The nutrient load in sewage can also promote the growth of unwanted aquatic plants.

- Do not discharge human waste directly into the water. If you have an installed toilet, use a sewage pump-out facility to get rid of waste.

- If you own a portable toilet, empty it in a restroom.

- Dispose of pet waste properly by using disposable bags for cleanup.

Waste and Trash. Appropriate disposal of solid and fish waste promotes a clean environment. Waterborne trash can be dangerous to both human and animal life. Wastes from fish cleaning may lead to a decrease in dissolved oxygen as discarded entrails decompose in water.

- Leave nothing on the dock to fall into or blow into the water.

- Do not discard fishing line, cigarette butts or other trash overboard.

- Bring back what you take out. It is illegal for any vessel to dump plastic trash anywhere in the navigable waters of the United States.

- Do not toss fish scraps into the water. Use designated containers at fish cleaning stations found at many marinas and boat launches. Otherwise, bag the waste and take it home for disposal.

Boat Cleaning and Maintenance. Cleaning and maintenance is important to keep boat safe and reliable. Choosing an appropriate cleaning location, products and methods go a long way toward minimizing adverse impacts.

- Avoid using toxic paints and other products. When cleaning a boat, use non-phosphate and biodegradable cleaning products.

- Properly maintain boat engines to prevent leaks and achieve maximum fuel efficiency while running.

- To prevent the spread of exotic species, clean all mud, plants and aquatic organisms from the boat, trailer, propeller, live well and anchors before leaving the boat launch.

Wisconsin Meets Federal Mandate for Clean Coastal Waters. In 1990, Congress amended the Coastal Zone Management Act (CZMA) by requiring states with approved coastal management programs to develop a Coastal Nonpoint Pollution Control Program. The Wisconsin Coastal Management Program (WCMP) and Wisconsin Departments of Natural Resources (DNR) and Agriculture Trade and Consumer Protection (DATCP) assembled a suite of existing authorities and new initiatives that received federal approval in December 2002.

Wisconsin's approved program includes management measures to address nonpoint source pollution from marinas, agriculture, forestry, urban impacts and hydromodification. Wisconsin's Coastal Nonpoint Pollution Control Program provides a framework for cleaner Lakes and ensures Wisconsin will continue to receive full federal funding for several Great Lakes and Clean Water Act programs.

Clean Boating Guide Available to the Public. The WCMP and DNR developed "Shipshape: A guide to reducing pollutants for marinas, boaters and other coastal customers." This booklet helps marina owners and boat operators follow Wisconsin's official best management practices to reduce pollution.

"Shipshape" was originally published in *Natural Resources* magazine and reached an initial audience of over 120,000 readers. The full document continues to be available to boaters and marina operators at www.wnrmag.com/supps/2002/ aug02/intro.htm or by contacting Wisconsin Coastal Management at (608) 267–7982 or coastal@doa.state.wi.us.

Wisconsin's waters will continue to be enjoyed by more than a million boaters every year. By practicing clean boating, Wisconsin water enthusiasts will minimize any potential adverse impact from their sport.

In 2003, Mike Friis was Nonpoint Source Pollution and Public Access Programs Coordinator for the Wisconsin Coastal Management Program.

---

1. Wisconsin Statewide Comprehensive Outdoor Recreation Plan (2000–2005), Wisconsin Department of Natural Resources website at www.dnr.state.wi.us/org/ land/parks/reports/scorp/2000/
2. Wisconsin Recreation Facts, 2003, Wisconsin Department of Natural Resources website at www.dnr.state.wi.us/org/water/division/yow/recreation.htm
3. Wisconsin's Great Lakes Shoreline, 2001, Wisconsin State Cartographer's Office website at www.geography.wisc.edu/sco/maps/shoreline.html
4. The Economic Impact of Expenditures by Travelers on Wisconsin 2001, Davidson-Peterson & Associates, as cited by the Wisconsin Department of Tourism.

COASTAL COMMUNITIES: GROWING SMART, TENDING THE PAST

Geoffrey M. Gyrisco, Ph.D.

Donovan Rypkema, nationally known consultant in historic preservation economics, emphasizes that historic preservation is true smart growth. He observes that well-designed, compact communities fully use existing public infrastructure, land and buildings, provide for a mix of uses, offer a variety of housing types, create new jobs and provide choice in transportation.

People seek to live and work in places with high quality urban design and historic buildings. That is the finding of Richard Florida in his provocative best seller, *The Rise of the Creative Class*. Mr. Florida shows that in order to win the economic development race communities must attract knowledge workers. And, he argues, artists, teachers, scientists, engineers, technicians, medical professionals and office managers value creativity, individuality, differences and merit. The experiences of several Wisconsin coastal communities support the concepts of Rypkema and Florida.

The historic character of Bayfield draws many culturally oriented tourists. Studies show that these visitors stay longer and spend more than other tourists. Historic preservation in Bayfield began with a survey in the 1970s, followed by a historic preservation ordinance and a law to preserve the brick streets. Mayor Larry McDonald states, "The key to the continued success of Bayfield and its livability and community satisfaction is historic preservation."

Climate and location limit Bayfield's tourism economy: half of its business occurs in 60 days and 90 percent in six months. To provide additional economic base, Chequamegon Bay area leaders created the Alliance for Sustainability to promote high technology education, telecommuting and a technology center. The project and the beauty of the area drew technology entrepreneur Jerry Johnson to invest $2 million in projects centered in Bayfield. Thus, Chequamegon Bay may find itself on the verge of becoming silicon bay.

Richard Florida identified diversity as a critical ingredient in a community's ability to attract knowledge workers. Business and community leader Einar Tangen takes pride in the diversity and safety of Milwaukee's Third Ward where there is "no tolerance for intolerance." Here steel mill workers, investment bankers, techies and artists mix. This warehouse district—where three rivers meet and enter Lake Michigan—once seemed destined to become the city's red-light district. Business people saw greater potential. They created a Business Improvement District, gained a listing on the National Register of Historic Places and established an historic preservation commission for the district. Talented people working together created a mixed-use community centered on the historic district. In less than ten years, the value of property in the district rose from $40 million to $240 million today. Planned projects will raise the value to $500 million in three years.

Racine has realized much of Rypkema's vision of historic preservation as true smart growth. Its downtown retail and cultural center occupies a late 19th and early 20th century Main Street historic district. A new art museum, the Johnson Building and a planned history museum ensure that this street remains vital. The arts businesses of 6th Street will soon be joined with the conversion of a large factory for artists' live-work lofts. Industry, a charter school and a day care share a historic factory.

Racine is an easily walked city with a bus system centered on a revitalized historic train station. Metra train service may soon connect Racine to Chicago and Milwaukee. The city has agreed not to expand its boundaries and will continue to grow through compact redevelopment.

Ashland's draft comprehensive plan positions the city as a regional center providing services to smaller surrounding communities. The plan calls for compact redevelopment on underused land with little urban expansion, and connects the city's historic downtown with the bluff overlooking Chequamegon Bay. A new historic preservation commission works with the various churches to provide leadership in preserving the community character that makes it attractive to visitors and new residents.

In the Door County Town of Nasewaupee, citizens demanded a unique, creative and detailed plan that would protect the distinctive character of the town in lieu of traditional zoning. They began with a community character inventory. The inventory incorporated photographs of many historic landscapes and building features that give the township a distinctive sense of place. The inventory helped define land use management areas that were assigned goals and policies specifically designed to allow new development and maintain the town's character.

Historic preservation approaches used throughout Wisconsin's coasts vary as much as the communities themselves. However, general principles of historic preservation apply widely. Working together, creative citizens successfully identify their community's historic assets and comprehensively plan for the preservation of historic resources, cultural character and local identity. By maintaining and using their historic heritage, communities can draw in new financial resources and people to create their chosen future.

In 2003, Geoffrey M. Gyrisco, Ph.D., of Gyrisco Associates was a historic preservation and history consultant in Madison.

2004

Foreword

Governor Jim Doyle

Dear Friend of Wisconsin's Great Lakes:

The Great Lakes are one of America's greatest resources. The lakes are used in manufacturing, transportation and energy, and draw thousands of tourists to their shores. They provide drinking water for millions and habitat for animals as diverse as the piping plover and the coaster brook trout. Wisconsinites understand the need to preserve and protect the Great Lakes—the largest body of fresh water in the world.

My administration has done much to improve the quality of the Great Lakes and their coasts. Over the past year, we have accomplished several objectives.

- I requested that the federal government site a National Estuarine Research Reserve (NERR) on the shores of Lake Superior, the first on the western Great Lakes. A Wisconsin NERR would improve coastal decision making, increase awareness of coastal resources and promote stewardship of estuarine natural areas.

- I signed into law a bill that expands the state's Harbor Assistance Program (HAP) to privately owned ports and docks, facilitating economic development by allowing private businesses to improve their port facilities. Additionally, I signed a bill that requires HAP-supported facilities to be held open for public use for at least ten years after the improvements are made.

- The Wisconsin Coastal Management Program awarded $1.55 million in grants to preserve and enhance Wisconsin's Great Lakes coasts. Nonprofit organizations, universities, and various levels of governments will support 39 projects totaling $4.2 million.

- We took an important step towards educating our youth about the importance of our Great Lakes by distributing

Paddle-to-the-Sea, a classic children's book, to every elementary
school and public library in Wisconsin.

- All state agencies have been directed to work towards the protection and restoration of the Great Lakes.

Looking ahead, Wisconsin is poised to do even more for the benefit of
our Great Lakes. As Chair of the Council of Great Lakes Governors, I have
invited the other members of the Council to Wisconsin to discuss Great
Lakes diversion requests and consumptive use of Great Lakes water within
the basin. The Council must act to prevent the diversion of Great Lakes
waters to faraway places like Las Vegas and Phoenix.

I will join with the federal government, port authorities and the shipping industry in identifying and implementing creative approaches to
prevent the discharge of ballast water from ocean going vessels. Together,
we will limit the entry of new invasive species to our Great Lakes and help
prevent further invasions of inland waters.

Finally, I am pleased that Lake Michigan will form the backdrop for
the 86th PGA Championship at Whistling Straits. Through this event, the
world will discover the beauty of Wisconsin's Great Lakes.

The investments we make now to protect and restore Lakes Michigan
and Superior will benefit future generations. I ask all Wisconsinites to join
me in working toward a healthier Great Lakes system.

Jim Doyle served as Wisconsin's 44th Governor from 2003 to 2011.

Coaster Brook Trout Rehabilitation in Lake Superior

Laura Hewitt

The brook trout fishing about Bayfield can scarcely be equaled in all respects in any part of the world. There are not less than fifty trout streams of easy access from Bayfield for both ladies and gentlemen; and the "rock fishing" for brook trout all along the shore, which is shielded by the Islands, affords the grandest sport that the disciples of Walton can find . . . The size of the brook trout caught about Bayfield run from one half pound to four pounds.—The Ashland Press, May 12, 1877

A palpable buzz among anglers and fishery biologists followed the confirmed March 2004 catch of a nine-pound coaster brook trout in Lake Superior off the Bayfield Peninsula. Coaster brook trout, a variant of the small stream dwelling brook trout, migrate from streams to grow large and glorious in the big waters of Lake Superior. Historical newspaper accounts talked of area streams that "seem to possess exhaustless numbers of brook trout."

Sadly, by the early 1900s the limits of the brook trout fishery were all too evident. Overzealous fishing was the first major blow. Widespread logging, mining, agriculture and road building subsequently took a heavy toll on the condition of streams and ultimately decimated the fishery.

Repeated attempts since the 1930s to reintroduce coasters have met with little success. Since the mid-1990s, renewed undertakings to rehabilitate coasters in the Lake Superior basin have been bolstered by improved scientific understanding of this unique fish and the partnership of 26 public and private organizations in the United States and Canada.

The appearance of a large brook trout in these waters, bearing no discernible fin clips that indicate a hatchery origin, is tantalizing. While the catch of a solitary fish does not necessarily indicate the imminent return of healthy populations, it does offer a glimmer of hope that it is indeed possible. Today, a basin wide effort to rehabilitate the coaster focuses on the steep sandy land of the Bayfield Peninsula and its neighboring waters.

The Habitat Connection. In some ways, coaster brook trout could be viewed as the animate link between Lake Superior and her tributaries. In a cycle that resembles that of salmon, most coasters return to the streams to spawn over groundwater upwellings. The young mature in the streams and then migrate out to the lake where they grow large. While the conditions of habitat in the streams and the lake are important, the streams have borne the brunt of environmental damage over the past century.

In response to the growing recognition that habitat may play a critical role in coaster rehabilitation efforts, partner organizations sponsored a comprehensive watershed assessment of five streams around the Bayfield Peninsula. The assessment documented the current state of stability in the watersheds, identified problem areas and recommended watershed rehabilitation management strategies.

The study—funded through a grant from the Wisconsin Coastal Management Program—was conducted as a cooperative effort among Trout Unlimited, Bayfield County, the Wisconsin Department of Natural Resources, Inter-Fluve, Inc., the United States Geological Survey, the United States Fish and Wildlife Service, the Red Cliff Band of Lake Superior Chippewas, Northland College and Windway Capital Corp. The report made recommendations that address land use and forestry management to reduce nonpoint pollution and runoff, and specific remedies to improve instream habitat. Partners are now actively working to implement those recommendations.

Conservation Stocks and Reintroductions. One aspect of the overall rehabilitation strategy involves strategic reintroductions of brook trout that are known to exhibit the coaster migratory life history. The USFWS Iron River hatchery and the Red Cliff hatchery are the only sites within the basin that rear conservation brood stock from Lake Superior remnant populations. These fish are used in multiple sites across the lake for reintroduction experiments.

In late 2003, several partners initiated a reintroduction experiment at Whittlesey Creek National Wildlife Refuge. Over the next few years, brook trout from two coaster strains will be reintroduced at varying times and stages, from eggs to fry and fingerlings. Partners will closely monitor the response of the populations to determine which strategies hold the most promise. The Wisconsin Department of Natural Resources has also strengthened fishing regulations for brook trout on Whittlesey Creek, other streams and Lake Superior to help protect these sensitive fish from over harvest during this critical period.

Learning and Building Support. Coaster brook trout rehabilitation efforts will not succeed in the absence of broad public awareness and support. The partners are collaborating on a basin wide education and outreach campaign that includes newsletters, brochures, a web site and regional meetings. They will host a Coaster Brook Trout Symposium at the August 2004 American Fisheries Society Annual Meeting in Madison, Wisconsin, to communicate the lessons learned from the numerous research and management experiments occurring across Lake Superior.

The journey to return self-sustaining populations of coaster brook trout to at least a portion of their historic home waters will take many years. It will be possible only through the coordinated efforts of a committed group of partners and public support for this unique fish.

In 2004, Laura Hewitt was Upper Midwest Conservation Director at Trout Unlimited.

RESTORING THE WEST SHORE OF GREEN BAY

Kendra Axness

The west shore of Green Bay is home to some of the finest remaining coastal wetlands in the Great Lakes system. Along with the valuable wetland functions of shoreline protection and nutrient cycling, these wetlands provide exceptional breeding, nesting and feeding habitat for birds and spawning habitat for fish.

However, they are threatened by hydrologic changes that have resulted from increased development of the watershed, invasion by exotic species and greater recreational use of waterways and undeveloped lands. To counter these threats, agencies, non-profit organizations and interested individuals are partnering and working across traditional jurisdictional boundaries to ensure that this resource will be available for future generations to enjoy.

A Unique Natural History. Over the last two million years, glaciers advanced and retreated, eroding the relatively soft sedimentary bedrock underlying the west shore coastal zone. The process left behind lowlands that are fundamentally influenced by the ebb and flow of water. In pulses that mimic a slow and life-giving heartbeat, the springtime landscape fills with water, cycling nutrients and providing fish with passageways to marshes for spawning.

During late spring and summer, the water retreats to the bay. This seasonal fluctuation is superimposed over short-term changes resulting from seiches and storms and long-term cycles related to climate trends. These constantly changing water levels fuel dynamic wetland ecosystems that are home to, among many other species, the state-endangered Forster's tern and common tern. The hydraulic connection to the bay enables important game fish species, such as northern pike, to move inland for spawning and feeding.

A Tradition of Conservation. Coastal wetlands have long been recognized as critical to supporting migratory bird, waterfowl and fish populations.

Louis Henry Barkhausen, a Green Bay area businessman and co-founder of Ducks Unlimited, established the Barkhausen Waterfowl Preserve in 1926. In 1936, a federal waterfowl refuge was designated on Long Tail Point. State of Wisconsin activity on the west shore began with the acquisition of the Sensiba Wildlife Area in 1948.

Leroy Lintereur, a state wildlife manager, developed the Green Bay West Shore Project in the 1970s. The project defined boundaries within which the Wisconsin Department of Natural Resources (DNR) could acquire land and establish management of state-owned lands on the west shore for wildlife protection, wildlife-based recreation and habitat preservation. UW-Green Bay Professor Hallet J. (Bud) Harris began sponsoring research studies of west shore ecology in the 1970s. Through their participation in the US Environmental Protection Agency-funded Great Lakes Environmental Indicators Project, UW-Green Bay faculty continue to lead west shore research projects that have national significance for understanding wetland ecology.

Growing Recognition of West Shore Importance. While state and federal agencies have managed project areas, guided restoration and protection efforts, and conducted research during the past decades, other individuals and organizations are beginning to turn their attention to the west shore wetlands. The Lake Michigan Shorelands Alliance—a coalition of land trusts working in the Lake Michigan basin—has identified three priority conservation areas on the west shore that together cover nearly all the shoreline between Green Bay and Marinette. The Nature Conservancy, an organization with an international presence, identifies the west shore as a priority and is beginning to apply its site conservation planning process to the area.

New Opportunities for Protection, Planning and Restoration. The role of headwater streams in protecting west shore wetlands habitat and water quality has become more apparent as uplands in the watersheds are developed. Consequently, a broader watershed approach to conservation has been promoted and is taking shape.

In 2002–2003, the DNR protected some of these important headwaters and coastal areas through their scattered fish habitat project, funded by a Wisconsin Coastal Management Program grant. Bay-Lake Regional Planning Commission defined environmental corridors for Marinette, Oconto and Brown Counties with local citizen input. By providing a regional view of natural resources, these corridors foster watershed-level thinking in local communities as they develop comprehensive plans. The west shore area is eligible for funds through the Fox River PCB Natural Resource Damage Assessment. These funds present a unique and significant opportunity for area resource managers to implement restoration projects that benefit the health of the Green Bay watershed.

Partnering for Conservation. The agencies, organizations and individuals involved in west shore projects have recently initiated efforts to strengthen existing and develop new partnerships to ensure efficient and collaborative use of resources along the west shore. These partners recognize the need for a strategic approach to conservation that includes not only continued research and land acquisition, but also participation in comprehensive planning, outreach and education, land protection through easements, and cooperation with private landowners to implement management practices. Projects that build on these partnerships include an educational water trail at the mouth of the Peshtigo River and low-order stream mapping in Oconto County to enhance understanding of local watersheds.

With over 50 percent of Wisconsin's Lake Michigan coastal wetlands located along the west shore of Green Bay, it is clear that these wetlands are a resource of regional and statewide importance. The sustained and coordinated efforts of partners to protect the coastal wetlands of the west shore have been and will continue to be critical to maintaining them into the future.

In 2004, Kendra Axness was a Basin Educator for Natural Resources for the University of Wisconsin-Extension.

Signs of Stress: Lake Michigan Algae

Victoria A. Harris and John Karl

During the past four summers, heaps of rotting algae have piled up on some beaches of Lake Michigan. The powerful stench turns otherwise inviting beaches into repulsive wastelands where walking is difficult, swimming is unthinkable and breathing turns the stomach. Similar conditions have been reported along the shores of Lakes Ontario and Erie.

The offending plant is known as *Cladophora*. It is a filamentous green alga common in the Great Lakes and many other fresh waters. Growing on submerged rocks, it looks like long, green hair waving in the water.

Cladophora is an important component of freshwater ecosystems, providing food and shelter for invertebrates and small fish. The recent excessive blooms in the Great Lakes, however, may be the response of a dynamic ecosystem to natural changes and human impacts.

Decaying *Cladophora* is more than an annoyance to people strolling on the beach. It may lower property values and has been linked to taste and odor problems in drinking water. In addition, it may exacerbate levels of *E. coli* and enterococci bacteria in swimming waters, raising questions about beach safety.

E. coli is an indicator of fecal contamination, and high numbers prompt managers to close beaches. Recent research shows *Cladophora* mats may nourish the growth of bacteria that come from gull droppings, sewage overflows or runoff from urban and agricultural areas.

Problems with *Cladophora* date back to the mid-1950s when nutrient levels, particularly phosphorus, were higher throughout the Great Lakes. Following the 1972 Amendments to the Clean Water Act, wastewater discharges of phosphorus were limited. Phosphorus levels in the lakes declined and nuisance algae blooms in Lake Michigan largely subsided.

Conditions Favoring Cladophora's Growth. The most important factors governing growth of *Cladophora* are substrate (the material it grows on), temperature, light and nutrients.

Cladophora generally grows attached to rocky substrates or other hard surfaces like piers, breakwalls or woody debris. *Cladophora* requires high levels of calcium and thus grows well on the dolomite (limestone) bedrocks of the west shore of Lake Michigan.

Optimal water temperature for *Cladophora* is 15–25°C (59–77°F). It does not grow well in the cold waters of Lake Superior, but is commonly found in the other Great Lakes. Abundance generally peaks in the spring and again in the fall. Die-offs occur in mid-summer, possibly due to higher water temperatures. Then, filaments break free from their substrate, and waves and currents carry the dead algae ashore.

Cladophora thrives in shallow and clear waters where light easily penetrates to the lake bottom. In freshwater ecosystems, phosphorus is usually the essential plant nutrient in shortest supply. Therefore, additions of phosphorus will usually stimulate *Cladophora* growth.

The causes of the *Cladophora* resurgence in the Great Lakes are not known for certain, but experts increasingly agree they probably include changes involving zebra mussels, lower water levels and possibly rising phosphorus inputs.

Zebra mussels. During the past decade, water clarity in the Great Lakes has increased substantially because zebra mussels filter suspended particles from the water as they feed. Light now penetrates to much greater depths, expanding the areas of well-lit, hard substrates where *Cladophora* can grow.

Zebra mussels also may be increasing phosphorus concentrations in nearshore waters. As the mussels feed, they filter algae and other phosphorus containing particles out of the water and excrete them onto the lake bottom—fertilizing the habitat they share with *Cladophora*.

Finally, the vast beds of zebra mussels now found in the Great Lakes also provide *Cladophora* with new substrate to grow on. *Cladophora* grows directly on the hard shells of the mussels and may draw upon the rich nutrients the mussels deposit.

Lower water levels. Lower lake levels may have expanded the areas of suitable substrate that receive sufficient light for *Cladophora* growth.

Possible increased phosphorus. Although inadequate funding seriously hinders water quality monitoring, there is limited evidence that phosphorus inputs may have increased in recent years from some streams that flow into Lake Michigan. Runoff is known to be the largest source of phosphorus to the Great Lakes. While phosphorus concentrations in the open waters of Lake Michigan remain low, levels in the nearshore waters may be much higher due to inputs from fertilizers, livestock manure, soil erosion or urban storm water.

What Can Be Done? In the short term, mechanically removing *Cladophora* from beaches and composting it may mitigate the offending conditions. However, zebra mussels are unfortunately here to stay, and little can be done to control water levels in the Great Lakes. Reducing the amounts and sources of phosphorus entering the lakes is clearly the best means available of controlling the growth of *Cladophora* and other algae.

New regulations are helping curb runoff pollution in Wisconsin. Smart Growth guidelines promote low-impact development that minimizes urban pollution. Farms near streams and lakes must meet new agricultural performance standards, and urban stormwater management programs are required for larger communities. Some municipalities also prohibit the sale of phosphorus-containing lawn fertilizers.

Nuisance *Cladophora* blooms indicate an ecosystem under stress. They remind us of the vulnerability of Great Lakes ecosystems to disturbances from urban and agricultural runoff, introductions of exotic species and changes in weather and climate.

In 2004, Victoria A. Harris was a Water Quality Specialist at the University of Wisconsin Sea Grant Institute. John Karl was a Science Writer at the University of Wisconsin Sea Grant Institute.

Bayfield County Shoreviewer

David Lee

Bayfield County's Lake Superior shoreline is a treasured resource with a valued natural heritage. Unfortunately, through forces of nature and consequences of man, we find this vulnerable resource increasingly threatened. However, confluence of advanced scientific understanding of the shoreline and a resurgence of land use planning allowed Bayfield County to take proactive measures to address issues of coastal hazards.

In recent decades, many studies have been conducted—and a great deal of information generated—on the characteristics and dynamics of Lake Superior coastal hazards, particularly coastal erosion. Excellent and relevant information has been developed by numerous local, state and federal agencies, and academic institutions.

A concern that these messages were not reaching coastal landowners and other stakeholders prompted the Bayfield County government to initiate a community outreach project focused on coastal hazards. The project, funded in part by the Wisconsin Coastal Management Program (WCMP), allowed Bayfield County to develop innovative data products and outreach materials that were integrated into a series of informative, live presentations on coastal erosion and shoreline recession.

Representatives from the WCMP, the University of Wisconsin-Madison, the University of Wisconsin Sea Grant Institute, the Wisconsin Department of Natural Resources and others presented current research on shoreline dynamics to help coastal stakeholders understand the processes causing erosion and learn more about specific ways to protect and manage their shoreline. The information generated through the outreach sessions, as well as much of the coastal research itself, has been incorporated into the Bayfield County website as a permanent reference for the public.

A particularly interesting component of the much larger outreach project is *Bayfield County ShoreViewer*, a series of oblique aerial photographs documenting the current condition of Bayfield County's Lake Superior shoreline. Although images depicting the Lake Superior shoreline abound, this project was the first to build a comprehensive library of images covering the entire stretch of Bayfield County shoreline.

Inspired in part by the California Coastal Records Project and Washington State's shoreline aerial photos, Bayfield County saw this as a means for providing a visual baseline for observing shoreline changes over time, whether from natural forces such as erosion, or from development. This visual shoreline archive also provides a ready source of imagery that can be useful for land use planning efforts, educational displays, public meetings and a multitude of other shoreline-related issues and events.

Bayfield County ShoreViewer was created to meet several objectives. It sought to capture close-range, oblique aerial images of the entire Bayfield County Lake Superior shoreline of approximately 87 miles in length. *ShoreViewer* would obtain high-resolution images and maximize shoreline visibility by taking photos during "leaf-off" conditions.

Bayfield County also sought to create a system to record the geographic position of the camera when each image was taken for use in an Internet application to permit site visitors to view and download shoreline images. Where possible, the County placed a premium on minimized costs and the use of local expertise. Finally, *ShoreViewer* was expected to include recent shoreline research and educational information on factors of Lake Superior shoreline erosion.

Bayfield County ShoreViewer met these objectives and more. Using a Cessna 1726 flown at approximately 500 feet above Lake Superior and about 1,200 feet parallel to the shoreline, 513 overlapping oblique photos were taken extending from Fish Creek to the Brule River. A Nikon D100 digital camera captured the high-resolution (3008 x 2000 pixel) images in November 2002. GPS recorded the flight path and GPS-PhotoLink software assigned a geographic coordinate value to the position of the aircraft when each photo was taken.

Flight costs were significantly reduced by collaborating with the Bad River Band of Lake Superior Chippewas Natural Resources Department. The skills of pilot and biologist Tom Doolittle and GIS Specialist Matt Eitrem are showcased by the aerial images they captured. This fortuitous partnership not only provided Bayfield County excellent photography, but also allowed the Bad River Natural Resources Department to hone technical skills directly applicable to other natural resources projects on which they are working.

A web-based map interface was developed to provide instant access to the shoreline images. The architect of this application, consultant Mark Miller, created *ShoreViewer* to permit site visitors to explore the Lake Superior shoreline using the oblique aerial photographs. Users employ locator maps to navigate to the particular reach of shoreline they wish to examine, or simply click to advance photos incrementally and literally *walk* along the shoreline. If greater detail is desired, all photos are downloadable; while file sizes are large, the high-resolution images are rich in detail.

Shoreline bluff profile and erosion information from UW-Madison researchers David Mickelson, Lindsay Anderson, et. al., can be accessed from *ShoreViewer*. The Lake Superior shoreline portion of the Bayfield County Land Records Department web site, www.bayfieldcounty.org/landrecords, also contains extensive information, resources and publications on coastal processes.

Bayfield County is dedicated to protecting its Lake Superior shoreline. The Wisconsin Coastal Management Program continues to further our shared goal to provide objective scientific information to our community so that, together, we may chart the best future for this valued resource.

In 2004, David Lee was the Land Records Administrator for Bayfield County.

PROJECTED POPULATION CHANGE IN WISCONSIN COASTAL COUNTIES

David Egan-Robertson

The Wisconsin Demographic Services Center in 2004 completed a set of long-range projections for Wisconsin including the state's fifteen coastal counties. These projections, from 2000–2030, help public officials and others anticipate and plan for future growth and decline.

As a group, Wisconsin's fifteen coastal counties are projected to increase by 14.9 percent in population through 2030. This change is less than projected statewide growth of 19.6 percent. Numerically, the coastal counties' population is projected to increase by 296,000 persons, from 1.99 million in 2000 to 2.29 million in 2030.

Lake Superior Counties: Modest Growth. Overall, the four counties bordering Lake Superior—Ashland, Bayfield, Douglas and Iron—are projected to increase in population by 7.5 percent, from 82,000 in 2000 to 88,200 in 2030. Of particular note, Iron County is forecast to decline by approximately -4.5 percent while Ashland, Bayfield and Douglas are each expected to grow (8.9 percent, 8.0 percent and 8.7 percent, respectively). Bayfield County's population is projected to peak at 2025 and then decline thereafter.

The primary reasons for this relatively slow growth and decline are the aging population of the area over the next 30 years and minimal net in-migration. At the 2000 Census, Iron County had the second-highest median age (45.0) of all Wisconsin counties; Bayfield, the seventh highest (42.1). In the 1990s, both of these counties experienced natural decrease (more deaths than births). For instance, in Iron County deaths exceeded births by nearly 400 from 1990–2000.

By 2020–2030, this difference increases to more than 500, and the predicted net in-migration will be inadequate to offset it. Furthermore, net in-migration across all four counties is expected to be modest: In-migration across the 30-year period is expected to be 5,800 residents, increasing the base population by roughly seven percent.

Bay-Lake Counties: Fast and Moderate Growth. Overall, the seven
Bay-Lake counties on Lake Michigan—Brown, Door, Kewaunee, Manitowoc, Marinette, Oconto and Sheboygan—are projected to increase in
population by 19.9 percent, from 549,400 in 2000 to 658,700 in 2030.

Growth in these counties will be bifurcated based on proximity to the
city of Green Bay. Following Census 2000, the Green Bay Metropolitan
Statistical Area—formerly consisting of Brown County only—was expanded to incorporate Kewaunee and Oconto Counties. Together, these
three counties will contain the bulk of this region's growth.

Brown County is projected to grow by 28.8 percent, Oconto County by
27.0 percent and Kewaunee County by 15.3 percent. Their growth is expected to occur in both natural increase (18 percent) and net in-migration
(10 percent). Manitowoc and Sheboygan Counties are also anticipated to
demonstrate solid growth of 10.2 percent and 18.1 percent, respectively.

On the contrary, Door and Marinette Counties will display population
change similar to Bayfield County: moderate growth until 2020, and then
gradual decline with net gains over the 30-year period of five and three
percent, respectively. At 2000, Door County had the fifth highest median
age (42.9) and Marinette County had the fifteenth (40.5).

Door County, which experienced natural decrease of about -300 in
the 1990s, is likely to see this negative value soar to -2,600 in the 2020–30
period. Marinette County, with a natural decrease of -400 last decade, will
probably see this negative value rise to -1,800. While net in-migration
is still expected to be strong in these counties through 2030—adding 22
percent to the year 2000 population in Door County and 11 percent in
Marinette County—by the last decade of the projection period, it will not
overcome the imbalance between births and deaths.

Southeastern Wisconsin Counties: Solid Gains. Overall, the four southeastern counties on Lake Michigan—Kenosha, Milwaukee, Ozaukee and
Racine—are projected to increase in population by 13.3 percent, from
1,360,900 in 2000 to 1,541,500 in 2030.

Again, it is instructive to view these counties in sub-groupings. Due to
their relatively young populations, Milwaukee and Racine Counties are
projected to gain population on the basis of strong natural increase, adding
19 percent to the base population in Milwaukee and 15 percent in Racine.
However, Milwaukee and Racine Counties are also predicted to experience

outmigration during the 30-year period, resulting in net population gains of 9.6 percent and 13.8 percent, respectively.

Kenosha and Ozaukee Counties are expected to gain in both natural increase and net migration through 2030. Kenosha County, as the northernmost county in the Chicago metropolitan area, is predicted to increase its 2000 population by 23 percent through natural increase and 10 percent through migration (32.5 percent overall). Ozaukee County is expected to show a more modest increase of 18.6 percent.

Regional Population Distribution. The fifteen coastal counties will lose a portion of its share of Wisconsin's overall population to other areas of the state. In 2000, the coastal counties comprised 37.1 percent of the state's population; in 2030, their share will fall to 35.7 percent. The Lake Superior counties' share will fall nominally from 1.5 percent to 1.4 percent in 2030, and the Bay-Lake region's portion will grow slightly from 10.2 percent to 10.3 percent. However, the Southeastern Wisconsin coastal counties' proportion will drop from 25.4 percent to 24.0 percent. As was the case in past decades, the southeastern region remains the most significant driver of population trends in Wisconsin's coastal counties.

In 2004, David Egan-Robertson was the Demographer at the Demographic Services Center, Wisconsin Department of Administration.

WISCONSIN'S MARITIME TRAILS

Russ and Cathy Green

Wisconsin has by any standard a rich maritime history. Bordered on the east, west and north by some of America's most important navigable waterways, the Badger State sits at the maritime crossroads of Middle America. The state's economic, industrial and cultural development has been influenced substantially by its proximity to water. Evidence of Wisconsin's maritime legacy is found in the unique stories of its people, its towns, on the state flag, and in a large and well-preserved collection of marine archaeological sites.

Shipwrecks and other submerged sites offer a fascinating way to learn about Wisconsin's past. Kept extremely well preserved by the Great Lakes' cold, freshwater, shipwrecks are virtual underwater museums. Historic documents indicate that over 700 shipwrecks sites may exist in Wisconsin's Lake Michigan and Superior waters alone.

To encourage preservation and visitation of these unique sites and foster wider public appreciation for Wisconsin's maritime cultural resources, the Wisconsin Historical Society (WHS) began the Wisconsin's Maritime Trails initiative in July 2001. Winding above and below the waves, the Maritime Trails encompass four stretches of Wisconsin coastline linking shipwrecks, lighthouses, historic waterfronts, historic vessels, museums and shore-side historical markers and attractions. When viewed as a metaphorical "trail," these resources vividly illustrate the state's diverse maritime history.

Under the Maritime Trails initiative, the state is divided into four regional trails. From the waterfront remains of the logging industry in Washburn to the dramatic wreckage of the steamer *Sevona* in the Apostle Islands, the *Lake Superior Maritime Trail* celebrates the harsh realities that characterized this northern-most region of the state. The *Door County Trail* highlights this vacation peninsula's unique maritime heritage, from its once thriving stone industry to the cargo schooners that sailed this busy shipping corridor.

Upper Lake Michigan Trail attractions include the Wisconsin Maritime Museum and historic Port Washington where the story of the sinking of the steamer *Niagara,* one of the most tragic passenger ship disasters in the Great Lakes, is told along the city's waterfront. Finally, the *Lower Lake Michigan Trail* relays the story of the vibrant ports of Milwaukee, Kenosha and Racine and the histories of immigrants traveling to and the products of industry traveling out of the area via the Great Lakes transportation network.

Some of the Wisconsin's Maritime Trails' major elements include:

Archaeological Research. The documentation of Wisconsin's submerged cultural resources, primarily historic shipwrecks, is the foundation of the Maritime Trails initiative. Beyond academic and resource management applications, the results of this research form the basis of most interpretive and outreach projects.

Shipwreck Moorings and Dive Guides. With volunteer assistance, the WHS maintains permanent moorings on 18 historic shipwrecks. The moorings facilitate recreational access to the sites, offer a means of interpreting the wreck to visitors, provide a safe point of descent for divers and eliminate damage to the site from recreational boat anchors. Rugged waterproof dive guides supply divers with maps, and unique ship construction and dive site details.

Public Presentations. Given at a variety of venues, public presentations provide a direct, personal connection between the WHS and the public. WHS underwater archaeologists and volunteers have reached over 14,700 people via public presentations since the Wisconsin's Maritime Trails inception.

Interpretive Signage and Kiosks. By summer 2004, the WHS will have installed 15 shore side informational markers for historic shipwrecks and waterfronts. All of the signs utilize an identical template unifying them as attractions and information points within the statewide Maritime Trails program. In addition, interactive computer kiosks highlighting Wisconsin's historic shipwrecks will be installed at the Wisconsin Maritime Museum, the Kenosha Public Museum and at WHS headquarters in Madison.

Web Sites. Three sites dedicated to Wisconsin's historic shipwrecks, underwater archaeology, and maritime history provide access to timely and useful information.

- Wisconsin's Maritime Trails at www.maritimetrails.org

- Notes from the Field at www.maritimetrails.org/participate

- Wisconsin's Great Lakes Shipwrecks at www.wisconsinship wrecks.org

Partnerships. The Wisconsin's Maritime Trails program collaborates with federal, state and local agencies, chambers of commerce, private businesses, non-profits and individuals. Funding partners include the Wisconsin Coastal Management Program, UW Sea Grant Institute and the Wisconsin Department of Transportation.

Dozens of volunteer groups such as the Wisconsin Underwater Archaeological Association and the Great Lakes Shipwreck Research Foundation, as well as a growing list of project specific partners and individuals, ensures that all of those with a stake in Wisconsin's maritime cultural resources share in their management and interpretation.

In 2004, Russ and Cathy Green served as Underwater Archaeologists at the Wisconsin Historical Society.

WISCONSIN HARBOR TOWNS: PROMOTING COASTAL COMMUNITIES

Tom Lyons

Dotted along 1,100 magnificent miles of scenic coastline, Wisconsin's harbor towns have welcomed visitors to our shores for more than 150 years. From sophisticated cities to quaint fishing villages, Wisconsin's harbor towns feature outdoor recreation, museums, shopping, arts, dining, relaxing scenery and hospitality.

The Wisconsin Harbor Towns Association—a non-profit organization with membership from communities on Lake Michigan, Green Bay and Lake Superior—formed in 2000 to promote the beauty and attractions found along Wisconsin's coastline under a single brand image. The scope of the organization has evolved from its original focus of attracting cruise ships to include recreational boating, sailing and land-based tourism in coastal towns.

Assisted by a $26,000 grant from the Wisconsin Coastal Management Program, the group in 2003 produced a full-color guide to the Wisconsin harbor towns. The guide beautifully showcases each of the member communities with pictures, marina maps, attractions and special events, and information for boaters, sailors and land-based tourists. Visitors took more than 20,000 copies of the guide in its first six months.

Wisconsin Harbor Towns has since launched online promotional efforts at www.WisconsinHarborTowns.org. The site includes much of the information and images in the printed guide as well as interactive features. Additionally, the group received a crucial $40,000 grant from the Wisconsin Department of Tourism to promote coastal communities in key markets through advertising and public relations. Wisconsin Harbor Towns will also host members of the Midwest Travel Writers Association on a weeklong guided tour along our eastern seaboard in 2004.

The Wisconsin Harbor Towns Association believes that sustainable tourism is an excellent way for people to learn to appreciate and value our shoreline's environmental assets through enjoyment of the many activities they offer. People tend to protect what they value and they value what has personal meaning to them.

Tourism promotion is only the start for Wisconsin Harbor Towns Association. Future efforts under discussion include ways to share information and strategies for dealing with issues such as beach water quality and homeland safety as it applies to our major ports.

With the continued support of our members and strategic partners, the Wisconsin Harbor Towns Association will be a force for positive and sustainable economic growth in the state's shoreline communities.

In 2004, Tom Lyons served as President of the Wisconsin Harbor Towns Association.

Recreational Boating Facilities Program

Larry Freidig

*It's a beautiful summer evening. There is just a whimsy of breeze
from the west and the sun is beginning its final descent. You stand in
a park overlooking the boat basin, the melody of wind in the sailboat
rigging filling the area. The sun reflects off the masts and hulls of the
moored boats and catches the shimmer of an incoming boat, the last
sport-fisher of the day . . . .*

For over 25 years, a small but effective grant program has made this image
a reality for Wisconsin coastal communities. More than creating just an
image, the state's Recreational Boating Facilities Program has made a substantial contribution to the safety and convenience of boaters using our
state's water resources.

This grant program was patterned in 1978 after Michigan's highly
successful boating facility program, but with a significant difference.
Rather than rely on a state agency for investigation, planning, design and
construction of boating facilities, Wisconsin's program offered financial
assistance to local communities to undertake these activities.

Funds for this state cost-sharing program started as general purpose
revenue and bonding. The Legislature in 1985 changed the source to a for-
mula transfer of gasoline excise tax attributed to recreational boating use.

The original legislation also created the Wisconsin Waterways Commission to supervise the program. Each of the five Commissioners represents a particular water "geographical" area: Lake Michigan, Lake Superior, the Mississippi River, the Lake Winnebago watershed and the state's
inland waters.

The Commission supervises the Recreational Boating Facilities Program by assessing the need and feasibility of recreational boating projects either through its own study activities or financial assistance to local

sponsors. It then provides financial assistance to local sponsors for the construction or rehabilitation of eligible facilities.

On coastal waters, these recreational facilities have largely been harbors of refuge, often including multiple lane launch ramps and associated car/trailer parking areas. Prohibited by law from participating in the construction of marinas, the Commission has directed its financial assistance at creating large boat basins protected by breakwater structures to provide flatter water conditions for non-trailerable watercraft during periods of stormy weather.

These harbors also provide for protected launching and retrieving launch lanes for trailerable boats. One only needs to observe the retrieving of sport-fishing boats during a storm event to understand the value of this protection for boater safety.

As coastal communities have recognized the value of once dormant waterfront properties for public recreation and downtown development, the construction of these protected boating facilities have become the catalyst for a variety of urban renewal activities. Public and private development spurred by the construction of harbors in Racine, Kenosha, Port Washington and Sheboygan highlight the importance of safe boating facilities in community redevelopment.

In 2004, Larry Freidig was the Recreational Boating Facilities Program Administrator in the Wisconsin Department of Natural Resources.

PADDLE-TO-THE-SEA

James M. Langdon

The Great Lakes are as impressive and vast as any natural feature in Wisconsin. Their physical enormity notwithstanding, they may also be the most overlooked geographical contributors to our state's history, culture and economy.

The Wisconsin Coastal Management Program (WCMP) has launched numerous initiatives to educate the public about Lakes Michigan and Superior and their shores. In fact, *Wisconsin Great Lakes Chronicle*—first published in 2002—was created to enlighten the citizenry in matters concerning their Great Lakes. More recently, however, the WCMP strove to reach a new audience with its Great Lake education campaign: Wisconsin's children.

The WCMP celebrated its 25th anniversary in 2003 with a gift to the youth of Wisconsin. It distributed to every elementary school and public library in Wisconsin *Paddle-to-the-Sea*, a classic children's book that illustrates the history, character and importance of the Great Lakes.

Paddle-to-the-Sea, written by Holling Clancy Holling in 1941, follows a wooden Indian and canoe as it travels from the headwaters of Lake Superior through the Great Lakes and into the Atlantic Ocean. Although *Paddle-to-the-Sea* won a Caldecott Medal in 1942—presented annually to the most distinguished American picture book for children—its images and story hold up well for today's youth.

The WCMP anniversary edition of *Paddle* includes a classroom activity drawn from *Working with Water: Wisconsin's Waterways*, by Bobbie Malone, Jefferson J. Gray and Anika Fajardo. Guided by the activity, elementary students learn about the ecological and geographical features of the Great Lakes. In addition, children study how the Great Lakes and St. Lawrence River connect the producers of Wisconsin commodities to world markets.

The real strengths of *Paddle-to-the-Sea*, however, are Holling's well-crafted story and engaging illustrations. Children—and adults—learn about the character of the Great Lakes from the water-level perspective of a child's toy. They develop a sense of scale and direction by tracking the path of the toy as it travels throughout the Great Lakes and into the Atlantic Ocean. Holling leaves the reader aware that the Great Lakes are a special place deserving of care and protection.

Teachers, librarians and students from as far away as Italy have expressed interest in the WCMP's *Paddle-to-the-Sea* project. However, the real proof of the project's impact will come years from now when today's children have grown to adults who are more aware and protective of their Great Lakes.

In 2004, James M. Langdon was a Director in the Wisconsin Department of Administration. The WCMP thanked Cathy Techtmann, Bobbie Malone, Houghton Mifflin Company and others for assisting in the development of this project.

2005

FOREWORD

Governor Jim Doyle

Dear Friend of Wisconsin's Great Lakes:

The 1,100 miles of Great Lakes shoreline in Wisconsin shape who we are in this state. Lake Superior and Lake Michigan are critically important for commerce, safe drinking water and countless recreational opportunities. The Lakes are a freshwater resource that is unique on our planet, supporting thousands of species—including our own.

My new *Conserve Wisconsin* environmental agenda is a broad package of legislation and executive orders that will safeguard Wisconsin's great environmental legacy. In addition to initiatives to conserve our lands and ensure a sustainable energy future, the agenda includes many initiatives to protect our waters. We will regulate ballast water in ocean-going ships and work to stop the spread of invasive species.

As the Co-Chair of the Council of Great Lakes Governors, I am working with other governors to develop and implement policies on a region-wide basis to restore and protect the Great Lakes for future generations.

In 2004, nine priorities were identified by the eight Great Lakes governors for restoration and protection of the Lakes. Since that time, these priorities have been adopted by the Great Lakes Mayors and the Great Lakes Commission. Among them:

- Confront the challenge of invasive species and guard against ballast water discharges from oceangoing ships that can damage the Lakes forever.

- Protect the sustainable use of our water resources while confirming that the States retain authority over water use and diversions of Great Lakes waters.

- Ensure the waters stay open as highways of commerce while protecting their fragile ecology.

While the Governors together play an important role, the strength of our recent efforts has been the partnership of our regional collaboration. A robust working relationship has developed with the states, our region's mayors, Native American Tribes, the federal government and nongovernmental organizations concerned about our natural resources.

In December 2004, I joined hundreds of people representing stakeholders from across the Great Lakes basin to develop a restoration and protection plan for our Great Lakes. Our initial draft action plan has been completed and is now available for public review and input. It calls for greater investment of resources and better coordination of efforts to protect and enhance our Great Lakes. Working together, we can make a difference. For more information about the Great Lakes Regional Collaboration, please visit www.epa.gov/glnpo/collaboration.

The responsibility to restore and protect the Great Lakes is not limited to state and local government. We call upon the federal government to recognize the value of our Great Lakes and the influence they have on our country's welfare. We need a commitment of federal resources comparable to those provided for ecological restoration in the Gulf of Mexico, the Everglades and San Francisco Bay.

One of Wisconsin's—and America's—greatest leaders was profoundly aware of the value of the Great Lakes. Former Governor and US Senator Gaylord Nelson passed away in 2005 after a life dedicated to many important issues including protection of the Great Lakes. I was honored to attend a ceremony in August naming the Gaylord Nelson Wilderness area within the Apostle Islands. Gaylord Nelson laid out a clear vision for the environment in 1970 when he founded Earth Day:

"Our goal is an environment of decency, quality and mutual respect for all human beings and all other living creatures—an environment without ugliness, without ghettos, without poverty, without discrimination, without hunger and without war. Our goal is a decent environment in its deepest and broadest sense."

A critical component of this goal is the restoration and protection of the Great Lakes. I invite you to join me in working toward the fulfillment of Gaylord Nelson's vision.

Jim Doyle served as Wisconsin's 44th Governor from 2003 to 2011.

Apostle Islands Wilderness

Harald (Jordy) Jordahl

Lake Superior's Apostle Islands archipelago in Ashland and Bayfield Counties is among the most beautiful and culturally rich places in our state.

The Apostle Islands National Lakeshore is a unique collection of rugged coasts, deep green forests, sea caves and undeveloped sand beaches. Native Americans, voyageurs, loggers, farmers, commercial fishermen and people working in quarries all played a role in the Islands' history. Starting with the Ojibwe people—the original inhabitants of the area—the Islands have provided food, trade and now recreation for generations of people. Its six historic light stations are the most found in any national park. Many still provide beacons to ships on Lake Superior and some remain open to visitors.

Today, the cold blue waters of Lake Superior are covered in summer months by visitors in kayaks, sailboats and motorboats while the Apostle Islands' forests have tents and trails for hikers. Nearly 200,000 people visit every year, a number that has grown as the popularity of kayaking has increased over the last three decades.

The process to protect the Apostle Islands took decades of work and the leadership of Governor and later US Senator Gaylord Nelson. It required nearly 10 years of work by Senator Nelson and a large group of supporters to finally pass federal legislation protecting nearly all of the Islands.

The Apostle Islands National Lakeshore was established on September 26, 1970 "to conserve and develop for the benefit, inspiration, education, recreational use, and enjoyment of the public."

Twenty-one islands in the Apostles are included in the National Lakeshore managed by the National Park Service. The 69,372-acre park includes 21 islands and the waters ¼ mile around their shores. A 12-mile stretch of mainland in Bayfield County is also included. Madeline Island, the remaining island, is mostly privately owned although the State of Wisconsin manages the highly popular Big Bay State Park on its shores.

Although part of the Lakeshore, community leaders believed an official federal Wilderness designation would also provide permanent protection for the Islands' unique natural features. Some form of Wilderness designation for the Islands was considered for decades—even before the federal Wilderness Act was passed in 1964 and before the Apostles became a part of the National Park system in 1970.

The National Park Service initiated a formal three-year Wilderness study in 2001. Strong community feedback supported continuing to protect and manage the Apostle Islands' natural resources and maintaining access to the Islands. Dozens of public meetings were held and thousands of public comments were received over the three years. After formal alternatives were presented for public review, more than 99 percent of the formal public comments supported some form of Wilderness protection.

In 2004, with the leadership of Senator Russ Feingold and Congressman Dave Obey, the US Congress passed a law designating much of the Islands as an official Wilderness Area under the protection of the 1964 Wilderness Act. In so doing, Congress honored the man most responsible for protecting the Apostles by naming the area the Gaylord A. Nelson Wilderness.

The designation of 35,000 acres—about 80% of the land area—as official Wilderness makes permanent the current management for most of the Islands. Sand, Basswood and Long Islands are excluded from the Wilderness because of their highly visible evidence of human history and use. These islands will be used to provide visitors with more opportunities for cultural interpretation and educational materials.

Of the remaining 18 park islands, eight will be managed entirely as Wilderness while the other ten are more than 90 percent Wilderness. Wilderness status ensures that our children and grandchildren find these places much the same when visiting them far into the future.

All of the park's public docks, lighthouses and facilities where visitors congregate are excluded from the Wilderness designation. None of the waters in the Lakeshore are included—guaranteeing continued access to the Islands by boat and without impact on existing rules for snowmobilers who have access to the frozen surface of Lake Superior in the winter. This balance shows the possibility of protecting wild places as Wilderness while also protecting areas for visitors for cultural history and interpretation.

Park Superintendent Bob Krumenaker noted public comment on the Wilderness study confirmed what "Senator Nelson instinctively knew all along—that these islands were meant to be visited, enjoyed and experienced, but that they shouldn't ever be allowed to lose the wild and primitive character that brings people here in the first place."

The Wilderness designation will protect this vision.

In 2005, Harald (Jordy) Jordahl was Director, Intergovernmental Relations, at the Wisconsin Department of Administration.

SUSTAINABLE DEVELOPMENT
IN THE MENOMONEE VALLEY

Mary Beth Driscoll

At 1,500 acres, the largest collection of brownfield properties in Wisconsin continues on the path to restoration. Broad and sustained support from entities like the Wisconsin Coastal Management Program (WCMP) has generated significant progress on a long list of objectives in Milwaukee's Menomonee River Valley: environmental remediation, stormwater treatment, flood abatement, improved water quality and natural areas incorporating habitat restoration.

With partnership and imagination, this contaminated corridor is being transformed into a community destination featuring creative environmental restoration and new economic development. Guided by principles of sustainable development, this long-term collaborative effort is attracting high-quality investors and family supporting jobs capable of adding long-term value and pride to the community.

Starting with a 1999 US Environmental Protection Agency-sponsored Sustainable Development Design Charrette, or visioning exercise, new ideas were generated for development plans that would accommodate sustainability and smart growth objectives. The charrette involved over 140 local architects, engineers and planning professionals from the public and private sectors who engaged in brainstorming and listening sessions and volunteered to create drawings and plans. Their results—published as "A Vision for Smart Growth"—gave form and substance to the vision for sustainable development.

To further accelerate the vision for sustainable development, Sixteenth Street Community Health Center (SSCHC) assembled a broad community partnership to host a design competition in 2002—sponsored in part by the National Endowment for the Arts, the WCMP and foundations—that focused on a specific 140-acre parcel that lies in the shadows of Miller Park. The winning submission, created by a team lead by Wenk Associates of Denver (CO), includes an industrial park that will provide family-supporting jobs while adding to the City's property tax base. While meeting the city's immediate economic needs, the Wenk plan also allows for the integration of natural and open-space elements including a storm-water park that prevents water pollution, a community green and the Hank Aaron State Trail.

With continued encouragement from the WCMP, the national design competition's winning concept has moved much closer to reality with the creation of detailed drawings and engineering specifications for the stormwater park, including an innovative stormwater treatment train that mimics regional habitat types. The stormwater park provides the nec-essary non-point pollution control to allow a portion of the parcel to be densely developed as an industrial park, which in turn will bring jobs back to the Valley and give a boost to the regional economy. The stormwater park provides the ecological benefits of habitat restoration and species di-versity along with a community commons that provides active and passive recreational opportunities.

Designed in concert with the new Canal Street extension, construc-tion of the stormwater park has begun so that it will be capable of treat-ing stormwater from Canal Street starting in 2006. The stormwater park is already serving as a demonstration site by influencing other similar projects, resulting in a more comprehensive approach to water resource management throughout the entire Menomonee Valley.

Principles from the Menomonee River Valley Sustainable Design Guidelines have provided the private sector development community with performance standards for ecological enhancement, restorative techniques and a "how to" for employing a Best Management Practices approach to address these sustainability goals.

The Menomonee Valley Benchmarking Initiative (MVBI) will track and study environmental, economic and community development indicators to gauge impacts of redevelopment in the Valley, including changes to water quality and aquatic habitat. The Menomonee Valley Partners, Inc. (MVP), SSCHC and the University of Wisconsin-Milwaukee Great Lakes Water Institute have collaborated on a WCMP-supported project that will assist the MVBI in measuring changes to the Menomonee River.

This partnership has deployed water quality monitoring technology in the lower reaches of the Milwaukee River basin including two devices in the Menomonee River. These sampling points will provide critical data to the MVBI while also making water quality information available to the general public through a network of kiosks and web-based applications.

Although redevelopment of Milwaukee's Menomonee River Valley has only recently begun, its central location and other attributes have already drawn investors such as The Sigma Group, a private sector firm that has built a highly attractive, sustainable facility in the heart of the Valley. The enthusiastic response Sigma has received to its new offices portends well for the mutual benefits that can be achieved as the Valley's environment is cleaned up and new family-supporting jobs improve the health and livability of the surrounding community.

From a more strategic perspective, it is clear that the revitalization of the Menomonee River Valley offers a compelling story for achieving environmental restoration in urbanized areas that already have the infrastructure needed to support quality development and are close to an available workforce. This pattern of development reduces pressure on farmland and existing open spaces, and protects water quality and water recharge areas that are under enormous pressure from sprawling development. The story of the Menomonee River Valley can play out up and down Wisconsin's magnificent Great Lakes shorelines.

In 2005, Mary Beth Driscoll was Manager of Collaborative Projects, Department of Environmental Health, at the Sixteenth Street Community Health Center.

PROTECTING BEACH HEALTH
IN DOOR COUNTY

Vinni Chomeau

Door County's beaches draw millions of people with diverse interests to the water's edge: swimmers, limnologists, boaters, bird lovers, fishermen, home owners and sunset watchers. All of these persons are connected by a common desire for themselves and future generations to enjoy the thrills and pleasures of Door County beaches without suffering the ill effects of contaminated water.

Door County is an ecological haven for biodiversity. It provides habitat to many threatened and endangered species, is a destination for nearly 2.2 million visitors per year and is the home of 28,000 residents. The health of Door County's 250 miles of Lake Michigan and Green Bay shoreline and near shore waters is invaluable to the county and the State of Wisconsin.

In 2003, the Door County Public Health Department (DCPHD) began regular monitoring of 28 public beaches utilizing Federal Beach Act funds. Additionally, the Door County Soil and Water Conservation Department (SWCD) began the task of determining the sources of beach contamination at all 28 monitored beaches. Each agency contracts with the University of Wisconsin-Oshkosh Biology and Microbiology Department to collect the monitoring and source identification water samples. A comprehensive team of conservationists, health professionals, microbiologists, ecologists, limnologists, statisticians and shoreline/beach experts analyze and interpret the beach data.

Door County has beaches with sand and rock substrates with various degrees of water circulation based on their location within bays and the predominant wind directions. Some of the beaches are in urban areas with stormwater runoff on the beach and others are in rural areas with no stormwater runoff. All of these different beach characteristics make determining potential contamination sources an individual and challenging pursuit at each beach, and establish Door County as an excellent site for researching beach contamination sources and persistence.

With assistance from Wisconsin Coastal Management Program (WCMP), the SWCD in 2003 conducted watershed surveys for every monitored beach. The surveys included mapping the beach watershed and stormwater conveyance systems, determining beach slope and substrate, quantifying land use and identifying potential contamination sources. With a WCMP grant and donations from local governments and organizations, SWCD used the 2003 beach data to enact a water sampling project in 2004 with the sole purpose of identifying beach contamination sources.

In 2004, SWCD water sampling for source identification included expanded sampling at five high priority beaches and a system of rain gauges within five miles of every beach. Source identification sampling included spatial sampling for *E. coli* in 12, 24 and 48 inches of water.

The results showed that *E. coli* concentrations significantly decreased as water depth increased. The average of the samples taken in 48 inches was below the swim advisory level of 235 MPN per 100 ml of water, revealing that the sources of beach contamination are localized from onshore/watershed sources. Analysis of the rainfall events at several beaches with stormwater outlet pipes revealed that *E. coli* concentrations stayed above 235 MPN for eight to 12 hours after rain events of 0.5 inches.

Bird populations were observed using both bird count and bird waste count methods. Bird populations were correlated with *E. coli* concentrations at selected beaches. Genetic codes and the antibiotic resistance of *E. coli* isolates that were recovered from five beaches revealed that there were human and avian sources of *E. coli* present at all five beaches. Four of the five beaches had a significant amount of human derived *E. coli*.

As a result of the 2004 source identification project, two beaches in the City of Sturgeon Bay now issue pre-emptive beach closures based on rainfall. The City of Sturgeon Bay and the Village of Ephraim have extended the source identification water sampling into the stormwater and surface water conveyance systems to isolate sources of contamination. The City of Sturgeon Bay and the Town of Gibraltar have made improvements to their stormwater discharge areas on the beach to improve swimmer safety and beach health.

In 2005—with the assistance of a WCMP grant and local donations—thirteen beaches are being sampled for contamination source identification using the same 2004 methods with an emphasis on isolating sample locations during rainfall events to determine specific sources of contamination.

The efforts of Door County to ensure the safety of water users and protect this valuable resource have not gone unnoticed. After an unfavorable review of their beach monitoring activities in 2003 by the Natural Resource Defense Council, this comprehensive regimen of water quality sampling and bacterial source inventory has placed the county on its Beach Buddy list.

The beach contamination source identification project has provided the county one method of accessing and abating non-point pollution sources. It is essential to the residents, tourists and ecosystem in Door County to monitor and improve near shore water quality for human health protection, water recreation and ecological integrity.

In 2005, Vinni Chomeau was a Conservationist with the Door County Soil and Water Conservation Department.

LAKE MICHIGAN COMMUNITIES REINVENT FOR TOURISM

Jennifer Garrett

Travelers spent nearly $12 billion in Wisconsin last year, and it is easy to see why. The range of activities, accommodations and amenities makes it easy for everyone from earthy campers to highbrow art lovers to find a place to visit, rest, play and enjoy.

However, tourism does not happen by accident. Even lakeshore destinations—blessed with beautiful scenery and access to fishing, sailing and other water-based activities—must constantly reinvent themselves to remain attractive and accessible to visitors.

Some waterfront communities are transitioning from manufacturing to vacation spots. Others are focused on small niches, like nature or cultural tourism. Longstanding favorites continue to improve and evolve as they earn widespread attention and attract visitors from around the globe.

Kenosha. Once an automotive manufacturing center, nearly 90 percent of Kenosha's lakefront is today dedicated to public recreation in the forms of parks, gardens, trails, beaches and fishing piers. Getting from attraction to attraction is easy thanks to the two-mile electric streetcar that connects the historic district, downtown business district, parks and marina.

Paula Touhey, director of the Kenosha Public Museum, says residents are proud to tout their city as a destination that offers unique shopping, great restaurants, good fishing and nature. "Our location between Chicago and Milwaukee is ideal. People can easily enjoy the lakefront, and costs in this area are reasonable."

Racine. Racine, well known for manufacturing, is also making strides with its cultural tourism industry. Jessica Zalewski, marketing specialist for the Racine Art Museum, says the new museum sends a clear message about the importance of investing in tourism as a means of economic growth. "If there is more to see and do, there are clearly more reasons to visit for a longer period of time and more often."

Milwaukee. Milwaukee has been a hotbed of tourism development thanks to a $2.2 billion boom that includes the stunning Calatrava addition to the Milwaukee Art Museum, the Milwaukee Brewers' new home at Miller Park, the Potawatomi Bingo Casino and the Riverwalk. The newest attraction on Milwaukee's lakefront will be Discovery World at Pier Wisconsin due to open in 2006. The redeveloped municipal pier will feature a science, economics and technology museum including special exhibits on freshwater and the Great Lakes. Pier Wisconsin will also be the summer home to S/V *Denis Sullivan*, a 137-foot replica of a 19th century Great Lakes schooner that provides scenic tours and serves as a floating classroom for water and conservation programs.

Port Washington. As long-time manufacturing businesses closed, Port Washington balanced its changing economy by investing in tourism. Concentrated efforts to capitalize on the city's New England-style maritime charm have worked as the local tourism industry has outpaced statewide tourism growth. Kathy Tank, executive director of the Port Washington Tourism Council, says the community has learned to embrace tourism—and not just to fuel the economy. "A town that is attractive to tourists also adds greatly to the quality of life of its residents."

Manitowoc. During World War II, the Manitowoc Shipbuilding Company built 28 submarines for the Pacific War effort. Now Manitowoc's shipbuilding heritage is at the heart of its tourism industry. Every year, thousands of people head to Wisconsin's Maritime Capitol to visit the World War II submarine USS *Cobia*, now an international memorial and historic landmark. The Wisconsin Maritime Museum recently finished a multi-million-dollar addition, and car ferry travelers on their way to Luddington, Michigan, embark from Manitowoc.

Kewaunee County and the Door Peninsula. One has to look no further than Door County to understand how tourism can drive a local economy. The popular lakefront destination draws nature lovers to its beaches, state parks, bikeways and waters. Art lovers can take in live theatre performances or peruse more than 80 galleries and museums. Sturgeon Bay, Algoma and Kewaunee are employing their well-deserved reputations as great fishing communities to attract sport travelers with top-notch charter fishing.

Marinette. Marinette is using its abundant waterfalls and parks to develop a nature-based local tourism industry. Kay Eaton, owner of Eaton

Design Studio which publishes the Marinette County Visitors Guide, says Marinette is focusing on a narrow segment of the traveling population with sport fishing and natural attractions. "We realize that we're not a Wisconsin Dells that has amazing water park attractions, but we do have nature and that really is a nice draw. We like to call ourselves 'Nature's Waterpark.'"

Special Events. Large—sometimes international—events can drive tourism industry development locally and statewide. For instance, the 2004 PGA Championship held at Kohler's Whistling Straits golf course impacted numerous communities along Lake Michigan. Hotels, resorts and restaurants filled up fast when Tiger Woods and the rest of the golf world showed up.

Regional and worldwide visitors are attracted to the beauty and history of Wisconsin's Lake Michigan shores. Coastal communities are using their assets to meet the needs of the traveling public and improve the quality of life for residents.

In 2005, Jennifer Garrett was a freelance writer.

Coastal Performance Indicators

Elizabeth Mountz

How should the nation determine whether it is successfully managing coastal areas? How should limited resources be allocated among numerous coastal priorities such as habitat restoration, coastal hazards and providing public access to the coast?

These are the types of questions that Congress and the federal Office of Management and Budget have asked the national network of state and territory Coastal Zone Management (CZM) programs. In an era of increasing governmental accountability, federally-funded programs are required to develop performance measurement systems to evaluate program effectiveness.

Over the past three years, the National Oceanic and Atmospheric Administration (NOAA) and the 34 state and territory CZM programs have worked to develop a system of performance indicators—using measurable and quantifiable data—that will tell the story of coastal management in the United States. This system is referred to as the National Coastal Performance Measurement System. The Wisconsin Coastal Management Program (WCMP) has played a leading role in this process, participating in both developing and testing the proposed performance indicators for coastal zone management.

Developing Performance Indicators. The process of developing performance indicators first sought to define objectives for which CZM programs are responsible. At first glance, this seems to be an easy task since the Coastal Zone Management Act (CZMA)—the legislation authorizing federal support for state CZM programs—prescribes a wide range of goals and objectives.

However, the CZMA was also designed to give each state or territory the flexibility to develop a management program best suited for its specific needs. The 34 state and territory CZM programs encompass a wide range of variability in climate, geography, cultural norms and political structure. For example, the Puerto Rico CZM program works in a tropical ecosystem that is dramatically different from California's Pacific coastline which in turn differs from Wisconsin's Great Lakes shoreline. Regardless of these differences, each state and territory CZM program works to protect, restore and ensure responsible development of its share of the nation's coastal communities and resources.

In 2003, a NOAA and state CZM program working group developed a draft list of approximately fifty performance indicators based upon six key areas within the CZMA:

- Public access

- Coastal habitat

- Coastal water quality

- Coastal hazards

- Coastal dependent uses and community development

- Government coordination and decision making

In addition, the working group developed a list of contextual indicators that will provide insight to the socio-economic and environmental trends influencing coastal management needs at both state and national scales. For example, the contextual indicators "population density" and "percentage of population change" demonstrate the extent of human-generated pressures upon the coastal environment. The WCMP brought a Great Lakes perspective to the working group ensuring that the resulting indicators would be applicable to both Great Lakes and oceanic coastal systems.

Testing the Indicators. In 2004, the WCMP was one of seven state CZM programs to volunteer for a year-long pilot program to test the usefulness and feasibility of the draft indicators. The WCMP focused on testing the coastal habitat, public access and coastal hazards draft indicators by partnering with programs such as the University of Wisconsin-Madison Sea Grant Institute and the Department of Natural Resources Wisconsin Wetland Inventory program.

During this phase, the WCMP worked to determine whether existing data sources could be used to answer questions such as the number of acres of coastal wetlands in Wisconsin and the acreage of coastal wetlands impacted by permitting decisions within any given year. The WCMP also worked with the University of Wisconsin-Madison Botany Department to adapt Species Dominance Index indicators—originally developed through the Great Lakes Environment Indicators project—for use as coastal management habitat indicators.

Next Steps. In July 2005, all state and territory CZM programs began tracking performance indicators to quantify the national impact of the Coastal Zone Management Program. During the next year, the programs will concentrate on collecting information on the public access and government coordination and decision making indicators. The set of indicators will be expanded to include coastal habitats and coastal water quality.

By the third year of the program, state and territory CZM programs will track coastal hazards and coastal dependent uses and community development indicators providing a strong picture of the condition of coastal management across the United States. A list of the performance indicators and contextual indicators are available online at www.coastalmanage ment.noaa.gov/cpd/welcome.html.

The WCMP will continue to work with NOAA and the other Great Lakes CZM programs to coordinate on a regional level. Data and methodologies will be shared between state CZM programs and with other regional indicator initiatives such as the State of the Lakes Ecosystem Conference and the Great Lakes Environment Indicators project.

The addition of the National Coastal Management Performance System will provide data specifically tailored to the needs of coastal policy makers and resource managers at the state, regional and national levels.

In 2005, Elizabeth Mountz was a Coastal Management Specialist with the NOAA Office of Ocean and Coastal Resource Management.

WATERFRONT REDEVELOPMENT

Andrew Savagian

Our coasts are the places where much of the business of humanity takes root. They are the points where water greets the land, where societies are gathered up and brought together into communities, and where the booms and busts of history have played out for centuries.

Along our Great Lakes shorelines, Wisconsin has marked the passage of time through Native populations, the influx of early European settlers and the rise of manufacturing industries. Today, many of our cities are dealing with polluted places where industries ran their course.

The empty factories, abandoned warehouses and old gas stations that dot the Great Lakes landscape present unique and often difficult issues. They are, however, issues that must be dealt with before communities can reclaim and redevelop these coastal eyesores now labeled "brownfields."

The Benefits of Coastal Redevelopment. A combination of common sense and data are driving our coastal cities, suburbs and small towns to tackle brownfields. Communities benefit financially by replacing vacant properties with thriving businesses. Recent studies have shown that brownfields redevelopment can raise the value of surrounding commercial property by as much as ten percent and residential property by 30 percent.

Waterfront redevelopment also helps protect public and environmental health and preserve valuable green space. Shoreline redevelopment is typically at a higher density, provides ready-made transportation routes and often saps fewer natural resources.

The State can play an important role in successful waterfront redevelopment projects. In Wisconsin, recent figures show that for every one dollar spent in State brownfield grant money, 14 dollars of local funding was invested in redevelopment. These State/local collaborations are creating success stories across Wisconsin.

Sheboygan's Blue Harbor Resort. A high profile coastal redevelopment is playing out on the western shore of Lake Michigan in the City of Sheboygan.

In the 1880s, the city's C. Reiss Coal Company opened its doors for business. More than 100 years later, the company ceased operations and left a waterfront property with environmental contamination problems.

City officials stepped in with new brownfield tools available through the Department of Commerce and Department of Natural Resources (DNR). Utilizing the DNR's technical assistance, the city was able to clean up the soil and groundwater contamination, remove leftover storage tanks and begin redevelopment. In addition to a Commerce brownfield grant of $1.1 million and a DNR Land Recycling Loan, the city invested an additional $3 million on cleanup.

Today the former waterfront eyesore is home to Blue Harbor Resort, a 183-room hotel and conference center with more than 350 employees. The project not only provides an increased tax base of more than $100 million, it also contains a beach restoration area created with funding from the Wisconsin Coastal Management Program. The property is the centerpiece to Sheboygan's coastal redevelopment plan and an excellent example of balancing commercial interests with public access and green space preservation.

Kenosha's Harbor Redevelopment. Part of the fast-growing corridor running from Chicago to Milwaukee, Kenosha had one of Wisconsin's most troublesome coastal brownfields. In the early 1990s, much of its shoreline was taken up with an old American Motors manufacturing plant including more than 40 acres of abandoned buildings, underground tanks and contaminated land.

Working with a host of partners—including the DNR, Department of Commerce, the US Environmental Protection Agency, the Urban Land Institute and private consultants—Kenosha officials began piecing together an impressive array of redevelopment tools and technical assistance.

With more than $2.5 million in funding from these federal and state agencies, Kenosha began remediation by removing eleven underground storage tanks and more than 6,000 cubic yards of contaminated soil.

Cleanup and redevelopment took several years, but today the city boasts two new museums, bike and walking trails, condominium developments and a trolley service to downtown. Not only has the harbor redevelopment created jobs, coastal property values have also increased $50 million since 1989 and nearby property values increased by more than $13 million.

Even more impressive is the city's ability to blend green space preservation with economics, creating a community destination where 90 percent of Kenosha's coastal area is accessible to the public.

Waterfront Revitalization Awareness. The success of brownfield redevelopments depends upon the input and support of citizens who live and work along our Great Lakes coasts. With that in mind, Wisconsin state agencies teamed up with the Great Lakes Commission to host the 2005 Waterfront Revitalization Conference at Blue Harbor Resort. The meeting drew 200 individuals seeking to redevelop contaminated Great Lakes waterfronts.

Conference participants learned about success stories like those in Kenosha and Sheboygan. They also discussed how community participation has helped hundreds of cities all over the Great Lakes turn their blighted shorelines into coastal treasures.

Future conferences and a comprehensive, statewide "one-stop" web site are in the works. Everyone involved in coastal redevelopment believes this momentum will bring new ideas to Great Lakes communities, each one dedicated to the goal of making coastal brownfields a place to gather once more.

In 2005, Andrew Savagian was a Brownfields Outreach Specialist with the Wisconsin Department of Natural Resources.

State and Federal Coordination on Wisconsin's Great Lakes

Kathleen Angel

Enjoy and protect Wisconsin's Great Lakes. This simple statement guides the Wisconsin Coastal Management Program (WCMP) and underlies all of its efforts. The WCMP is best known for providing matching grants to communities and organizations working on economic development and preservation projects along Lake Michigan and Lake Superior. The WCMP's work, however, goes well beyond funding and grants management. An equally important task is monitoring the federal government's activities in the coastal zone through a process called federal consistency review.

Federal consistency is an agreement between a state and the federal government. It comes from Section 307 of the Coastal Zone Management Act (CZMA), the federal legislation under which the WCMP formed. Federal consistency requires that *federal actions that will have reasonably foreseeable effects on land or water uses or natural resources of the coastal zone* must be consistent with a state's federally-approved Coastal Management Program.

Federal Actions. Federal consistency review applies only when the federal government takes an action. Actions include those taken directly by or on behalf of the federal government, such as dredging, construction or planning. Actions also include indirect activities such as federal permitting. Federal financial assistance activities are also subject to federal consistency review. Applications for funds from the Department of Housing and Urban Development, for example, may be subject to federal consistency review.

Reasonably Foreseeable Effects on Land or Water Uses or Natural Resources. Not all federal actions require federal consistency review. In addition to involving the federal government, the activity must have reasonably foreseeable effects on land or water uses or natural resources in the coastal zone. Uses include recreation, fishing, floodplain management and historic preservation. Resources include biological and physical entities such as air, rivers, lakes, aquifers, minerals, plants, fish, reptiles and mammals.

The Coastal Zone. Federal consistency review is subject to the physical boundaries of the coastal zone. States delineate their coastal zones in different ways. In Wisconsin, the coastal zone consists of the 15 counties bordering Lakes Michigan and Superior. All direct actions that involve federal development projects and many federal permitting actions are automatically subject to federal consistency review if they occur in Wisconsin's coastal zone. Even if the planned activity is outside of the 15 counties, the action may be subject to federal consistency review if the project will likely affect the land, water or other resources of the coastal zone.

The Review Process. If the proposed activity is a direct action, the federal agency will determine whether there are any foreseeable coastal effects. If coastal effects are reasonably foreseeable, the federal agency will make its own consistency determination. The agency must give notice to the WCMP at least 90 days before the activity begins. The WCMP then has 60 days to concur with or object to the federal agency's determination.

In the case of a federal license or permit activity, the individual, organization or government agency applying for the federal permit must submit a Consistency Certification to the approving federal agency and the WCMP. The program then has six months to respond. The federal agency may not grant the permit or license until the consistency process is complete.

When reviewing a proposed project, the applicant, federal agency and WCMP will look to the WCMP's enforceable policies. These are the state laws, rules and regulations that the WCMP has identified as related to coastal uses and resources. They can be found on the WCMP's website at www.coastal.wisconsin.gov.

The enforceable policies are a part of the WCMP's federally-approved program. That is, the federal government has reviewed the policies and agreed to abide by them. Furthermore, the WCMP does not develop regulations of its own; its enforceable policies come from state statutes and the regulations developed by other agencies such as the Department of Transportation and the Department of Natural Resources. As statutes and rules evolve over time, the WCMP must revise its policies in response. The WCMP is currently updating its enforceable policies.

Consistency as a Coordination Tool. Federal consistency protects Wisconsin's coastal resources by requiring the federal government to follow state regulations when taking actions that may affect our Great Lakes. The federal government may not approve permits or licenses that violate identified state regulations.

Federal consistency also encourages cooperation between the federal government, state government, local governments and individuals. Furthermore, because the WCMP's enforceable policies are tied to the Wisconsin statutes, rules and regulations, the federal consistency process requires coordination between state agencies.

Federal consistency requirements also help the WCMP stay up to date with projects throughout the coastal zone. Program staff uses this information to share innovative ideas and best practices throughout coastal communities. The WCMP is also better able to make informed decisions on grant requests and provide useful technical assistance to local governments and organizations.

Wisconsin's coastal zone is best managed when all levels of government work together. Federal consistency creates an environment where all may enjoy and protect Wisconsin's Great Lakes.

In 2005, Kathleen Angel was Federal Consistency Coordinator with the Wisconsin Coastal Management Program.

2006

Foreword

Governor Jim Doyle

Dear Friend of Wisconsin's Great Lakes:

All of us here in Wisconsin benefit from the Great Lakes, one of the world's greatest natural resources. Nearly two million Wisconsin residents live along or near the Lake Michigan and Superior shorelines while almost all state residents visit the coasts for work or play. The Lakes and their coastal resources provide abundant beauty, unique natural and cultural resources, recreational opportunities and a source of drinking water.

The Lakes are also important for our state's economy by supporting transportation, manufacturing and energy production. Ecological diversity thrives in the Lakes, even as we continually battle the threat of invasive species. The people of Wisconsin understand and value the need to preserve and protect Lake Michigan and Lake Superior. To commemorate these lakes and what they provide the state, I have proclaimed September 2006 as Coastal Awareness Month.

My administration is committed to improving the quality of the Great Lakes and their coasts. Over the past year, we have accomplished several objectives:

- I requested that the federal government designate a National Estuarine Research Reserve (NERR) on the shores of Lake Superior, the first on either Lake Michigan or Superior. Estuaries are found at the mouths of the many Wisconsin tributary streams to Lake Superior where the inland sea and the Northwoods meet. A Wisconsin NERR would provide needed research to help state, local and tribal governments better manage coastal resources, increase awareness of coastal resources through education and promote stewardship of estuarine areas.

- The Wisconsin Coastal Management Program in the Department of Administration awarded $1.5 million in grants to preserve and enhance Wisconsin's Great Lakes coasts. Nonprofit

organizations, universities and various levels of governments
will support 42 projects totaling $4.1 million.

- Protecting and enhancing our coastal resources—including our
coastal communities—is a priority in my Conserve Wisconsin
conservation agenda that guides the efforts of all state agencies.

Looking ahead, Wisconsin is poised to do even more to protect and
preserve our Great Lakes.

As Chair of the Council of Great Lakes Governors, I hosted a meeting
of the Great Lakes Governors and Canadian Premiers with the goal of de-
veloping a strategy to address proposals that would divert waters from the
Great Lakes and consumptive uses of Great Lakes water within the basin.
On December 13, 2005 in Milwaukee, we joined to sign the *Great Lakes–
St. Lawrence River Basin Sustainable Water Resources Agreement.*

This landmark agreement commits ten state and provincial governments to work together to better manage and protect this unique international resource. It is a good-faith effort between the eight Great Lakes
states and the Canadian provinces of Ontario and Québec. This agreement
is critical because all of the governments committed to collectively manage
our precious Great Lakes. Some of the key parts of the agreement include
new protections against water diversions from the Great Lakes, standards
for in-basin water consumption, provisions for regional water conservation and an affirmation of Native American treaty rights.

These investments we make now to protect and restore Lakes Michigan
and Superior will benefit us and future generations. I ask all Wisconsinites
to join me in working toward a healthier Great Lakes system. These are our
lakes to enjoy and protect.

Jim Doyle served as Wisconsin's 44th Governor from 2003 to 2011.

THE GREAT LAKES–ST. LAWRENCE RIVER BASIN WATER RESOURCES COMPACT AND AGREEMENT

Kathleen Angel

The Great Lakes contain almost 20 percent of the world's fresh surface water. They hold about 23,000 km3 (5,500 cu. mi.) of water, or six quadrillion gallons. Only the polar ice caps and Siberia's Lake Baikal hold more.

The quantity of water in the Great Lakes is enormous. Consumption of Great Lakes water is enormous as well. The Great Lakes provide 56 billion gallons of water per day for municipal, agricultural and industrial use. Forty million people depend on the Great Lakes for drinking water. As populations have grown, pressure to withdraw water from the Great Lakes has also increased.

In 1998, a company named the Nova Group sought permission to remove water from Lake Superior. The proposal would have allowed it to withdraw 160 million gallons of water per day from the lake for sale to Asian markets. The Province of Ontario approved the permit. Although Ontario has since rescinded the permit, the situation heightened public concern over water diversions. The need for inter-state and international coordination also became clear.

Concerns over jurisdiction and management of the Great Lakes are not new. In 1985, the Governors of the Great Lakes states—Wisconsin, Illinois, Michigan, Indiana, Minnesota, New York, Ohio and Pennsylvania—and the Premiers of Québec and Ontario signed the Great Lakes Charter. The Charter is a voluntary agreement that provides for management of the Great Lakes. The Council of Great Lakes Governors, currently chaired by Wisconsin Governor Jim Doyle, assists the Governors and Premiers in coordinating activities under the Charter. Within the United States, the Water Resources Development Act (WRDA) of 1986 prohibited the diversion of water from the Great Lakes to outside the basin unless the diversion was approved by the Governor of each of the Great Lake states.

Nevertheless, Ontario's approval of the Nova Group's proposal and other discussions for water withdrawals demonstrated that the protections were not adequate.

On June 18, 2001, the Great Lakes Governors and Premiers met in Niagara Falls where they signed an agreement to develop binding compacts to protect and preserve our Great Lakes. The agreement was an amendment to the Great Lakes Charter named the Great Lakes Charter Annex of 2001 (the Annex).

Since signing the Annex, the states and provinces have developed implementing agreements. On December 13, 2005, the Governors and Premiers met in Milwaukee where they signed The Great Lakes–St. Lawrence River Basin Sustainable Water Resources Agreement (the Agreement) and The Great Lakes–St. Lawrence River Basin Water Resources Compact (the Compact). The Agreement is a good-faith effort between the Great Lakes States, Ontario and Québec. The Compact is an interstate agreement.

The Compact and Agreement set minimum standards for new diversions—that is, removing water out of the Great Lakes Basin. They prohibit new or increased diversions with a few exceptions: straddling communities (where the water will be taken outside of the Basin, but the community's boundaries are partly inside and partly outside of the Basin), intra-Basin transfers (moving water from the watershed of one Great Lake to another), and straddling counties (where the community is outside of the Basin, but the county is partly within it). The Compact and Agreement also express that a Supreme Court decision, rather than the new agreements, will govern withdrawals from Lake Michigan for Chicago's use.

To qualify for an exception, a proposal must meet a number of requirements that vary depending on the type of project and how much water the community proposes to divert. Proposals for diversions to communities in a straddling county and some intra-Basin transfer proposals need approval by the Council of Great Lakes Governors. Each governor has veto power in such cases.

The Compact and Agreement go beyond addressing diversions. They also create standards that apply to withdrawals and consumptive uses within the Basin. All of the water withdrawn needs to be returned to the source watershed, less an allowance for consumptive use (water that is incorporated into products or lost through evaporation). A withdrawal or consumptive use must be implemented so as to ensure it causes no significant adverse impact to the waters of the Great Lakes.

The proposal must incorporate conservation measures and meet municipal, state and federal laws and international agreements. Finally, the proposed use must be reasonable. The proposal must show that diverted water and existing water supplies will be used efficiently, there is a balance between economic and social development and environmental protection, and potential adverse impacts are considered. The proposal must include a plan for restoration efforts.

The states and provinces are currently undergoing efforts to ratify the Agreement and Compact. The Great Lakes states have committed to working with each of their own legislatures to ratify the Compact. The Compact sets out minimum standards for states. States may, however, adopt more stringent standards. The states will also ask Congress for its approval. State ratification and congressional consent will make the Compact enforceable. Through the Compact and Agreement, the states and provinces are taking steps to protect the quantity as well as the quality of the waters within our Great Lakes.

In 2006, Kathleen Angel was the Federal Consistency Coordinator with the Wisconsin Coastal Management Program.

Spreading the Word about Stormwater Pollution

Kari Jacobson-Hedin

When research assistants from the City of Superior come for a visit, expect to get wet. And muddy. You might even be asked to stick your head and shoulders in a barrel, handle bugs with long legs and lug bags of rocks. It is all for the good of Lake Superior.

Wisconsin identifies stormwater as the leading cause of water quality impairment for Lake Superior, and the City of Superior is in the spotlight for its pollution prevention and stormwater management efforts. The City's Environmental Services Division (ESD) Stormwater Education Program provides Superior residents of all ages the opportunity to participate in hands-on projects that teach ways to prevent stormwater pollution. Activities include planting rain gardens, stenciling storm drains, recruiting volunteer stream monitors and selling rain barrels.

Sixth-Graders Soak Up Science—and Learn How to Plant Rain Gardens. About 125 sixth-graders from Superior Middle School recently spent the entire year immersed in rain gardens. Rain gardens are mini wetlands that collect stormwater and allow it to soak into the ground where contaminants are removed and groundwater reserves are slowly recharged. Rain gardens differ from normal gardens in that they are bowl-shaped and contain native plants that can withstand the fluctuations of wet and dry periods.

Teachers Pat O'Connell and Becky O'Brien partnered with ESD research assistants Kari Hedin and Amber Westerbur to get students involved in the entire process of creating rain gardens. Each activity carried a message about stormwater pollution and the role of rain gardens.

In October 2005, students designed their gardens on paper and held class-wide votes for their favorite designs. They transferred these designs to the grounds of the Middle School by spreading landscape fabric over areas where rainwater naturally collects. In winter, they chose plants using a computer program that allowed them to create virtual gardens, and they grew native seedlings from seeds collected by Ms. Hedin.

Once the five rain gardens were dug out, they helped back-fill them with rocks, sand, peat, compost and mulch—a wet and muddy process! Everything came together in June 2006 when the students planted hundreds of native seedlings. Over their ensuing years at the middle school, they will be able to point out the beautiful blooming gardens that they helped create, and it will remain fresh in their minds that they, too, can keep Lake Superior clean.

Dump No Waste—Drains to Lake! These were the words shouted far and wide by Superior's fifth-graders as they walked city streets using their traffic cones as megaphones. They spread this message in another way—by stenciling storm drains around their school in May 2006. Nearly every fifth-grader from Superior's six schools participated in the stenciling, and approximately 735 drains were stenciled.

Keeping Current on Northern Wisconsin Streams. Visitors to Amnicon State Park in May 2006 were not enjoying a lazy lunch as they sat at picnic tables under the shade of pine trees. They were trying to determine whether the macroinvertebrates in the trays were mayflies or stoneflies. These types of macroinvertebrates caught in the Amnicon River would tell these volunteer monitors something about water quality.

They also strapped on waders and climbed in the river to learn how to measure dissolved oxygen, temperature, water clarity, water flow and habitat condition. The University of Wisconsin-Superior Extension (UWEX) Program and the ESD coordinated the stream monitoring program by recruiting and training volunteers and helping them find wadable monitoring sites on rivers from Superior to Ashland.

"Monitoring is an important way to obtain baseline and trend data, especially in streams where little is known about water quality and habitat condition," said Sue O'Halloran of UWEX.

"Consistent monitoring information is needed to make informed resource decisions," said Scott Toshner, Wisconsin Department of Natural Resources fisheries biologist. "It will help us protect areas with good water quality and point out areas where additional management efforts should be made by our agency."

After a season of monitoring, volunteers will submit their data to an online statewide database managed by Wisconsin Water Action Volunteers. Their hope is to continue this monitoring program and get a clear idea of the water quality of northern Wisconsin streams.

From Pickles to Rainwater. "Time to do the rain barrel reach!" announced Kari Hedin as she reached waist-deep into an empty rain barrel to secure a spigot with a washer and locknut. Afterward, rain barrel workshop participants approached her and fellow research assistant Amber Westerbur to ask if they could get help securing the spigots on their barrels.

They had just learned how rain barrels can keep rainwater from becoming polluted stormwater runoff and are excited to take their rain barrels home. The recycled plastic barrels that once carried pickles from Greece now serve as catch basins for water running off the roofs of hundreds of Duluth and Superior homes. Approximately 420 rain barrels have been sold since 2005.

In 2006, Kari Jacobson-Hedin was a Research Assistant with the City of Superior Environmental Services Division.

Wisconsin Lake Superior National Estuarine Research Reserve

Travis Olson

Lake Superior is the largest and most pristine of the Great Lakes. As such, it has the most at stake in the ongoing efforts to protect and restore coastal ecosystems. Scientific research and regulatory actions are focused primarily on reducing toxic pollution and protecting populations of native species from non-native invaders. Local communities and state and federal agencies are also addressing the effects of land use and runoff pollution through comprehensive planning and improved land management practices.

Despite the impressive achievements of scientists, coastal managers and local communities to increase public awareness and appreciation for restoring Lake Superior's ecosystem, more remains to be done. Much could be accomplished by increasing the knowledge of citizens and decision-makers about the challenges to the lake, and the opportunities for restoring the lake's fisheries, wetlands and other coastal resources.

National System of Coastal Research and Education Centers. Wisconsin is beginning the process of adding a Lake Superior site to a national program that provides opportunities to learn more about managing and restoring coastal resources. The National Estuarine Research Reserve (NERR) System consists of 27 sites that are living laboratories for studying coastal wetlands and neighboring natural communities. Research at these sites is used not only to increase scientific knowledge, but is also translated into practical, on-the-ground actions that citizens and communities can take to protect their quality of life.

Each NERR site begins as a partnership between the state and federal governments to identify a site that contains a type of estuary, or coastal wetland, that has value for research and education. Once a site is selected, a partnership of state, federal, tribal and local governments, as well as citizens and nonprofit organizations, develops a management plan that describes what resources the NERR will manage and the type of information that is most important for local communities to learn from research activities.

The management of a NERR is the state's responsibility, and there are no federal restrictions on the use of a NERR's land and water resources. Existing sustainable uses such as hunting and fishing can continue.

A typical NERR has a boundary that encompasses the core estuarine area from the lake or ocean to a point upriver where the influence of lake or ocean water diminishes. Although the state must control the majority of the area within the boundary, it does not need to own all of the land.

The NERR System provides annual federal cost share grants to support site operation, research and education programs. Construction and acquisition grants are also available. NERR sites are managed by a variety of state agencies including natural resource departments and universities.

Each NERR is part of the national system of reserves. NERR managers across the nation regularly exchange information about estuarine science, land conservation and management and education programs for coastal communities.

Benefits to Wisconsin and Lake Superior. Establishing a NERR on Lake Superior will bring national recognition to the value of freshwater estuaries and the Great Lakes ecosystem. There is currently only one freshwater NERR at Old Woman Creek on Lake Erie in Ohio. Researchers at that site have for over twenty years studied the relationship between agricultural practices and water quality in Lake Erie. Lessons learned there have been used to improve land use planning and educate landowners and communities about how to reduce soil erosion and runoff pollution of local waterways.

A Wisconsin NERR would enhance existing research and education programs throughout the Lake Superior basin. Research on Wisconsin's Lake Superior coast is currently conducted by several institutions including the University of Wisconsin-Superior's Lake Superior Research Institute, Northland College's Sigurd Olson Environmental Institute, the University of Minnesota-Duluth's Natural Resources Research Institute, the US Environmental Protection Agency's Mid-Continent Division in Duluth, and several departments of the University of Wisconsin-Madison. The Wisconsin and Minnesota Sea Grant programs participate in and support much of this research.

Much like the "Wisconsin Idea," the NERR System uses the results of research to improve the design and implementation of government programs. Through the Coastal Training Program, for example, local community leaders and land management professionals learn about how to apply science-based lessons to better manage coastal resources. A Wisconsin NERR would also build on existing community education, public school programs and teacher professional development courses provided by University of Wisconsin-Extension programs, Northland College and the Cooperative Education Service Agency for northwest Wisconsin.

Next Steps for a Wisconsin NERR. The University of Wisconsin-Extension is leading the process, in collaboration with the Wisconsin Coastal Management Program, Wisconsin Department of Natural Resources and The Nature Conservancy, to identify the most appropriate site for a Lake Superior NERR. A Site Selection Technical Team will provide shared leadership and scientific expertise, and will include representation by local individuals and organizations. The site selection and designation process is expected to take three to five years and includes several opportunities for public involvement. The final result of developing a NERR on Lake Superior will be better understanding of Lake Superior's coastal ecosystems and greater integration of research and education for Wisconsin's coastal communities.

In 2006, Travis Olson was the Wetland Protection and Land Use Planning Coordinator with the Wisconsin Coastal Management Program.

THE MILWAUKEE URBAN WATER TRAIL

Cheryl Nenn

When asked what they value most about the greater Milwaukee region, people frequently refer to the close proximity to Lake Michigan or one of the area's three rivers. This is reflected in the building and redevelopment boom along Milwaukee's rivers, improved public access to the waterways, and increasing numbers of anglers and paddlers using the rivers and lakefront.

This change in perception has been brought on in part through improved water quality and river conditions. For instance, the removal of the North Avenue Dam reopened the Milwaukee River to fishing and paddling, and helped flush pollutants out of previously stagnant stretches. As a result, residents and visitors increasingly use our rivers for recreational boating and enjoyment of the natural, cultural and historical attractions that can be discovered from the water.

However, a growing gap existed between interest in riverfront recreation and information about public access to our rivers. Milwaukee River information was primarily passed along through word of mouth rather than by any readily available public source. Access information on the other two rivers, the Kinnickinnic and the Menomonee, was virtually non-existent.

The lack of information on legitimate public access points has lead people to use makeshift, and at times illegal and unsafe, access points.

Problems with these unofficial access points include trespassing on private property, unsafe boat launching points and portages, inadequate or inappropriate parking and damage to sensitive shorelines. In addition, increasing riverfront development is making it harder for paddlers to find access points from the land and distinguish between a throng of unsigned private and public piers from the water.

There was also very little information available for local paddlers on trip planning, water safety hazards and features along our three rivers. Due to these reasons, Friends of Milwaukee's Rivers (FMR) developed the

Milwaukee Urban Water Trail with the support of the Wisconsin Coastal Management Program.

The concept of a water trail is new to many people. Essentially, water trails are liquid pathways that enable non-motorized boaters to find legal access points, resting sites and nearby cultural, historical, and natural attractions. Unlike a hiking or bicycling trail, water trail advocates do not need to acquire land or invest in landscape improvements. Water trails connect people with places, both natural and human-made, connect past to present, and bring the boater into contact with the rivers and surrounding lands. These connections help provide a sense of place within our watersheds, promote stewardship and bring us together as a community.

The Milwaukee Urban Water Trail is a canoe and kayak route through the urban portions of the Milwaukee, Menomonee and Kinnickinnic Rivers containing more than 25 miles of paddling opportunities. The trail includes 33 access sites (including portages), passes through portions of five cities and two counties, and connects the three rivers to paddling opportunities on Lake Michigan.

The Milwaukee Urban Water Trail was created through a collaborative process involving FMR, the National Park Service Rivers and Trails Program, the Wisconsin Department of Natural Resources, the City of Milwaukee, Milwaukee County Parks, several private landowners, environmental groups and concerned citizens. The map was officially released in fall 2005, and is available to the public as a free paper map and digitally on the FMR website at www.mkeriverkeeper.org. All of the Water Trail sites have posted signs identifying them as official public sites to minimize confusion about which sites are public and private.

More than 9,000 Water Trail maps have been distributed and thousands of visitors have viewed the map on the FMR website. As the Milwaukee Urban Water Trail becomes more popular, people increasingly realize that they do not need to travel long distances to go canoeing or kayaking. Instead, they can enjoy the rivers right in their own backyards.

As part of the water trail process, FMR also created a report to provide information on how to physically improve and enhance existing water access sites and associated facilities, identify gaps in access and prioritize development of new access sites and facilities. The recommendations included in this report are meant to serve as a starting point for managing agencies, landowners and interest groups that are encouraged to utilize and build on this information.

The Wisconsin Coastal Management Program is an important partner in these efforts to improve access to our coastal waterways. In addition to the Milwaukee Urban Water Trail, Wisconsin Coastal Management has funded other river access projects including the design of the Urban Ecology Center launch along the Milwaukee River and the new launch on the Hank Aaron State Trail along the Menomonee River.

The Milwaukee Urban Water Trail builds on a series of efforts to bring life back to the rivers of the greater Milwaukee area by improving river access, water quality and wildlife habitat. The Water Trail connects people more closely to their rivers and encourages responsible use of our rivers and Lake Michigan. By getting people out on the water, more residents and tourists will be inspired to become stewards of our rivers.

In 2006, Cheryl Nenn was Riverkeeper/Project Director with Friends of Milwaukee's Rivers.

MASHKIIGIMIN (CRANBERRY) IN THE KAKAGON SLOUGHS

Leah Anne Gibala

The Bad River Band of Lake Superior Tribe of Chippewa Indians is a federally recognized Tribe organized under the Indian Re-organization Act of 1934. There are approximately 7,000 enrolled tribal members with about 2,700 living on or near the reservation. Our reservation has 124,654 acres of land within the exterior boundaries and is located in northern Wisconsin approximately 72 miles east of Duluth, Minnesota. The heart of our community is within the town of New Odanah, (Ō-day´-nǎ), translated loosely in English as *town*. To outsiders, we are known as *Anishinabe Odeto´win*, or *Place of the People with Good Hearts*.

Wetlands cover nearly 25 percent of the Bad River Reservation, the largest being the Kakagon/Bad River Sloughs. Comprising 12,000 acres, and formed behind a series of sand spits on the south shore of Lake Superior, this single freshwater ecosystem is the Band's most culturally important wetland. It is described in the Federal Registry as "perhaps the finest marsh complex on the Upper Great Lakes."

Within the Bad River Integrated Resources Management Plan (IRMP), wetland conservation is considered a high priority. Specifically, threats to the ecology of the Kakagon/Bad River Sloughs are of concern and include nutrient loading, increased sedimentation, increased recreational and developmental activities, the introduction of exotic species and fluctuations of Lake Superior surface levels.

Native wild cranberry is a historically significant resource in the Kakagon/Bad River Sloughs. Two types of trailing cranberry—*Vaccinium macrocarpum* (large cranberry) and *Vaccinium oxycoccos* (small cranberry)—are commonly found in tamarack swamps and wire-grass sedge meadows that have a sphagnum moss component and wet acidic soils. Both plants grow low on creeping stems, but the small cranberry has branches that can reach up to ten inches high. The large cranberry has alternate leathery leaves and pale pink flowers with recurved petals and stamens that form a beak resembling a crane. The small cranberry has alternate evergreen leaves with rolled edges and a pale underside and small pink to white flowers.

Aniibimin, as large cranberry is called by the Great Lakes Ojibwa, has a round to oval tart red berry that may stay on the vine throughout the winter. Traditionally, the berry was eaten raw or drunk as a tea. An infusion of the plant was occasionally used as a remedy for nausea. *Mashkiigimin*, as small cranberry is known, is red and sour. The Ojibwa took this plant to treat slight nausea and ate the berries as food.

Anecdotal evidence from Band members suggests a significant decline in the abundance of wild cranberry over the last forty to fifty years. Currently, there is little harvest of this culturally important plant because of the scarcity of harvestable stands.

In order to initiate a restoration of the historically significant sites or a reintroduction of viable plants into the system, it is necessary to establish baseline information with regard to cranberry presence and environmental conditions in the areas of interest. This project comprises the initial assessment of sites based on cultural importance and historical significance, and the evaluation of long-term monitoring protocols to study trends in cranberry productivity. The project also provides the Bad River Natural Resources Department with the baseline data needed to develop a long-term monitoring project within the Kakagon/Bad River Sloughs to effectively manage wild native cranberry habitat in coastal wetlands.

This project is part of an integrated and cooperative effort to preserve native plants in coastal wetlands on the Bad River Reservation in the Kakagon/Bad River Sloughs. Bad River agencies—Bad River Natural Resources Department, Bad River Legal Department, Gitiganing Gardening Committee and the Bad River Vistas—will work with the Natural Resources Conservation Service and the Great Lakes Indian Fish and Wildlife Commission on the following three components:

Wetland Protection and Habitat Restoration. Methods in tracking trends in wild native cranberry will be assessed in the coastal wetlands of the Kakagon/Bad River Sloughs which will enable the Band to effectively recognize changes and potential threats to the conservation of the ecosystem. The establishment of regular sampling in the sloughs will begin our tracking of the effects of lake level changes on the vegetative communities of the Kakagon/Bad River Sloughs.

Great Lakes Education. At the completion of the project, an educational brochure will be distributed to the community that discusses appropriate activities within the sloughs, sustainable harvest techniques and the historical and cultural significance of cranberry and the Kakagon/Bad River Sloughs. The brochure will provide community members and those living off reservation with background information on the importance of the Kakagon/Bad River Sloughs and the conservation of native plant communities.

Coastal Resources and Community Planning. The project will result in the development of a guidance document and a detailed map to be included into the Bad River GIS database. These resources will depict cranberry densities in areas of interest and be incorporated into the Tribe's existing IRMP as a management tool to preserve culturally significant native plants in coastal wetlands located in the Kakagon/Bad River Sloughs.

In 2006, Leah Anne Gibala was a Wetlands Specialist with the Bad River Natural Resources Department.

Project Shipshape

Carolyn Colwell and Virginia Schwartz

Milwaukee sits on banks where three rivers gather, gazes out across the waters of Lake Michigan and welcomes visitors from all over the world. Transportation activity on these inland seas was in the early days by paddle and sail, later by steam and today by a variety of propulsion systems. Documenting past Great Lakes' marine activity is an important task because it helps educate twenty-first century citizens about their world and prepare them to deal with the future.

The Wisconsin Coastal Management Program has helped streamline the documenting process by funding Project Shipshape, but we are getting ahead of our story . . .

Milwaukee Public Library. Just one mile from Lake Michigan, the venerable Milwaukee Public Library's Central Library houses one of the largest collections of information on Great Lakes vessels: The Great Lakes Marine Collection. Books, magazines and journals, nautical charts and many other materials are included in the collection, the heart of which is the Great Lakes Vessel Files containing information on over 9,000 ships. The cornerstone of the Great Lakes Vessel Files is the Herman G. Runge Collection, acquired by the library in 1958.

Mr. Runge devoted almost 70 years of his life to collecting and preserving information on all aspects of marine activities on the Great Lakes. He journeyed to the principal lake ports to visit with government and shipping officials, captains and crews of lake boats, ship photographers and fellow collectors. He also kept up a heavy correspondence with other compilers, government agencies and shipping lines. At his death in 1958, he was one of the most knowledgeable and colorful collectors on the lakes.

The Runge Collection contained information on thousands of ships that sailed the lakes as well as approximately 17,000 photographs of Great Lakes ships. It was later augmented by other collections—including the Stevenson and Kramer collections—and together today form the Vessel Files.

Heavily used, the Vessel Files are individual folders of data on more than 9,000 vessels that sailed the Great Lakes from 1679 up to those that are on the Lakes today including diesel-powered, sailing, barges, cargo vessels, passenger boats, military ships and even pleasure craft. The file for each vessel includes a datasheet outlining the vessel's size and history, captains and changes of name. Many of the files also include photographs. The collection is extensively used by divers, genealogists, historians, students and others.

Project Shipshape. Years ago, the Milwaukee Public Library and the Wisconsin Marine Historical Society—a nonprofit organization founded to care for the Runge Collection—recognized the need to make the Vessel Files more widely available and secure. Staff decided that the information on the datasheets should be digitized—converted into an electronic database with the goal of preserving the collection and making the information available on the Internet.

In the maritime world, shipshape means the arranging of things properly, neatly and trimly. Therefore, this effort was called Project Shipshape. An undertaking of this size might overwhelm a city-funded library and its generous, but small, friends group. However, this goal is today being realized with the assistance of grants from the Wisconsin Coastal Management Program.

The library and Marine Historical Society received Coastal Management matching grants for Project Shipshape to create a database containing the information from 9,000 datasheets on Great Lakes vessels. These include 2,000 files on vessels that sailed prior to 1870, an important period in Great Lakes history and a distant time for which relatively little information is available. The funding will also realize the goal of making the database available on the Internet.

Private citizens generously give their time and talent to make the project a success. Many of the volunteers are members of the Marine Historical Society, college students and retired library and other City of Milwaukee employees. The volunteers perform research, data entry, proofreading, photocopying, filing, software advising and inventorying of the photo collection.

The digitized files are currently available on a standalone computer at the Milwaukee Public Library and by June 2007 will be available on the Internet. It will be possible to search by vessel name, when, where and by whom the vessel was built, type of vessel, number of masts, and official number.

With the completion of Project Shipshape, historians can use the speed of the computer as their assistant. The collection will also be more readily available to recreational and archeological divers. Genealogists will discover information on ancestors through names of owners, captains, shipbuilders and others associated with a vessel. Once the vessel file datasheets are available online, researchers will be able to order the entire contents of the file—including photos and articles—for a small fee.

Project Shipshape has put the Vessel Files in convenient order: neat, tidy and soon on the Internet. The online Vessel Files will become an even more valuable source of information to researchers and others throughout the world.

In 2006, Carolyn Colwell was the Great Lakes Marine Librarian and Virginia Schwartz was the Arts and Humanities Coordinator with the Milwaukee Public Library.

COASTAL COMMUNITY PLANNING

Angela Pierce

By 2010, Wisconsin law requires that local and regional land use decisions be based upon an adopted comprehensive plan. As a result, communities have been actively adopting new plans or updating existing plans to be consistent with the State's comprehensive planning laws.

While similar issues are addressed in most comprehensive plans, coastal communities face unique planning challenges. It is essential that coastal communities embrace their distinctiveness as they envision their future and develop meaningful comprehensive plans.

Wisconsin defines a coastal community as located within a county that has shoreline on Lake Michigan or Lake Superior. Wisconsin has fifteen coastal counties and about a third of the state's population resides within these coastal areas.

With continued growth pressures on coastal resources, it is important that communities address unique coastal issues and opportunities as they relate to each of the nine elements of their comprehensive plan:

- Agricultural, Natural and Cultural Resources

- Housing

- Economic Development

- Transportation

- Public and Community Facilities

- Intergovernmental Cooperation

- Land Use

- Issues and Opportunities

- Implementation

Coastal issues are intertwined with every element, and management decisions in each area will likely impact coastal resources. When addressing *agricultural, natural and cultural resources*, coastal communities need to consider issues and assets unique to the Great Lakes including shore erosion, coastal wetlands, invasive species, lake level fluctuations, public access, historical and archaeological resources, coastal hazards, and beach health and safety.

Coastal communities need to balance residential *housing* development and maintaining the health and natural beauty of the coast. Growing numbers of landowners and visitors to coastal areas can cause user conflicts, create stress on finite resources and significantly impact the sustainability of the coastal environment.

Coastal communities must also balance *economic development* and natural resources. The coastal ecosystem is an economic asset that provides a variety of aesthetic, ecological, recreational, industrial and life-sustaining benefits that must be properly managed. The complex physical and biological processes of coastal ecosystems provide value to people and communities in many ways that can be measured in both dollars and non-monetary ways.

In addition to typical *transportation* issues, coastal communities need to consider unique transportation features such as ports, harbors, marinas, dredging and waterfront storage facilities.

As part of the *public and community facilities* element, coastal communities must discuss the availability of public access to the shoreline for recreational activities. As growth in coastal areas increases, many public access sites are lost to development or conversion to private lands. Moreover, user conflicts may develop because many existing public access areas are unclearly marked or have no signage at all. Coastal communities must also contend with distinctive facilities considerations related to water supplies, sanitary systems, stormwater management, coastal safety, emergency services and beach health.

A community's relationship with neighboring communities can influence planning, public facilities and services. An examination of these relationships and the identification of existing or potential conflicts can help communities address situations systematically. *Intergovernmental cooperation* can be even more significant when communities share coastlines and resources.

The *land use* element includes an inventory and discussion of existing land use controls within the community that may affect or restrict the use of land for specific purposes. Land use issues of particular importance to coastal communities include bluff setbacks and recession rates, shoreland housing densities and lot sizes, second tier development, shoreline overlay zoning and commercial port development.

The *issues and opportunities* element discusses community development goals, objectives and policies. The community should identify specific concerns and values it holds about coastal assets and issues. It is also important that coastal communities develop a vision for protection of its coastal resources. Visioning should identify coastal resources that need to be protected or preserved and the manner in which it will be accomplished.

The final element in a comprehensive planning program is *implementation*. Various implementation tools are available to help turn a community's vision into reality including erosion control ordinances, setback ordinances, shoreline overlay zoning and stormwater management ordinances.

As Wisconsin coastal communities undertake the task of developing comprehensive plans or updating existing plans, a planning guidebook entitled *A Guide to Planning for Coastal Communities in Wisconsin* can prove quite helpful. The *Guide* was developed by the Bay-Lake Regional Planning Commission—with financial assistance from Wisconsin Coastal Management Program—to help Wisconsin communities address coastal issues and opportunities within their comprehensive plans.

The *Guide* discusses coastal issues as they pertain to each of the nine elements of a comprehensive plan and offers information and planning tools on Great Lakes coastal issues, implementation ideas to achieve common coastal planning goals, and references and contacts for further assistance. A copy of the *Guide* is available for download at www.baylakerpc.org or by contacting the Bay-Lake Regional Planning Commission.

In 2006, Angela Pierce was a Natural Resources Planner with the Bay-Lake Regional Planning Commission.

2007

FOREWORD

Governor Jim Doyle

Dear Friend of Wisconsin's Great Lakes:

Here in Wisconsin, our beautiful Great Lakes are not just a part of our heritage. They are a part of who we are. Lakes Michigan and Superior and their coastal resources provide the State with abundant beauty, unique natural and cultural resources, recreational opportunities, a gateway to the world economy and clean drinking water. Helping people enjoy and protect our Great Lakes is one of my top priorities as Governor.

Over the last several years, we have made great strides to help citizens and visitors enjoy our Great Lakes. Earlier this summer, I dedicated Wisconsin's newest state park—Lakeshore State Park—in Milwaukee. This new state park provides yet another reason to visit Milwaukee and greatly benefits Milwaukee residents who no longer have to drive outside the city to experience Wisconsin's natural beauty—instead, it is right in their backyard.

Further north, we permanently protected thousands of acres of beautiful recreational and conservation lands including nearly nine square miles along the Brule River—a Lake Superior tributary famous to people who fish, canoe and kayak—and nearly four miles of the North Country National Trail. Working together with the federal and local governments, the Bayfield Regional Conservancy and the Wisconsin Coastal Management Program, we also protected miles of hiking and ski trails surrounding Bayfield County's Mt. Ashwabay with breathtaking views of the Apostle Islands in Lake Superior.

Another initiative—funded in part by a Wisconsin Coastal Management grant—will help people use the power of their computers to see, learn about and plan visits to sites along out Great Lakes coasts. The Great Lakes Circle Tour–Coastal Access Guide follows the Circle Tour driving route and provides visitors with information about and pictures of coastal parks, beaches, lighthouses, shipwrecks and other features along the way. This project and others like it helps make our coastal sites, communities and attractions easier than ever to visit and experience.

As Chair of the Council of Great Lakes Governors, I am working with other state and provincial leaders to protect both the quality and quantity of the Great Lakes. The *Great Lakes–St. Lawrence River Basin Sustainable Water Resources Agreement* commits the ten state and provincial governments to work together to better manage and protect this unique international resource. The Agreement includes new protections against water diversions from the Great Lakes, standards for in-basin water consumption, provisions for regional water conservation and an affirmation of Native American treaty rights.

I am also working closely with the Legislature, Tribes, local governments and organizations to enact the *Great Lakes–St. Lawrence River Basin Sustainable Water Resources Agreement* here in Wisconsin. Implementation of this agreement will help the region ensure the quality and long-term protection of the Great Lakes for future generations.

The Great Lakes belong to us all and so does the responsibility to protect them. I ask all Wisconsinites to join me in working toward a healthier Great Lakes system. These are our lakes to enjoy and protect.

Jim Doyle served as Wisconsin's 44th Governor from 2003 to 2011.

REVITALIZING RACINE'S NORTH BEACH

Dr. Julie Kinzelman

As recently as 2000, Racine's North Beach was posted as unsuitable for swimming for 66 percent of the bathing season. Concerned citizens turned to the City of Racine to return this stretch of Lake Michigan coastline to a valuable community asset.

Identifying Contamination Sources and Initiating Remediation. The Racine Health Department embarked on a five-year course of research initiatives to identify the pollution sources responsible for swimming bans and develop cost-effective solutions to improve recreational water quality.

In one instance, research identified elevated fecal bacterial levels at a storm water outfall that discharged rainwater collected from 400 acres of the city directly at the beach. Rick Jones, Commissioner of Public Works, made reengineering the site a priority.

The new design called for the installation of two primary treatment systems capable of removing street waste and diverting the initial—and dirtiest—surge of stormwater to a series of infiltration basins. The constructed basins are wetland areas planted with over a dozen varieties of native wetland plants such as bulrushes, grasses and sedges. This natural treatment system reduced the median fecal indicator bacteria from 3,000 CFU/100 ml in 2000—the year immediately preceding construction—to 448 CFU/100 ml in 2004.

Sands also contributed to North Beach's contamination problem. Research studies indicated that sands were acting as a reservoir for fecal bacteria deposited by the large resident population of seagulls. Certain conditions—such as surface run off, wave action or groundwater exchange—promoted the delivery of bacteria to near shore waters.

Three major efforts were taken by the Department of Parks, Recreation and Cultural Services (PRCS). First, mechanical beach grooming was altered to promote the drying of the beach sand, demonstrated to significantly reduce fecal indicator bacteria density. Second, the initial re-surfacing of beach sand after removal of snow fencing in the spring was done in a way to promote drainage and prevent the formation of swales that could retain water on the beach. Third, additional waste receptacles with rigid, removable liners were placed on the beach to encourage the proper disposal of litter by beach goers as a deterrent to attracting more seagulls.

Other potential sources of pollution, such as algal blooms and the Root River, likely exist and the City of Racine Departments of Health, Parks and Public Works continue to work cooperatively to investigate and mitigate as necessary.

Research also revealed that water quality may vary suddenly in response to certain environmental conditions. Therefore, better methodologies are needed to more rapidly analyze water samples. The Health Department is currently working on faster ways to detect pollutant loading using real-time DNA-based tests.

Creating Public Awareness. Municipal efforts identifying and mitigating pollution sources must be partnered with public education to realize maximum benefits. Several public awareness campaigns centered on water quality issues are helping citizens become stakeholders and stewards of coastal areas.

In 2007, the PRCS Department and City of Racine will enter into an agreement with UW-Parkside to establish a Center for Community Partnership to improve public awareness of Great Lakes resources and related ecological issues. The City also enacted an ordinance prohibiting the feeding of seagulls (prominently displayed near the concession area at the beach), placed educational signage along the Lake Michigan Pathway and distributed hangtags to numerous homes to inform the public about the relationship between storm water and surface water quality. Keep Our Beaches Open, a local environmental group based out of the River Bend Nature Center, initiated campaigns to flag dog waste left by pet owners, provided bags for pet waste removal and volunteered to stencil city storm drains.

The Spirit of Volunteerism is Alive and Well in Racine. Several volunteer efforts have also been instrumental in improving and maintaining North Beach. Volunteers assisted the City in installing wetland plants in the infiltration basins. Earth Day and Make-A-Difference Day activities have focused on beach clean-ups, the construction of a new walking path bordered by native plants and the formation of vegetated dunes to reduce blowing and drifting of sand near public access points.

Adopt-A-Beach groups—an initiative of the Alliance for the Great

Lakes—routinely conduct citizen monitoring and litter removal from designated areas along the shore. In 2003, Make-A-Difference Day volunteers constructed Kid's Cove Playground, a 20,000 square foot play area.

Revitalizing the Lakefront. In 2006, North Beach was open 95 percent or more for two consecutive bathing seasons. Once an under-utilized and lonely stretch of Lake Michigan coastline, North Beach is now buzzing with activity and host to a variety of nationally recognized events including the Spirit of Racine Triathlon and the Corona Light EVP Volleyball Tour. The Kid's Cove Playground is a year round attraction for children.

The Lake Michigan Pathway, completed in 2006, provides almost ten miles of scenic Lake Michigan views for pedestrians and bikers. The North Beach Oasis provides concessions and live music from Memorial Day to Labor Day. In Racine, scientific research, municipal teamwork and community efforts have resulted in a vibrant, revitalized lakefront that is home to Wisconsin's only Blue Wave beach (certified by the Clean Beaches Council, Washington, D.C.)

In 2007, Dr. Julie Kinzelman was an Environmental Microbiologist with the City of Racine Health Department.

THE NIAGARA ESCARPMENT: A UNIQUE WISCONSIN COASTAL RESOURCE

Angela Pierce

The Niagara Escarpment is generally not a recognized name in Wisconsin. However, most northeast Wisconsin locals are familiar with the feature known commonly as *The Ledge* that runs along Door County's Green Bay shoreline into Brown County. The Niagara Escarpment is a distinguishing natural resource area due to its unique geology, the presence of rare plants and animals, and growing development pressure.

The Niagara Escarpment is a geologic landform that was formed 430 to 450 million years ago when current day North America was near the equator and submersed under a shallow warm sea centered on what is now the State of Michigan. The outer rim of this ancient sea, crossing present state and national borders, now marks the location of the Niagara Escarpment.

The escarpment is a sickle-shaped ridge with a steep face on one side and a gentle slope on the other that begins in south-central Wisconsin, arches east through Michigan and southern Ontario and ends in western New York State. The best-known portion of the Niagara Escarpment is the section of the ledge over which the Niagara River falls to form Niagara Falls. The Niagara Escarpment in Ontario, Canada is a United Nations Educational, Scientific and Cultural Organization (UNESCO) designated World Biosphere Reserve, making it part of a network of more than 400 reserves in 95 countries.

Since the Niagara Escarpment was formed prior to glaciations, glacial ice cover and melt water have dramatically altered it. The Escarpment in Wisconsin varies from prominent rock faces with 150-foot cliffs to a series of ledges, low cliffs and pavement including areas where the escarpment is completely buried—and may only be evident in a quarry. The visible effects of the glaciation seen on the escarpment today were shaped during the most recent stage of glaciation called the "Wisconsin Glaciation."

The Niagara Escarpment is sometimes overlooked as a coastal resource in Wisconsin even though the escarpment is the shoreline of much of the

Door Peninsula on the Green Bay side. The Niagara Escarpment in Wisconsin is present almost continuously from the tip of Washington Island to the northeast side of the city of Green Bay. Beyond the city of Green Bay, the Niagara Escarpment becomes intermittent as it is covered with glacial till for several miles in sections and reappears in other sections as it continues into south-central Wisconsin.

The climate, ecology and geology of the escarpment are significantly influenced by the Great Lakes that surround it, creating unique microenvironments that support a diversity of life including many threatened and endangered resources. The landscape of the Niagara Escarpment supports unique natural relationships and communities that include alvars, oak savannas, communities of threatened dwarf lake iris, and cliff face communities of slow-growing cedars that are over 1,000 years old. Additionally, the escarpment provides habitat for a number of migratory birds, bats, the endangered glacial Relict land snails and the Hines Emerald dragonfly.

The cultural resources on and along the Niagara Escarpment are numerous as well and include archeological sites, pictographs and petroglyphs, mounds, lighthouses, lime kilns and caves, historic farmsteads and over 500 historic sites, 37 of which are on the National Register of Historic Places.

According to a study completed by the Bay-Lake Regional Planning Commission, *An Inventory and Assessment of the Resources of the Niagara Escarpment in Wisconsin* (March 2001), the Niagara Escarpment area is experiencing steady population growth and development pressure, especially along the coastal Niagara Escarpment area adjacent to Green Bay. This sensitive shoreline ecosystem is vulnerable to misuse from improper land development and resource extraction.

Although much of the Brown and Kewaunee County shoreline along Green Bay is already developed and experiencing second and third tier development, a significant amount of the Green Bay shoreline in Door County along the escarpment remains undeveloped as wooded or agricultural land. Current trends reveal that development will likely continue to consume the escarpment since few land use controls exist to protect it.

The Niagara Escarpment is a special coastal resource in Wisconsin and we are fortunate to have it here. It is important that we all work to ensure that this unique resource will be available in a natural state for future generations to marvel. We should follow the lead of our Ontario neighbors and work at preserving the remaining undeveloped portions of the escarpment before they are lost to us. The time to act is now.

The Niagara Escarpment Resource Network is a great organization to turn to for additional information on the Niagara Escarpment in Wisconsin. The Network is a coalition of federal, state and regional agencies, local and county governments, academia, non-profit organizations, landowners and citizens whose purpose is to provide a common forum for discussion and action promoting balanced land-use decisions and an appreciation for the unique ecology of Wisconsin's Niagara Escarpment. Involvement with the Network is a great way to learn more about the escarpment. The group meets regularly and always welcomes new members. For more information on the Niagara Escarpment Resource Network, check out its website at www.escarpmentnetwork.org/.

In 2007, Angela Pierce was a Natural Resources Planner for the Bay-Lake Regional Planning Commission.

Lake Superior Coastal Visual Quality

Jason Laumann

In a rapidly developing world, visual resource planning and management are becoming increasingly important as means of preserving fundamental community character. Nowhere is this statement more relevant than along Wisconsin's Lake Superior south shore where natural scenic beauty is among the region's most prized natural assets. It is also one of the most compelling reasons why people choose to live and recreate in the shadow of the great Gitche Gumee.

The south shore coastal environment is rich in visual diversity and character. Unique local landforms, scenic shorelines, rock and cliff formations, vegetation and the land-water interface combine to create a striking visual landscape. The Apostle Islands add visual interest and provide an element of scale to the flat horizontal expanse of Lake Superior. The rugged natural beauty, visually distinctive architecture and historic resources of quaint coastal communities intertwine in a harmonious visual composition.

In recent years, the south shore has come under increasing development pressure that threatens to change the visual landscape. The relative remoteness of the region has not isolated the south shore from development. In fact, it is this very remoteness—and the natural scenic values associated with it—that attracts people and development. Increasingly, communities across the country have begun to recognize scenic beauty as a tangible resource critical to core community character, local economies, health, well-being and quality of life. Along the south shore, the winds of change have also focused increased attention towards the concept of sustainability and maintenance of the unique scenic and ecological values of the region.

The Northwest Regional Planning Commission (NWRPC) recently completed a guide to protecting the visual resources of Wisconsin's Lake Superior south shore, a project funded through a grant from Wisconsin

Coastal Management Program. This guide fosters a general understanding of the visual resources of the south shore coastal landscape and provides an overview of tools and techniques for the preservation of natural scenic beauty. This document is intended to assist south shore communities in planning for and protecting natural scenic beauty. It is also meant to serve as a companion document to Wisconsin's growing library of community planning assistance guides. While this guide focuses on the south shore of Lake Superior, its recommendations, tools and methods for visual resource protection could be applied in virtually any community, regardless of geographic context.

The guide provides an overview of the landscape and design elements used to characterize and evaluate scenic beauty. By exploring basic visual quality concepts such as vividness, intactness and unity along with the foundational landscape characteristics that contribute to scenic beauty, the reader is equipped with a basic knowledge and understanding of how scenic beauty can be defined and measured.

The guide also attempts to dispel the notion that scenic beauty is purely a subjective judgment by illustrating that there are objective, quantitative methods for assessing scenic beauty. Quantitative methods for analyzing visual resources are commonly used by federal and state resource management agencies to evaluate project proposals and management alternatives. By removing the element of subjectivity from the concept of visual quality—and by providing objective, reproducible methods for assessing scenic beauty—a basis is provided for regulating activities that influence visual quality.

The publication provides a range of implementation tools for local government and voluntary building and site design recommendations for private landowners. For communities, an overview of both regulatory and non-regulatory approaches serves as a primer to stimulate local discussion. The guide also strongly advocates the integration of visual resource planning into community comprehensive planning efforts and provides guidance on how this may be accomplished.

A key section of the document explores how subdivision design may influence scenic beauty. The guide uses 3-D visualizations of subdivision design policy alternatives applied to two actual sites along the Lake Superior south shore. These sites were first analyzed to identify existing environmental features such as surface waters, steep slopes and wetlands and then split into lots based on traditional subdivision design and a cluster-type conservation design. Three-dimensional homes were then placed on the lots in both developments.

To achieve the highest level of success, government regulation must work in concert with the voluntary efforts of private landowners who are willing to make a commitment to preserving scenic beauty. Collectively, private landowners can have a tremendous impact on the scenic beauty of the south shore. A step-by-step tutorial guides landowners through site analysis, building site selection and the site plan development process. The guide also examines the use of scenic beauty conservation techniques for structural design, exterior finishing, roofing and exterior lighting.

Education is the first step toward a sustainable future. It is hoped that this guide will foster a better understanding of the importance of scenic beauty and the ways in which it may be preserved. The motto of Scenic America is "change is inevitable, ugliness is not." If coastal communities and individuals are willing to embrace this idea and take action, collectively we can ensure that the scenic beauty of our magnificent south shore will be maintained for future generations to enjoy.

In 2007, Jason Laumann was Senior Planner at the Wisconsin Northwest Regional Planning Commission.

CLIMATE CHANGE COMES TO THE
GREAT LAKES COASTS OF WISCONSIN

Philip Keillor

A regional warming trend that appears to be part of global climate change apparently began to have an effect on Wisconsin around 1970. The evidence includes shortening ice cover seasons on the state's lakes and in lakes around the Northern Hemisphere (Magnuson et al 2000) as well as Lake Superior's warming waters (Austin and Colman 2007). Will continuing changes in our climate require getting used to low lake levels? Lake Superior water levels are now almost as low as the record lowest levels of 1926 and have been below average for nearly a decade. The levels of Lake Michigan have been below average since the end of 1998.

Confidence in the results of global climate models (global atmospheric circulation models) grows, supported by a steady stream of new scientific information as recently reported in Madison by a prominent climate scientist (Trenberth 2007). In sharp contrast to this confidence in global models and alarm at model results is the continuing absence of regional climate models that will realistically translate global model results at the scale of the Great Lakes Basin. There seems to be little awareness among Basin governments and the public that such regional models are needed and therefore little incentive for research managers to make regional climate model development a high priority.

There is a common, but mistaken, perception that climate change is happening somewhere else, but will not happen here. We know that dramatic changes are happening in the Arctic (Hassol 2004). Occasional climatic shifts known as El Nino occur in the southern Pacific Ocean, shift jet stream routes and storm tracks passing through the central United States, and bring warmer and dryer weather to Wisconsin thousands of miles from the South Pacific (Trenberth 2007). Clearly, Wisconsin is affected by climate changes happening in distant parts of the world.

Wisconsin and the Great Lakes Basin could experience sudden climate change as persistent shifts in storm tracks into (or out of) the state and

Basin (Trenberth 2007). Such situations have been considered by modelers of Great Lakes water level responses to hypothetical what if? scenarios. The effects of such shifts might include dramatic changes in water levels lower (and maybe higher) than the ranges we have become accustomed to in modern times.

I have recently discussed climate change with faculty knowledgeable about erosion and coastal slope stability. If climate change brings warmer, wetter winters (UCS 2007) with sufficient warmth to thaw frozen coastal slopes, more frequent and deep slump failures are likely.

More extreme rainstorms (also predicted) with rain falling on exposed, unfrozen coastal slope soils will bring more shallow landslides and more surface erosion. If climate change brings winters with open water and no ice ridges piling up on Wisconsin's coast, the state's shores will be more exposed to erosion by storm waves previously prevented by ice sheets or blocked by ice ridges. Some of the state's near shore lakebed continues to erode downward making our coasts more vulnerable to increases in storminess (another climate change prediction).

Owners of coastal property can improve the resistance of their property to the erosion impacts of climate changes by controlling surface water flow and groundwater flow that contribute to slope erosion. State and coastal governments and property owners need to identify and monitor sources of information about climate change. Good coastal risk management needs to be put into practice at various levels of government and private property ownership.

This summer, Alan Lulloff (Association of State Floodplain Managers) and I have been writing a new coastal erosion setback methodology for the Wisconsin Coastal Management Program. This report deals with climate change and managing the risks of coastal hazards. We also borrow from earlier work that we did for NOAA in adapting the Association's No Adverse Impacts policy for river floodplains to coastal floodplains (ASFPM 2007).

Right now, Wisconsin needs a good regional climate model so that we can get more specific regional predictions and prepare for climate changes expected to affect Wisconsin over the next few decades.

In 2007, Philip Keillor was a Coastal Engineer.

References

ASFPM. 2007. Coastal NAI Handbook. www.floods.org/home/ default.asp

Austin, Jay A. and Steven M. Colman. 2007. Lake Superior summer water temperatures are increasing more rapidly than regional air temperatures: A positive ice-albedo feedback. Geophysical Research Letters. Vol. 34, L06604. 5 pages.

Hassol, Susan Joy. 2004. Impacts of a warming Arctic. Arctic Climate Impact Assessment. Cambridge University Press.

Magnuson, J.J., et al. 2000. Historical trends in lake and river ice cover in the Northern Hemisphere. Science. 289. 1743–1746.

Trenberth, Kevin E. 2007. Keynote Presentation: Global warming is unequivocal. University of Wisconsin, Madison, Wisconsin and notes from an informal round table discussion. April 23, 2007. Part of lecture series: Climate Change in the Great Lakes Region. University of Wisconsin Sea Grant Institute. www.seagrant.wisc.edu/ ClimateChange. Dr. Trenberth is a principal author of one of the recently-issued assessment reports of the Intergovernmental Panel on Climate Change (IPCC).

UCS. 2007. Global Warming: Great Lakes Communities and Ecosystems at Risk. Union of Concerned Scientists. URL: www.ucsusa.org/greatlakes.

WISCONSIN SHIPBUILDING

Mike Friis

With 1,000 miles of Great Lakes coast, over 15,000 named lakes and 44,000 miles of rivers and streams, water is a big part of Wisconsin. This expansive maritime transportation network has for more than a century fueled a strong and dynamic sector of the Wisconsin manufacturing economy: shipbuilding.

Shipbuilding is big business in Wisconsin and throughout the Great Lakes states. The Shipbuilders Council of America estimated that the commercial shipbuilding industry alone accounted for more than $42 million of economic activity in Wisconsin in 2001. The Great Lakes Commission reports residents of Great Lakes states spent $2.025 billion on new power boats, outboard motors, trailers and accessories in 2003. More than 250 Great Lakes businesses and their 18,500 employees manufactured 182,700 watercraft in 2003.

Hundreds of shipbuilders and manufacturers in Wisconsin's coastal region produce maritime craft and marine products for commercial, recreational and military uses. It is impossible to catalog all such businesses in a single article. However, the following provides a sample of companies engaged in shipbuilding within Wisconsin's Great Lakes counties.

Fraser Shipyards Inc. Established in 1890, Fraser Shipyards resides in Superior and Duluth. The Twin Ports is the largest on the Great Lakes in terms of total cargo volume, and it is an important access point for many agricultural products from the Plains States. Superior/Duluth is a major winter layover port for Great Lakes bulk carriers; in the winter of 2006, eleven vessels wintered there undergoing a variety of repair and maintenance projects.

Fraser Shipyards has an 830' x 80' graving dock where hull damage is repaired, cargo hold steel is renewed and regulatory agencies perform required maritime safety inspections. Fraser also performs work on vessels afloat including piping system renewals, boiler repairs, turbine repairs and other routine maintenance work.

Manitowoc Marine Group. The Manitowoc Marine Group has two Wisconsin-based shipbuilding facilities: Marinette Marine in Marinette and Bay Shipbuilding in Sturgeon Bay.

Marinette Marine (MMC) was founded along the Menominee River in Marinette in 1942. It was started to supply naval materiel during World War II. Since its first contract to build five wooden barges, MMC has built more than 1,300 vessels.

Recent vessels completed by MMC include the famous Staten Island ferries. These diesel-powered vessels are each designed to carry 4,400 passengers and 30 vehicles. Each ferry has five passenger cabins on four decks.

MMC also built the new US Coast Guard Cutter *Mackinaw* (WAGB-83). This multi-purpose ship is designed for maintaining floating aids-to-navigation, icebreaking, search and rescue, marine environmental response, maritime law enforcement, national security and national defense. The *Mackinaw* is 240 ft. long, carries a crew of 50 personnel and is able to break 32 inches of level ice at three knots.

Bay Shipbuilding (BSC) has over 100 years of experience in shipbuilding. BSC constructs double hulled vessels, dredges, dredging support equipment and self-unloading bulk carriers.

BSC and its 700 employees specialize in large ship construction projects, vessel conversions, repowering and modernization. In addition to new construction business, BSC also provides repair work that routinely occurs during the winter lay-up season. The shipyard has a schedule to construct seven double hull tank barges and ship repair commitments well into the future.

Cruiser Boats. Founded in 1904 as the Thompson Bros. Boat Manufacturing Co. in Peshtigo, Cruiser Boats later moved to Oconto where it made 14- and 16-foot lap strake boats. Today, Cruisers Yachts produces fifteen models from 28- to 54-feet in its expanded Oconto facility and a new boatbuilding operation in Wilmington, North Carolina. Cruisers' 700 employees in its Oconto and Wilmington plants produce midsize to luxury pleasure yachts for markets around the world.

Palmer Johnson. Palmer Johnson of Sturgeon Bay has a worldwide reputation of excellence in boat design and manufacture. Founded in 1918, Palmer Johnson began as a small boatyard constructing wooden fishing vessels and commercial craft for the Great Lakes. During WWII, it made air-sea rescue boats and 65-foot Army T-boats. It branched out to sailboats in the 1950s.

Employing over 300, Palmer Johnson's sole business now is to build and service its highly styled sport-yachts. The company recently expanded its production facility to meet product demand. Two new construction bays can accommodate 250 footers and a new dedicated paint facility will be operational in the summer of 2007. Additional property adjacent to the existing facility has been purchased for further expansion. The company recently opened a new customer service center in the Mediterranean port of Golf Juan where it assists owners and captains maintain these Wisconsin-built yachts.

Burger Boats. The Burger Boat Company in Manitowoc was founded in 1863. It designs and builds custom motor yachts from 100 to 200 feet in length. The company typically launches two or three yachts per year with up to six projects at various stages of completion at a time. Its vessels are designed to capture the quality of classic yacht building and provide the latest technologies and systems available today.

The Burger Boat Company is considered among the oldest custom yacht builders in America. The company has a worldwide customer base and employs 300 people.

Wisconsin shipbuilders continue a tradition of craftsmanship that is well regarded internationally. Products from Wisconsin builders provide for commerce, personal transportation, recreation, safety and security on waterways around the world.

In 2007, Mike Friis was Manager of the Wisconsin Coastal Management Program.

THE SMART PREVENTION APPROACH TO MANAGING INVASIVE SPECIES

Jeff Maxted and Jake Vander Zanden

During the past century, the ease in which goods can be moved across the globe has increased dramatically. Every day, cargo ships depart from exotic ports with a host of items bound for sale in the United States. Many of these ships traverse the oceans, navigate the St. Lawrence River and unload at ports throughout the Great Lakes. Unfortunately, some of these cargo ships unload more than we bargained.

Aquatic invasive species are a serious concern in our coastal systems. Once an invader is introduced and establishes a new population, it can cause significant negative effects. For example, the zebra mussel—one of the most notorious invasive species in the Great Lakes—clogs intake pipes for drinking water systems, litters sandy beaches with sharp shells and causes major disruption to the Great Lakes ecosystems. Invasive species are nearly impossible to reverse and exceptionally costly to manage. Millions of dollars are spent in the Great Lakes each year to minimize the impacts of the zebra mussel alone.

Moreover, once aquatic invasive species establish in the Great Lakes, they can easily be transported inland where they threaten Wisconsin's cherished lakes and streams. Seemingly innocuous events—such as dumping leftover live bait into a stream or moving bilge water to another lake—can cause major ecological impacts if hitchhiking aquatic invaders survive in the new aquatic system.

State and federal agencies are working to prevent harmful impacts of invasive species, but it is a momentous challenge to prevent their spread in a region with thousands of lakes and streams. To address this challenge, we and our collaborators at the UW-Madison Center for Limnology are developing the Smart Prevention approach for managing invasive species. The goals of Smart Prevention are to identify the specific places that are vulnerable to specific invasive species and direct the appropriate prevention actions to these vulnerable sites—the places where prevention programs will produce the greatest benefit.

The research involves three questions to identify which places are most vulnerable to invasive species:

- Can the invasive species get there?

- Can the invasive species live there?

- Will the invasive species have adverse impacts?

To answer these questions, we collect information about invasive species distributions and combine it with lake and stream environmental data. If the answer to all three of the above questions is yes for a specific lake or stream, then that lake or stream is considered to be vulnerable to invasion.

For example, zebra mussels need high levels of dissolved calcium to build their shells. In addition, zebra mussels only survive in water with a particular pH level. Using available pH and calcium data for lakes and streams, we can map where zebra mussels are capable of establishing and causing detrimental impacts.

We can use a similar approach with the rainbow smelt, an invasive fish. Rainbow smelt prefer deep, unproductive lakes and can have negative impacts on native fish species such as lake whitefish, lake herring, yellow perch and walleye. We can combine fish survey data with existing information about Wisconsin lakes to determine where rainbow smelt are capable of negative impacts.

For other species, information about lake access, the presence of native species and proximity to the Great Lakes can be used to ask the other Smart Prevention questions. Our research is finding that only a fraction of the lakes and streams in Wisconsin are vulnerable to any particular invasive species. It is our belief that these vulnerable lakes and streams should receive attention from resource management agencies responsible for stopping the spread of aquatic invasive species.

While this research is designed to guide the efforts of state and federal resource agencies, basic invasive species prevention steps need to be practiced by all people in all aquatic ecosystems. By removing plants from boats and trailers, disposing of unused bait in the trash and draining live wells and bilge water, the spread of harmful invasive species can be greatly reduced.

There is an old adage that an ounce of prevention is worth a pound of cure. In the case of invasive species, this is truer than ever. Through application of the Smart Prevention approach, we are developing and implementing ways to make invasive species prevention programs more efficient and effective.

In 2007, Jeff Maxted was a Research Specialist with the University of Wisconsin-Madison Center for Limnology. Jake Vander Zanden was an Associate Professor with the Center for Limnology and the Department of Zoology at the University of Wisconsin-Madison.

GREAT LAKES CIRCLE TOUR—
COASTAL ACCESS GUIDE

David Hart

A vacation on the Great Lakes Circle Tour can be the adventure of a life-time. But if one only sticks to the highways marked with the distinctive green Circle Tour signs, much of the show will be missed.

In 1996, my father and I took our own Circle Tour trip. We traveled through Ontario on the eastern shore of Lake Huron through the Bruce Peninsula and onto Manitoulin Island. We proceeded around the northern shore of Lake Superior and ended with a ferry ride across Lake Michigan from Manitowoc to Ludington.

The real delights were when we got off the main road and experienced the culture of the lake towns and the natural areas on the shore. My father, a geologist who served the Michigan Department of Transportation for many years, shared his knowledge as we explored the limestone geology of Manitoulin Island. There was the serendipity of discovering the music and ales of a Celtic festival in Goderich, Ontario. Experiences like these rest around each bend of the Lakes and inspired the development of Wisconsin's Great Lakes Circle Tour—Coastal Access Guide (www.aqua.wisc.edu/glct/).

The Coastal Access Guide builds upon several Web sites that promote cultural tourism and exploration, such as:

- the Green Map System at www.greenmaps.org/

- the Coastal Access Guide in Connecticut at www.lisrc.uconn .edu/coastalaccess/

- the Oregon Coastal Atlas at www.coastalatlas.net/

Drawing on these sites and others, we developed a Coastal Access Guide to map the Circle Tour route along with local roads, parks, beaches, lighthouses and shipwrecks on the Great Lakes. Hot links on interactive maps connect to other Web sites offering more information about each attraction.

A favorite feature of the site is the panoramic photo viewer. These photos show locations that provide public access and/or water views. The photos synchronize with a vicinity map that shows the field of view. One can rotate the photo 360 degrees to orient places on the map. Another feature links to webcams so one knows whether to pack a raincoat or bring sunscreen before venturing out.

A variety of Web mapping software used to develop the site allowed us to research the benefits and drawbacks of each technology. The main site is developed using the Google™ Maps interface thus making it easy to use with a Web browser like Windows® Internet Explorer or Mozilla Firefox®. Virtual Earth software such as Google™ Earth and NASA World Wind make it possible to integrate different features and simulate flying over the Circle Tour. Open source software such as MapServer, Chameleon and OpenLayers pull in information from other data custodians and share our maps as well. It is our intention to write how-to guides so others in the Great Lakes region and beyond can learn from our example.

The Great Lakes Circle Tour—Coastal Access Guide will be a useful tool for many groups in Wisconsin. It will benefit tourists planning trips on the Circle Tour as it will show where to pull off the busy highway to explore coastal parks and beaches, lighthouses, shipwrecks and other cultural and natural attractions. The panorama photos of parks and scenic vistas could provide a Great Lakes experience to elderly or handicapped people who are unable to travel.

The Coastal Access Guide will be useful in the classroom for students to study the diversity of the Great Lakes shore. The virtual globe applications will add to environmental science and social studies classes. Coastal managers will gain through improved access to Great Lakes coastal data. The panorama photos provide a benchmark to study potential changes to the scenic vistas along the coast. Finally, the project showcases the sizable public investment in coastal land acquisition and access infrastructure made over the years by the Wisconsin Coastal Management Program and Wisconsin Department of Natural Resources.

Several enhancements are planned for the Coastal Access Guide. The Wisconsin Department of Natural Resources recently completed an inventory and Web mapping site for boat and developed shore fishing access sites in the state; the Great Lakes boat ramps will be added to the

Coastal Access Guide. Historian Margaret Beattie Bogue finished writing the second edition of *Around the Shores of Lake Superior* providing valuable information about historic sites on the Circle Tour route. David Mickelson, professor emeritus of Geology at the University of Wisconsin-Madison, recently took oblique aerial photos of much of the Great Lakes shore in Wisconsin. These will provide a unique bird's-eye view of the coast.

Portal Wisconsin (www.portalwisconsin.org/)—maintained by the Cultural Coalition of Wisconsin—provides a calendar of cultural events in the state. We are exploring techniques to geographically reference this calendar into the site. These updates are just the beginning for creating the definitive Web site for exploring the Great Lakes.

In 2007, David Hart was the GIS Specialist at the University of Wisconsin Sea Grant Institute.

2008

FOREWORD

Governor Jim Doyle

Dear Friend of Wisconsin's Great Lakes:

The Great Lakes are a globally important natural, cultural and economic resource. Wisconsin is blessed with over 1,000 miles of shoreline on Lakes Michigan and Superior. From urban waterfronts to recreational and wild places, our Great Lakes shores and waters are the foundation for much of Wisconsin's heritage, economy and drinking water.

Protecting and enhancing our Great Lakes is one of my highest priorities as Governor. Over the past several years, we have made major strides to build a long term foundation to protect our Great Lakes. In this year—when we celebrate the thirtieth anniversary of the Department of Administration's Wisconsin Coastal Management Program—we have many Great Lakes victories to celebrate.

In December 2005, eight governors and two Canadian premiers representing the Great Lakes came together in Milwaukee to endorse the Great Lakes Compact. Our strong commitment to the water, land and peoples surrounding all of the Great Lakes has led the region's leaders to work together to ensure that the Lakes are protected, conserved and managed.

The Compact protects Great Lakes communities by creating standards for sustainable management of Great Lakes waters. The Compact bans long-distance water diversions, but also sets up a process for communities near the basin to receive water from the Great Lakes. These communities will have clear standards that allow for water use in sustainable ways.

Wisconsin ratified the Great Lakes Compact in 2008 creating unprecedented protections for the Great Lakes and ensuring their continued viability to support regional economic growth and resource protection for generations to come.

Containing more than 20% of the world's surface fresh water, the Great Lakes will continue to grow in importance. One of our greatest competitive advantages in a 21st century global economy is our water—water that will help Wisconsin businesses grow and draw new businesses to our state.

In July 2008, the last of the Great Lakes state legislatures ratified the Compact in coordination with the Canadian provinces of Quebec and Ontario; approving the agreement shows full regional coordination to protect our precious Great Lakes. As this is written in August 2008, we are working with Congress and the President to pass the Compact and give its protections the power of federal law.

As Chair of the Council of Great Lakes Governors, I want to thank all of the dedicated residents and local, tribal and Canadian government officials who supported the progress of the Great Lakes Compact. The Great Lakes region is uniting as never before to protect one of the world's greatest natural resources.

I would also like to thank the Wisconsin Coastal Management Council, the program staff and the many state, local and tribal governments, nonprofit organizations and individual citizens who for the past 30 years have worked cooperatively to protect and enhance our Great Lakes and coastal areas.

I hope you will celebrate with me this year's accomplishments and join me in protecting the future health of Wisconsin's Great Lakes system. Working together, we can ensure that our children and grandchildren have the same opportunities to enjoy the Great Lakes that we have today.

Jim Doyle served as Wisconsin's 44th Governor from 2003 to 2011.

St. Louis River Freshwater Estuary

Becky Sapper

People tend to think of areas like Chesapeake Bay when they hear the word *estuary*. They imagine large river mouths that empty freshwater into the ocean, or wetlands where fresh and saline waters mix. But another kind of estuary exists here in Wisconsin. If one has ever fished, hunted, paddled or hiked along Wisconsin's Lake Superior coast—or simply driven through Ashland or Superior—they have seen a *freshwater estuary*.

Sometimes called sloughs, freshwater estuaries occur where a drowned river mouth empties into the Great Lakes. While saltwater estuaries are affected by lunar tides, freshwater estuaries are affected by wind tides and soup bowl-like sloshing called a seiche. Differences between the river and lake water—such as pH, water temperature and conductivity—create a unique habitat where they come together in shallow wetlands. The dynamic mixing and water level changes within a freshwater estuary create habitat shared by species that use both the river and lake.

Lake Superior's freshwater estuaries are both nursery and kitchen for diverse populations of aquatic plants, fish, wildlife and waterfowl that rely on them for shelter, food and spawning. Estuaries also benefit people. These shallow coastal wetlands slow runoff and act as filters to reduce erosion and sedimentation. They provide places for hunting, fishing, recreation and tourism activities. Lake Superior's freshwater estuaries and coastal wetlands are an important part of what defines the quality of life in the Lake Superior basin.

More than 20 freshwater estuaries grace Wisconsin's Lake Superior shore. One of these freshwater estuaries occurs on the largest United States tributary to Lake Superior, the St. Louis River.

The St. Louis River flows 179 miles through a watershed encompassing 3,634 square miles within Wisconsin and Minnesota. As it approaches the City of Superior, the river slows and spreads into a 12,000-acre freshwater estuary characterized by numerous bays and islands. Undeveloped tracts are interspersed with parks, public access points, homes, businesses, industry and a major international port system. The St. Louis River discharges more than 17,000 gallons per second into Lake Superior.

The combination of ecosystems within the St. Louis River estuary is unique in Lake Superior, the Great Lakes region and the world. The estuary is home to a diverse array of native birds and a critical stopover location for migratory birds—more than 230 species have been documented.

The estuary provides prime breeding habitat for wildlife and fish including threatened, endangered and game species. Its large warm water fish community of roughly 54 species includes an estimated 50,000–90,000 spawning walleye. The bay mouth bar complex of communities—also known as the barrier spits of Minnesota and Wisconsin Points—is the world's largest freshwater sandbar.

The St. Louis River freshwater estuary provides one of the world's best examples of seiche interaction. While the back and forth movement of water is continuous, the size of the seiche varies depending upon weather and winds, usually fluctuating from 3 to 25 cm during an event. The seiche can reverse the flow of the river 11 miles upstream to the Oliver Bridge.

Another important aspect of the St. Louis River estuary is its active working port. With iron ore and coal docks, grain elevators and specialized cargo facilities lining the industrial waterfronts, the Duluth and Superior ports serve shippers and receivers throughout the Midwest, Great Plains and Canada. The port's navigation season usually begins in late March and continues until mid-January serving 1,100 vessels. Duluth-Superior is the largest port on the Great Lakes and ranked number one on the Lakes for total cargo volume of 45 million net tons annually.

The St. Louis River estuary has 96 miles of shoreline in the City of Superior alone. More than 10,000 acres on the Wisconsin side of the St. Louis River are in public ownership through the City, Douglas County, Wisconsin Department of Natural Resources and the University of Wisconsin-Superior. Numerous places along the Superior waterfront and many of the tributaries that enter the St. Louis River and Superior Bay provide public access.

The St. Louis River freshwater estuary was recently nominated by Wisconsin Governor Jim Doyle as a National Estuarine Research Reserve (NERR) site. The NERR program is a non-regulatory federal and state partnership administered by the US National Oceanic and Atmospheric Administration (NOAA). The program provides federal funding and technical support to advance estuary research, education and stewardship.

The only other Great Lakes NERR site is located hundreds of miles to the southeast on Lake Erie at Ohio's Old Woman Creek. The St. Louis River freshwater estuary is an excellent setting for research and education activities on the upper Great Lakes. A Lake Superior NERR designation would be significant for Wisconsin, the region and the nation.

Numerous Wisconsin and Minnesota-based academic institutions, government agencies, and advisory and action committees have played a critical role in telling the St. Louis River story. The proposed NERR designation would take their research from the St. Louis to the larger Great Lakes basin and the world.

In 2008, Becky Sapper was the Lake Superior Freshwater Estuary Outreach Coordinator at the University of Wisconsin-Extension.

SAVING THE KINNICKINNIC

Ben Gramling

Wisconsin's Great Lakes and their tributaries mean many things to Wisconsin's diverse population. Our open waters provide recreational boating opportunities and commercial shipping avenues. Our shorelines and river corridors offer respite from the urban grind and a hard day's work on the farm. They are a thread in the fabric of home to humans, plants and wildlife alike. Wisconsin's coastal resources add value to our lives and state every day.

But what if your neighborhood river looked more like a concrete highway than a pristine, meandering creek? What if you had a better chance of seeing a shopping cart in the water than a northern pike? Suppose that your experience with Wisconsin's water resources was shaped not by the Lake Michigan shoreline, but by the drainage ditch at the end of your block that swells with dangerously fast moving water after rainstorms? Would you see the local river as a neighborhood asset or a dreaded liability? For many residents of Milwaukee's Kinnickinnic River corridor, the city's "forgotten river" provides only fear and worry.

In the 1960s and 1970s, a concrete lining was installed to channelize most of the Kinnickinnic and its tributaries. This lining served as a flood control measure that moved water into Lake Michigan as quickly as possible. Much of this concrete-lined river flows through heavily residential neighborhoods. In fact, the Kinnickinnic is Wisconsin's most densely populated watershed.

Citing the concentration of development within this watershed, the nationwide advocacy group American Rivers in 2007 designated the Kinnickinnic as one of America's ten most endangered rivers. The group said "more than 1.5 million people have a front row seat to the problems and have a vested interest in restoring the river."

The Kinnickinnic's concrete channel presents a number of challenges locally and to the region. Each challenge must be addressed if the Kinnickinnic is to add value to the community like so many of Wisconsin's other water resources. Its current ecological value is minimal with little or no vegetation, poor habitat and physical barriers to fish migration. The Kinn-ickinnic lacks community value because local families do not connect to and appreciate the river. Residents generally perceive the river as a waste stream and serious drowning hazard, especially in summer months when heavy rains produce fast moving and dangerous currents.

Today, the concrete lining placed in the river forty years ago is nearing the end of its life cycle. A comprehensive long-term solution is needed to spur economic, ecological and community improvements along with floodwater management. It is with this outlook that Sixteenth Street Com-munity Health Center, Groundwork Milwaukee and the Milwaukee Met-ropolitan Sewerage District—with support from the Wisconsin Coastal Management Program—have teamed to tackle the Kinnickinnic River's concrete channel. These groups are planning for concrete removal along a 2.5-mile stretch of the Kinnickinnic River between 27th Street and Chase Avenue on Milwaukee's near south side.

The project area targeted for this effort is home to a significant portion of Milwaukee's Hispanic population including many immigrants recently arrived from Mexico, Puerto Rico and other parts of Latin America. Lan-guage and cultural characteristics of Milwaukee's south side immigrant population influence how community members perceive and interact with large public sector entities that are typically involved in a project of this magnitude.

If the Kinnickinnic River project is to succeed, it must be well under-stood that economic circumstances are tough for many of these families. Making rent payments and paying for groceries will always have a higher priority than participating in the environmental cleanup and revitaliza-tion of the neighborhood river.

As a trusted organization that has served Milwaukee's south side for nearly 40 years, the Sixteenth Street Community Health Center has built a strong reputation by providing culturally and linguistically sensitive health care services and successful educational outreach empowering local families to improve their health. The Kinnickinnic community planning project team will rely on this experience and a community partner ap-proach as it communicates the complex science and engineering work that must precede the ultimate restoration of the river.

Churches, schools, community centers, block watch groups and individual leaders in the community will serve vital roles in this planning process. These entities and individuals will engage the public in discussion about the future of the concrete-lined river and the benefits a revitalized river corridor will bring to their neighborhoods. The project team has also developed a strategy to ensure ongoing resident support to foster active participation in decision making about the future of their neighborhood and the health of their river.

Summer 2008 will be an important time of learning and engagement for local residents, for the planning process that will drive the removal of the Kinnickinnic River's concrete lining and for creating a long-term vision and plan for revitalizing Milwaukee's Kinnickinnic River corridor.

Every partner working on this project is committed to ensuring that these activities will lead to the kind of community value Wisconsin's coastal resources can generate for all residents—no matter where they live or which language they speak.

In 2008, Ben Gramling was Director of Environmental Health Programs at the Sixteenth Street Community Health Center.

Wind Point Lighthouse: Gateway to the Stars

Bill Schalk

The Wind Point Lighthouse is truly a gateway to the stars. Capt. Laurel Salton Clark, US Navy Mission Specialist on the ill-fated space shuttle *Columbia*, sent an e-mail to family and friends on January 31, 2003 stating: "The perspective is truly awe-inspiring . . . Magically, the very first day we flew over Lake Michigan and I saw Wind Point."

It is not strange that astronaut Clark saw Wind Point from outer space while traveling at 17,000 mph. This jagged point 25 miles south of Milwaukee and its lighthouse have been a beacon for mariners since the 19th century.

The majestic Wind Point Lighthouse was designed and built by Orlando Poe in 1880 for the federal government. It remained federal property until the Village of Wind Point acquired it in 1997. The light at the top of the tower stands 112 feet above the lake. The tower itself is 108 feet tall and contains 144 steps to the light.

From 1880 until 1964, only seven keepers maintained the lighthouse for the US Coast Guard. Their primary job was to maintain the light as a key navigation aid for ships and boats on the lake. In 1924, the light's kerosene lamp was replaced with an electrified 300-watt bulb that was changed monthly. In 1964, the lens was replaced by a fully automatic system. The new system used a 1,000-watt bulb and a reflector that amplified the light intensity to two million candlepower. Today, a 100-watt bulb accomplishes the same intensity. After the light was automated in 1964, the Wind Point Lighthouse no longer required a resident keeper.

In 1963, the Village Board learned there was a possibility of obtaining possession of the lighthouse property and appointed a committee to pursue the project. In 1964, the lighthouse committee signed a five-year renewable lease for the property with the Coast Guard. The Village and Coast Guard went on to sign seven consecutive leases through 1997.

The lease required no payment to the federal government, but the

Village assumed costs for maintaining the tower and property. The Coast Guard remained responsible for the beacon.

With the departure of the Coast Guard lighthouse keeper, the Village hired a caretaker to tend to the buildings and property. As it does today, the grounds consisted of the main building including the lighthouse tower and house with three apartments, the Horn House, a garage, a small storage building and two acres of land.

In 1964, the new caretaker moved his family into the largest apartment in the main building. The Village Board used the remainder of the building for a police station and municipal meetings, a configuration that exists to this day. The grounds have since been available for recreational purposes. The lighthouse was placed on the National Register of Historic Places in 1984.

In February 1997, the federal government notified state and local authorities that it would declare the lighthouse area and tower surplus property. According to the notice, "[A]ny party interested in acquiring it had twenty days to express interest by requesting an application to acquire the property."

John Schmit, the Village Deputy Clerk, spent several months creating an application book to acquire the property. Former caretaker Mike Cooper took photographs of every building inside and out. The effort worked! In September 1997, the Coast Guard signed the deed transferring the lighthouse from the National Park Service to the Village of Wind Point. Since the building and grounds are on the National Register of Historic Places, the National Parks Service must approve any modifications to the buildings.

The Friends of the Wind Point Lighthouse was formed in 1999 as a 501(c)(3) nonprofit organization to "promote, protect and encourage the historic preservation of the lighthouse."

Monies generated by membership dues and fund raising events have been used to increase awareness of the history of the lighthouse and beautify the grounds.

The members of the Friends pursue their mission with a passion that is evident in everything they do. Any municipality that takes over a historic property needs a group like the Friends to be part of the ongoing operation because local governments are limited in terms of peoplepower, finances and creativity to get things done.

Today, the Wind Point Lighthouse retains its 128-year mission as a key navigation aid along Lake Michigan. In addition, it is showcase piece for Racine County. The lighthouse appears on many magazine covers, brochures and travel itineraries; the Racine Convention Bureau estimates that more than 20,000 people visit this icon yearly.

One must balance the needs of the community, cost to maintain and political factors when dealing with an icon like a lighthouse. The issues are dealt with through responsible taxation, the balancing of the residents' desires and needs, and the entire community's right to public access of a publicly funded historic property. The beauty of the property along with the peace and joy it brings to every visitor is worth the effort.

In 2008, Bill Schalk was President of the Village of Wind Point.

References

Minton, MD, Richard. A History of the Village of Wind Point—Celebrating the 50th
    Anniversary of the Village. Racine: Angel Litho. 2005.
Wardius, Barb, and Wardius, Ken. Wind Point Lighthouse. Charleston: Arcadia, 2007.

Conservation Ensures Great Lakes Sustainability

Jeff Ripp

Wisconsin residents have access to abundant freshwater supplies in part due to the state's proximity to the Great Lakes. Throughout history, Wisconsin's coastal cities have relied on Lake Michigan and Lake Superior for clean, affordable water. Today, the waters of the Great Lakes basin—including its groundwater resources—provide drinking water to nearly half of Wisconsin's 5.6 million residents.

Forty-five Wisconsin public water utilities withdraw more than 100 billion gallons of water per year directly from the Great Lakes for domestic, commercial, industrial and public uses. Another 135 utilities rely on the basin's groundwater resources to supply an additional 25 billion gallons of water per year. Other water users—including agriculture, thermoelectric power plants and self-supplied domestic and industrial users—withdraw many more billions of gallons each year. While most of this water eventually returns to the Great Lakes after it is used and treated, some is consumed or diverted outside of the basin.

Despite the vast quantities of water in the Great Lakes—up to 20 percent of the world's fresh surface water—it is important to recognize that this resource is not limitless. In fact, some estimates show that only one percent of the available water is renewed every year. Nationwide, portions of 36 states are expected to face water shortages in the next decade. Even in Wisconsin, regional and temporal water shortages are emerging.

For example, groundwater withdrawals have exceeded the rate of natural recharge in some parts of the state. Elsewhere, contaminants limit the availability of groundwater for human uses. Further, there are increasing concerns about Great Lakes water levels, including the effects of climate change and diversions that permanently remove water from the basin. Finally, anticipated population growth and economic expansion throughout the basin are expected to place additional strains on the Great Lakes.

Historically, water utilities have developed new wells or increased their surface water capacity to meet growing demands for water within their communities. However, declining water levels, new groundwater laws and regional efforts to regulate withdrawals from the Great Lakes are making it more costly and difficult to develop new sources of supply. Instead, many water utilities are finding that water conservation is the most cost-effective way to stretch existing supplies, manage customer demand, reduce energy use, lower utility operating costs and protect valuable aquatic resources.

The Public Service Commission of Wisconsin (PSC), an independent state agency responsible for regulating the rates and standards of service of public utilities, is leading a statewide initiative to assist water utilities with implementing water conservation and efficiency programs. The PSC's efforts include both demand-side and supply-side solutions that will improve water efficiency. Specifically, the PSC is working with utilities to:

- Reduce water lost through leaky distribution systems and inaccurate meters.

- Establish water rates that encourage efficiency and discourage wasteful practices.

- Promote water-saving products and practices through partnerships such as the US Environmental Protection Agency's Water-Sense program.

- Raise public awareness of water efficient behavior through education and outreach

In 2008, the PSC will work with the Wisconsin Department of Natural Resources and other state agencies to develop water conservation and efficiency goals for the Wisconsin portion of the Great Lakes basin. This is one component of the Great Lakes-St. Lawrence River Basin Sustainable Water Resources Agreement signed in December 2005 by the governors of the eight Great Lakes states and the premiers of Ontario and Quebec. Among other things, this good-faith agreement requires the states and provinces to work towards adopting the Great Lakes-St. Lawrence River Basin Water Resources Compact and develop water conservation goals and objectives for the Great Lakes.

Each state's conservation goals and objectives must be consistent with region-wide goals adopted by the Council of Great Lakes Governors. Wisconsin's goals and objectives will not only identify where improvements in water efficiency can be made, but also recognize those things water utilities are already doing to promote conservation and efficiency. These include metering water sales, reporting water use and eliminating wasteful water use practices.

These goals and objectives will lead to a coordinated, statewide approach to water conservation and efficiency. However, this does not mean that a one-size-fits-all approach will be the answer for every water utility. It is important to recognize that water conservation and efficiency measures must be tailored to the unique circumstances of each community.

Water is fundamental to Wisconsin's culture and economy. All water users—including water utilities, industry, agriculture and private well owners—have a stake in the sound management of Wisconsin's water resources. Effective water conservation and efficiency programs will help Wisconsin meet its water supply needs, reduce energy costs and ensure the long-term sustainability of the state's water resources. Using water wisely today means that future generations will continue to enjoy and benefit from our unique national treasure, the Great Lakes.

In 2008, Jeff Ripp was a Policy Initiatives Advisor at the Wisconsin Public Service Commission and served as its Water Conservation Coordinator.

Economics of Great Lakes Recreational Boating

Dave Knight

Recreational boating is big business in Wisconsin. But just how big has historically been an elusive statistic.

A recent study estimated that Wisconsin boaters in 2004 spent almost $1 billion to keep and maintain their boats and another $1.5 billion on boating trips. Of those combined amounts, about one-quarter—or $650 million—was spent on recreational boating on the Great Lakes. The same study estimated that recreational boating in Wisconsin supported over 36,000 jobs.

The motivation to develop this state-centric economic portrait originated with the federal government. Under federal policy going back to the early 1980s, recreational harbors are a low priority for dredging and other maintenance; in fact, the US Army Corps of Engineers (Corps) is not allowed to include recreational harbors in its operation and maintenance budget. Therefore, all federal funds for the dredging of recreational harbors come from congressional earmarks.

In the Water Resources Development Act (WRDA) of 1999, Congress considered the broad economic impact of recreational boating in Great Lakes states. In so doing, it directed the Corps to quantify the economic benefits of boating in the Great Lakes and examine federal interest in the operation and maintenance of recreational harbors on the Lakes.

The study was assigned to the Great Lakes Commission, an organization created by compact of the eight Great Lakes states and Canadian provinces of Ontario and Québec and dedicated to the wise use and protection of the Great Lakes basin. The Commission in turn worked with Michigan State University's Recreational Marine Research Center (RMRC) to conduct an analysis in 2003–04.

US Coast Guard boat registration data for 2003 indicated almost 4.3 million recreational boats in the eight Great Lakes states including 611,000 in Wisconsin. Wisconsin ranked fifth in the country behind Florida,

California, Michigan and Minnesota for its number of registered boats. The Great Lakes states together are home to about one-third of all registered US recreational vessels.

The study found that nearly one quarter of all recreational boats in Great Lakes states belonged to people residing in Great Lakes shoreline counties. This was an important factor in calculating how many of the states' registered boats were used primarily on Great Lakes waters. In Wisconsin, 162,171 boats were registered in Great Lakes coastal counties, or about 26 percent of the state's total registrations.

From 1999 to 2003, five of the Great Lakes states saw recreational boat registrations increase or remain stable. Wisconsin experienced the region's strongest growth at 8.5 percent followed by Minnesota at 6.6 percent. Three states—Indiana, Michigan and Illinois—had declining boat registrations over that period. The typical boat in Wisconsin is an aluminum fishing boat; the most prevalent size is 12 to 15 feet in length. Among all Great Lakes states, the most popular boat is a 16 to 24-foot fiberglass runabout.

The study used a unique methodology to collect boater trip and craft spending information. Data was obtained independently from on-line assessments conducted by the RMRC using a National Boater Panel. The Panel consisted of boaters across the country who were asked to complete an on-line survey during the course of 2004 related to craft spending— cost to buy, keep and maintain the boat—and trip spending—the cost of actual outings.

Beginning in May 2004, 6,000 Panel members were surveyed every two weeks concerning their most recent boating trips. Each member received emails during the summer asking them to describe a boating trip they took during the preceding two weeks including those things on which they spent money.

Information was collected on approximately 8,000 boating trips taken by the owners of different size boats. Geographically indexed analyses indicated that Great Lakes boater spending did not vary to any significant degree from national patterns, so the Panel-generated data was deemed appropriate for the study's regional application.

According to the RMRC, an average Great Lakes boat owner spent about $3,600 per year including $1,400 on craft-related expenses (e.g., equipment, repairs, insurance, slip fees) and $2,200 on outings (e.g., gas and oil, food, lodging) involving an average of 23 boating days. These averages were dominated by a high percentage of smaller watercraft. Owners of larger boats spent considerably more than these averages with up to $20,000 per year for boats 41 feet and more.

Average spending per boat day on trips varied from $76 for boats less than 16 feet in length to $275 per day for boats larger than 40 feet. The greatest outing expenses were for boat fuel (22%), restaurants and bars (17%) and groceries (14%). The fuel percentage would likely be higher today than in 2004. The majority of annual craft expenses were for equipment (39%), maintenance and repair (29%) and insurance (14%).

One long-running joke defines a recreational boat as "a hole in the water into which vast sums of money are poured." Now, for the first time, we have a much better picture of how vast and precisely where those sums are poured. The aggregate contribution of recreational boating to Wisconsin's and the Great Lakes' regional economy is a powerful and potentially growing force.

In 2008, Dave Knight was Program Manager of Transportation and Sustainable Development at the Great Lakes Commission.

GREEN TIER CHARTERS

Jeffrey Voltz

Wisconsin's Green Tier Program offers a paradigm shift in environmental protection from traditional command-and-control to collaboration by calling to action individuals, companies and communities to commit voluntarily to superior environmental performance. This collaborative approach stands to benefit both Wisconsin's economy and natural environment including waters.

In 2004, the Wisconsin Legislature passed §299.83 Wis. Stats, commonly referred to as the Green Tier Law. The law included a unique opportunity to form charters as a new means of environmental management.

Charters represent a major departure from traditional environmental policies that tend to manage environmental risks within the confines of fence lines and political jurisdictions. Instead, charters align problem solving with the scope of the problem by bringing the right mix of people to the table. Charters give legal standing to new alliances to produce beyond compliance environmental performance, address unregulated or under-regulated risks and voluntarily restore, preserve or enhance natural resources.

Two recently signed Green Tier charters have moved environmental protection discussions from *proof of concept* to *concept in practice*. Each approach establishes a voluntary framework that includes the systematic improvement of water quality—one for dairy farms and another for municipalities.

Dairy Charter. Dairy farms impact Wisconsin in many positive ways. A Green Tier charter with the Dairy Business Association (DBA) is helping ensure environmental impacts from dairy farms are positive as well.

The Green Tier charter with the DBA is built on the results of two projects in the Lakeshore basin: The Dairy Gateway Project and the Agricultural Watershed Improvement Network. These initial efforts laid the foundation for further development of Environmental Management Systems (EMS) within the dairy industry.

Funding from the Wisconsin Coastal Management Program provided necessary support for the development of a dairy charter. The resulting DBA Green Tier Charter enables dairy producers, the DBA and the Wisconsin Department of Natural Resources (DNR) to collaborate on implementing tailored EMSs and systematically tackle a variety of environmental issues including manure management, storm water run-off and energy efficiency.

The DBA and DNR will provide opportunities for dairy producers to participate in pilot projects, mentorships and farm walks/tours to assist in understanding and adopting environmental practices that go beyond what is currently required by Wisconsin law. In addition, the DBA Green Tier Charter will establish a diverse group of interested persons, including the environmental community. This group is charged with three main tasks:

- Improve communication with stakeholders and the public through activities including workshops and promotional advertisements.

- Develop specific recommendations to further the goals of the charter including environmental goals for the dairy industry.

- Establish methods of monitoring and measuring the environmental performance of DBA Charter members.

The previous efforts within the Lakeshore basin and the recently signed DBA Charter address environmental, economic and social issues. All are critical components of alleviating the impacts of water pollution and other management issues affecting the Lakeshore basin and Wisconsin in general.

Municipal Mercury Charter. Mercury is a significant pollutant in Wisconsin's waters. For instance, DNR and the Department of Health Services have issued a statewide fish consumption advisory because of mercury levels in Wisconsin fish.

There exist two primary sources of mercury release in Wisconsin: combustion of coal for the production of electricity and breakage or waste from mercury-containing products. To address the latter, DNR is encouraging community mercury reduction programs that reduce the public's use of mercury products and increase recycling for mercury products that will continue to be used. The new Municipal Mercury Charter is a direct result of the DNR's action.

The Municipal Mercury Green Tier Charter is an agreement between the DNR and the Municipal Environmental Group-Wastewater Division (MEG), an organization of Wisconsin municipalities. Communities whose wastewater treatment plant effluent does not meet the Great Lakes Water Quality Standard for mercury are required by state administrative rules to implement community mercury reduction programs.

Under the Mercury Green Tier Charter, municipalities may voluntarily achieve compliance with mercury reduction requirements prior to regulatory deadlines in exchange for flexibility and certainty in implementing mercury source reduction activities. The charter focuses on mercury product elimination or capture for recycling from hospitals, dental offices, schools and other sectors of the community that have historically used mercury-containing products.

Fifteen Wisconsin municipalities have subscribed to the Mercury Green Tier Charter with representation from all areas of Wisconsin. These communities will collaborate on their mercury reduction activities. Additional municipalities can subscribe to the Mercury Green Tier Charter during the next two years. It is expected that substantial and measurable reductions in mercury release to Wisconsin's environment will be demonstrated by the participating communities.

Each Green Tier participant and charter is unique to the environmental issue it addresses. However, all agreements reflect a growing concern for environmental improvement beyond what is required by law.

To learn more about Green Tier Charters, visit the Green Tier website at www.greentier.wi.gov.

In 2008, Jeffrey Voltz was an Environmental Assistance Coordinator at the Wisconsin Department of Natural Resources.

WISCONSIN COASTAL MANAGEMENT AT 30

Mike Friis

The wonder of Wisconsin's Great Lakes shores would be apparent if one considered only a single beautiful location, critical habitat, working waterfront, recreational opportunity or center of commerce and transportation. However, when one thinks about them collectively, our coasts' diversity and abundance make clear we have something special at our doorstep.

In 1978, the federal and state governments began a special partnership to care for Wisconsin's nearly 1,000 miles of coastline on Lakes Michigan and Superior. The Wisconsin Coastal Management Program (WCMP) became the first federal Coastal Zone Management Act (CZMA) program established in the Great Lakes and among the first ten nationally.

The WCMP guiding principle of *enjoy and protect Wisconsin's Great Lakes coastal resources* embodies the balance of environmental sustainability and public use. The program has a long history of providing the technical assistance and financial catalysts needed to make local and coastwide projects successful.

Consider Sheboygan's South Pier District. This 42-acre brownfield site at the mouth of the Sheboygan River was for over 100 years used for storage of coal, salt, fertilizer and petroleum. A major redevelopment plan began with a small WCMP investment for beach restoration and trail development. These initial dollars were among the catalysts that transformed this under-used urban waterfront into a tourist destination that adds great value to the community.

In Milwaukee's Menomonee Valley, the WCMP has been involved in several projects that are revitalizing Wisconsin's largest brownfield. A strong group of local organizations including the City of Milwaukee, Sixteenth Street Community Health Center and Menomonee Valley Partners have used WCMP investments and technical support. Their work to plan, design and restore the Menomonee Valley is producing a place where people can again work and play.

Precious undeveloped tracts also benefit from WCMP partnerships. Lion's Den Gorge sits within a ¾-mile-long pristine stretch of Lake Michigan shoreline in Ozaukee County. Local desire to protect and make this property available to the public was often discussed between County and WCMP staffs. When it became available for purchase, the WCMP was ready to contribute to the funding package that now preserves this shoreline in perpetuity.

The WCMP's financial and technical contributions also extend to public health. Several years ago, Door County was faced with beach sites with elevated levels of *E. coli* bacteria. The WCMP participated with several public and academic partners to develop initial remediation plans and implement best practices at the affected beaches. Through local leadership and state support, Door County in one year went from the Natural Resources Defense Council's Beach Bums list to its Beach Buddies list.

The WCMP played an integral role in the process that led to the nomination of a National Estuary Research Reserve (NERR) site on Lake Superior. In 2005, WCMP-funded research produced "An Assessment of Wisconsin's Great Lakes Freshwater Estuary Applied Research, Management, and Outreach Needs," a project setting the foundation for the NERR site selection process. In 2006, the WCMP worked with the University of Wisconsin-Extension to facilitate a comprehensive NERR public stakeholder process. These initiatives produced fruit in 2008 when Governor Jim Doyle announced the St. Louis River estuary as Wisconsin's nomination for the nation's next NERR site.

How does the WCMP achieve these results? It works with partners to leverage resources and coordinate the many state and local government programs that affect Wisconsin shores. This networked approach is crucial when one considers the varied nature of the coast and the uses for the Great Lakes. No one state agency can be all things for the management of the Great Lakes. In this coordinating role, the program's placement in the Wisconsin Department of Administration ensures the program retains balance between environmental, economic development, transportation, recreation and many other objectives.

The WCMP has since its inception been responsive to local and tribal governments and the public through policy guidance from the Governor-appointed Wisconsin Coastal Management Council. The fourteen-member Council represents people from all areas of Wisconsin coasts including tribal and local governments, the Departments of Administration, Natural Resources and Transportation, the University of Wisconsin Sea Grant Institute and legislators.

The WCMP annually provides matching grants to local and tribal governments, academic institutions, nonprofits and other state agencies for the protection, sustainable use and study of Wisconsin's coastal resources. The grant program emphasizes wetland protection and habitat restoration, nonpoint source pollution control, public access and historic preservation, coastal resources and community planning, Great Lakes education and coastal land acquisition.

CZMA legislation provides the WCMP with a mechanism to review proposed federal government activities in the coastal zone. These reviews ensure federal actions along Wisconsin's coasts take place in a manner consistent with the policies of the WCMP.

The WCMP founders established a strong program that today is among the nation's most recognized for its effective implementation of CZMA goals. With the importance of the Great Lakes greater than ever, the WCMP will remain relevant and vital in the management of our Great Lakes coastal resources for many years to come.

In 2008, Mike Friis was Manager of the Wisconsin Coastal Management Program.

2009

Foreword

Governor Jim Doyle

Dear Friend of Wisconsin's Great Lakes:

Wisconsin's clean and plentiful fresh waters are integral to our history, our culture and our commerce. Whether one studies satellite images of Wisconsin's Great Lakes coastlines, walks along a beach or drives through one of our many coastal communities, it is easy to see the impact the Great Lakes have on our region and the greater global community. Together with the other Great Lakes states and Canadian provinces, the region is home to 100 million people and the world's third largest economy.

In Wisconsin, we are fortunate to have over 1,000 miles of Great Lakes shoreline running from our southern to northern borders. Our coasts include landscapes as diverse as urban river walks and waterfronts, isolated parks and wilderness areas. More than just pretty places, our Great Lakes shores and waters form the foundation for much of Wisconsin's heritage and economy, while providing us with recreation and drinking water.

The Great Lakes are a key route to the world and will continue to grow in importance to our region's economy in the years ahead. For generations, the Great Lakes have been the doorway for our earliest citizens and immigrants and the highway for the products of our mills, farms, factories and mines.

As Governor of Wisconsin and Chair of the Council of Great Lakes Governors, protecting and enhancing our Great Lakes is one of my top priorities. I am proud of the major strides we have made to build a long-term foundation to protect our Great Lakes.

In the last year, we have taken a number of steps to ensure the future of Wisconsin's Great Lakes resources. Working with the other eight Great Lake states, two Canadian provinces and the United States government, we passed and ratified the Great Lakes Compact. The Compact protects coastal communities by creating standards for sustainable management of Great Lakes waters.

Additionally, the Department of Administration's Wisconsin Coastal Management Program received high marks and praise following its latest federal review and onsite evaluation. The State also completed a revision of the Wisconsin Great Lakes Restoration and Protection Strategy to guide our actions into the future.

Despite these important steps forward, we still have work to do. Working together with private citizens and organizations, local and tribal governments, federal and Canadian government agencies, we will continue our efforts to protect the Great Lakes.

Fortunately, we have a strong partner in the federal government that has stepped up to help us protect the Lakes. In President Obama's 2010 budget proposal, the administration calls for an unprecedented $475 million investment to clean up contaminated sites, protect critical natural habitats and provide greater access to the Great Lakes. With this newly energized partner, we will likely be able to highlight many more successes for the Great Lakes in the years ahead.

In the 21st century, the Great Lakes continue to help define our state's economy. In the years ahead, as freshwater needs grow throughout the rest of the country and world, the value of protecting our Great Lakes will become even easier to see. With the cooperative measures we have taken to safeguard this invaluable resource, we have ensured that future generations of Wisconsin residents will continue to enjoy our precious fresh waters.

Jim Doyle served as Wisconsin's 44th Governor from 2003 to 2011.

Finding Solutions to a Mysterious Harbor Corrosion Problem

Gene Clark and Kathleen Schmitt Kline

Chad Scott, a structural engineer and commercially certified diver, was on a routine port structure inspection dive in the Duluth-Superior Harbor several years ago when he came face-to-face with a problem—one big enough to put his fist through.

"I've seen some corrosion here and there at other Great Lakes ports, but nothing like this," he recalled.

Further investigations found that corrosion is widespread throughout the harbor with all types of steel piling covered with pits and some with holes larger than a softball. By comparing older and newer sheet pile installations, it was found that some steel structures designed to last fifty to one hundred years are now deteriorating at a rate that would require repair or replacement in thirty years of service or less.

The accelerated corrosion could have significant financial and safety implications for the port that handles the largest total cargo volume in the Great Lakes. Over thirteen miles of steel sheet piling are corroding around the harbor and if the problem is not addressed soon, the structural integrity of the facilities may deteriorate to the point where the failing steel would have to be completely replaced.

"This is potentially a very costly problem," said James Sharrow, facilities manager of the Duluth Seaway Port Authority. "We have more than 100 million dollars of possible repairs in our harbor to steel that's being damaged by corrosion."

To begin a systematic approach to the problem, the Wisconsin and Minnesota Sea Grant programs, the Duluth Seaway Port Authority, the US Army Corps of Engineers and the University of Minnesota-Duluth formed a steering committee that invited an independent group of experts to visit the port. The specialists in corrosion, microbiology and chemistry came up with a list of possible causes of the corrosion as well as recommendations for addressing the damage.

One possible cause they identified is that microorganisms such as iron oxidizing bacteria could be eating away at the steel, a phenomenon known as microbiologically influenced corrosion (MIC). Researchers at the University of Minnesota-Duluth have identified bacterial communities living on the corroded steel, but more research is needed to prove conclusively that MIC is the true culprit behind the corrosion.

While several studies continue to probe the cause of the aggressive corrosion, companion studies have begun to investigate ways to protect new and existing steel structures from further damage. With support from the Wisconsin Coastal Management Program, Wisconsin Sea Grant initiated several studies to investigate methods to slow down or stop the corrosion affecting steel structures already in place with an eye toward saving port and harbor infrastructure before having to completely replace the damaged steel.

One common method for protecting steel from corrosion is to cover the steel with a protective coating. Several facilities around the Duluth Superior Harbor had already been treated with coatings, so the first study assessed and documented these coated areas to see how they were holding up over time. These areas will be inspected yearly to determine which coatings have the highest durability to withstand the scouring action of ice, impacts from vessels and wave action. There are additional studies ongoing within the harbor to determine if new coating products could work, especially in very severe ice conditions.

A second study explored three different options for protecting steel structures from corrosion. Two types of jackets were installed on steel pilings already in place in the harbor. Jackets appear to be promising techniques for extending the lifetime of originally unprotected steel that has been attacked by the rapid corrosion, but is still serviceable. The jackets will be monitored to see how well they hold up against Lake Superior's harsh winter ice conditions and protect the pilings from corrosion.

Another alternative option installed was a cathodic protection system (CPS), commonly used in salt water harbor facilities, but very uncommon in freshwater environments. CPS works by sacrificing anodes attached to the steel structure they protect. The corrosion attacks the anodes and keeps the steel from deteriorating. Various CPS configurations were installed in the harbor on both coated and uncoated steel and will be monitored to see if this is a financially viable method of protecting steel in a freshwater port.

The results of the studies are anticipated to provide effective and affordable options for extending the life of steel structures around many Great Lakes port and marina facilities. Deeply pitted steel has also been observed in Two Harbors, Minnesota, Thunder Bay, Ontario, Madeline Island and Bayfield, Wisconsin, and at locations along Michigan's Keweenaw Peninsula.

Because this type of rapid corrosion had rarely been seen previously in freshwater harbors, Wisconsin Sea Grant is working with the harbor corrosion committee to spread the word to other Great Lakes port authorities and marina owners to examine their steel structures closely. While corrosion problems around the region may have different causes, the results of the studies will be beneficial for all facility managers as they consider repair alternatives for prolonging the useful lives of their docks and supporting structures.

For more information about the ongoing studies, visit www.seagrant .wisc.edu/coastalhazards.

In 2009, Gene Clark was a Coastal Engineering Specialist at the University of Wisconsin Sea Grant Institute. Kathleen Schmitt Kline was a Science Writer at the University of Wisconsin Sea Grant Institute.

Marketing Wisconsin's Great Lakes Tourism Experience

Secretary Kelli A. Trumble

There is no question that the Great Lakes are a tremendous asset for Wisconsin's tourism industry. It is equally true that several of our neighboring states also offer travelers Great Lakes experiences. In the course of a recent two-year brand research process, we unearthed the reality that parity travel products—such as the Great Lakes—on their own are not enough to create a preference for Wisconsin. But the collective personality of Wisconsinites is.

The mission of the Wisconsin Department of Tourism is to inspire people to love the Wisconsin experience. To accomplish that and bring much needed revenue to the State in the process, we have done what all good marketers do: build a brand that is uniquely ours.

Travelers told us Wisconsinites have a knack for creating extraordinarily fun, original and welcoming experiences. They also view us as hardworking, genuine and true stewards of our natural resources. Visitors cite those attributes as the tie-break in choosing Wisconsin as their vacation destination. That is our competitive advantage in marketing the Great Lakes.

The Wisconsin advantage is evident throughout our coastal communities. For instance, many cities and villages offer original festivals that flourish because of their very location on the Great Lakes. However, it is their Wisconsin personality that makes them shine. Milwaukee's Summerfest is the world's largest outdoor music festival, and its success is inextricably tied to its Lake Michigan shoreline venue and the hospitality of the people of Milwaukee.

The Department of Tourism is working with coastal communities to enhance and promote the Wisconsin experience. For example, Tourism wisely provided joint-effort marketing grants to the *Discover Wisconsin* Harbor Towns project that promotes spring travel to a long list of Great Lakes cities including Racine, Kenosha, Manitowoc, Marinette, Sturgeon Bay and Superior, and many points in between.

The Port Washington Maritime Heritage Festival used Tourism grant dollars to turn what had been a small event into a spectacular weekend festival resplendent with the appearance of five tall ships that drew an attendance of 27,000 and generated visitor spending nearing $1 million.

It should come as no surprise that some of Wisconsin's most original thinkers invented brands that have to do with a day on the water. Some of the most notable include Evinrude Outboard, Mercury Marine, St. Croix Rods, Harken sailboat hardware, and Carver, Cruisers and Palmer Johnson yachts. That originality carries forward today with innovative travel products and services directed at our visitors.

For instance, our tourism industry's commitment to sustaining the Great Lakes and Wisconsin's other natural resources led the Department of Tourism to launch the nation's first eco-conscious travel initiative, Travel Green Wisconsin. This program certifies businesses that are doing their part to voluntarily reduce their environmental footprint and educate travelers on the State's precious resources.

Travel Green Wisconsin debuted just a few years ago and already boasts more than 260 certified businesses. The list of certified businesses includes five charter and ferry lines offering visitors environmentally sounds choices for exploring and traveling the Great Lakes and the Port Superior Marina Association, a marina located at the entrance to the Apostle Islands Lakeshore. A myriad of resorts and bed and breakfasts that rim the beautiful waters of the Great Lakes are also members of Travel Green Wisconsin, each demonstrating the importance of preserving the lakes both to their businesses and our future.

Wisconsin originality is prevalent throughout our coasts. The Great Lakes inspired Wisconsinites to create the charming one-of-a-kind arts enclaves of Bayfield and Door County that attract hundreds of thousands of visitors each year. Milwaukee's Discovery World at Pier Wisconsin with its incredible sailing school vessel, the *S/V Denis Sullivan*, and Whistling Straits golf course, sculpted into the Lake Michigan coastline in Sheboygan and host of the PGA Championship, both celebrate the beauty of Lake Michigan.

Whitefish Dunes State Park in Door County attracts more visitors than any other day-use park in the State. And let us not forget the wonderful lighthouse tours that honor the heritage and romance of our Great Lakes.

A July 2008 study of travelers from Chicago and the Twin Cities produced a list of their most memorable Wisconsin vacation activities, and six of the top ten have ties to the Great Lakes—boating, swimming, fishing, sightseeing, camping and hiking. The economic ripple effect picks up even greater momentum when one considers those same travelers who participate in Wisconsin Great Lakes activities—such as boating and charter fishing—also spend money on dining, shopping and lodging.

By celebrating the originality of Wisconsin's people and the extraordinary experiences they have created, especially experiences on the pristine waters and sweeping shorelines of the Great Lakes, we have built a preference for Wisconsin that last year translated to $13.1 billion in traveler spending, making tourism one of the top three industries in the State.

The State's tourism industry also supported 310,300 full-time job equivalents, and generated $1.5 billion in State government revenues and $664 million in local government revenues to fund education, public safety and other government services. That is a predictable revenue stream for the State that we can all appreciate now more than ever.

In 2009, Kelli A. Trumble was Secretary of the Wisconsin Department of Tourism.

Lake Superior National Estuarine Research Reserve: Closer to Reality

Travis Olson

Residents along Lake Superior's coast will soon benefit from the designation of the Lake Superior National Estuarine Research Reserve (NERR) at the St. Louis River freshwater estuary. The Lake Superior NERR will be only the second reserve on the Great Lakes and among a national network of 27 reserves designated by the National Oceanic and Atmospheric Administration (NOAA).

The Lake Superior NERR is proposed to include approximately 15,000 acres of public land and water centered on the City of Superior. The anticipated designation of the Lake Superior NERR in 2010 will recognize the national significance of the St. Louis River freshwater estuary and lead to innovative programs that will benefit residents throughout the Lake Superior region.

The Wisconsin Coastal Management Program (WCMP) has long supported the designation of a Lake Superior NERR. A 2002 WCMP grant supported an initial feasibility study by the University of Wisconsin-Extension and The Nature Conservancy. The Wisconsin Coastal Management Council in 2003 endorsed pursuing a reserve on Lake Superior. WCMP staff assembled a multi-agency partnership for the site selection process that resulted in the nomination of the St. Louis River.

The University of Wisconsin-Extension is presently leading an extensive partnership of government agencies and organizations to develop integrated programs for research, education and resource stewardship at the Lake Superior NERR. Advisory committees are developing priorities that will be incorporated into a management plan to guide the work of Reserve staff for the next five years.

Research and monitoring of the St. Louis River and its watershed are of great interest to scientists and natural resource managers. Research priorities at the Lake Superior NERR will include preventing and controlling invasive species, restoring native plants and animals (wild rice is of particular interest), measuring the effect of land uses on water quality, and predicting the effects of climate change on the river and Lake Superior. Several monitoring stations set up in the Reserve will measure water and air quality and link to a national data center used by researchers throughout the world.

The Reserve will leverage existing research programs at regional and national institutions. The Wisconsin and Minnesota Sea Grant Institutes have already issued a joint request for research proposals that focus on the St. Louis River. Future partners in research may include the University of Wisconsin-Superior (a core partner in the NERR), the University of Minnesota-Duluth, the US Environmental Protection Agency Mid-Continent Division, the University of Wisconsin-Milwaukee Great Lakes WATER Institute, and the Wisconsin and Minnesota Departments of Natural Resources. The Reserve will also attract research from other institutions through graduate research fellowships and a national research grant program.

The Lake Superior NERR will educate citizens and students about Lake Superior's freshwater estuaries and coastal resources. Onsite programs will provide opportunities for school field trips and hands-on research projects, teacher workshops and classes, and visitor education. Reserve programs will also reach students and residents in community settings. As with research programs, the Reserve will utilize partnerships with existing organizations such as school districts, colleges and universities, local and tribal governments, aquariums, zoos and nature centers.

The Lake Superior NERR will also promote natural resource stewardship of the estuary. All of the property within the proposed boundary is publicly owned by one of four partner agencies: The City of Superior, Douglas County, the University of Wisconsin-Superior and the Wisconsin Department of Natural Resources.

Much of the Reserve consists of second-growth forest and wetlands that are characteristic of the Superior Coastal Plain. The Reserve will be managed to protect the key features that make it a valuable setting for research and education, and focus on restoring native ecosystems and controlling invasive species.

In addition to managing natural resources for research purposes, the Reserve will continue to accommodate existing recreational uses. Hunting, fishing, boating, cross-country skiing, archery, bicycling and bird watching are some of the activities that will continue within the Reserve boundaries. The Reserve partners are also coordinating with the Great Lakes Indian Fish and Wildlife Commission to ensure that tribal members continue to have access to off-reservation natural resources.

Finally, the Lake Superior NERR will be a resource for the entire community. Area residents will be invited to serve on advisory committees to provide input on Reserve programs and management. Existing programs like the Water Action Volunteer program that measures and monitors water quality will continue and expand at the Reserve. In addition, research, education and stewardship programs will have a great need for adult and school-aged volunteers in many capacities.

The Lake Superior NERR will soon be up and running with benefits to the Twin Ports region and all of Lake Superior. Superior will be home to an internationally important research program, unique education opportunities, continued conservation of a freshwater estuary and a source of community pride and activity.

In 2009, Travis Olson was a Program and Planning Analyst with the Wisconsin Coastal Management Program.

Planning Brown County's Parks

Aaron Schuette

Brown County's system of parks covers the spectrum of recreational opportunities. From one of Wisconsin's top-rated public golf courses, to the natural beauty of L.H. Barkhausen County Park, to camping, fishing and boating at Cecil Depeau Bay Shore County Park, to rollerblading on the Fox River Trail, Brown County provides countless ways for visitors and residents to enjoy the outdoors.

Each of Brown County's eighteen county-owned parks and three state-owned and county managed recreational trails fills its own unique niche. The Brown County Park and Outdoor Recreation Plan: 2008–2013—funded in part through the Wisconsin Coastal Management Program—will ensure the needs of existing parks are met and future opportunities are properly planned.

The 2008–2013 Plan was prepared in 2008 by the Brown County Planning Commission and the Brown County Facility and Park Management Department with the assistance of a steering committee. The Plan updates goals, objectives, policies and implementation activities identified in the original 2001 Brown County Park and Outdoor Recreation Plan.

In developing the Plan, the committee identified short-term needs of each park and kept an eye on the long-term goals of the County relating to new recreational facilities and natural resource protection. Of particular importance to users of coastal resources are plans for improvements to L.H. Barkhausen County Park and Fort Howard Paper Foundation Wildlife Area located on Green Bay's western shoreline, and Cecil Depeau Bay Shore County Park located on the eastern shore.

L.H. Barkhausen County Park and the adjoining Fort Howard Paper Foundation Wildlife Area are critical to the Brown County Park System and the overall water quality of Green Bay because of their proximity to the fragile coastal wetlands associated with the west shore of the bay. Although L.H. Barkhausen County Park is not located directly on the coast, it is comprised of approximately 475 acres of natural marsh, wildlife ponds, meadow and forest that drain through a series of small streams approximately one-half mile to the waters of Green Bay.

The West Shores Interpretive Center at Barkhausen is a former duck-hunting lodge and contains a number of interactive displays related to the history of the site and the fragile ecology of west shore wetlands flora and fauna. Immediately southeast of Barkhausen on the bay shore sits the 440-acre Fort Howard Paper Foundation Wildlife Area also owned and managed by Brown County. Hiking trails traverse both parks to provide public access to the perimeter and interior of these beautiful natural areas.

Specific recommendations in the Brown County Park and Outdoor Recreation Plan for L.H. Barkhausen County Park and the Fort Howard Paper Foundation Wildlife Area include protection, access and restoration activities, including:

- Adjacent bay shore property acquisition

- Expansion of a marsh overlook platform

- Parking lot and trailhead expansion at the Fort Howard Paper Foundation Wildlife Area

- Restoration of a former agricultural field to wetlands and wildlife habitat

- Restoration of a waterway to improve access for northern pike to critical spawning habitat

Cecil Depeau Bay Shore County Park is an 81-acre site on the rocky eastern shoreline of Green Bay where the Niagara Escarpment bluff meets the water. Scenic hiking trails follow the ledge of the escarpment—a geologic formation created over 400 million years ago by an ancient sea—and provide breathtaking views of the waters of Green Bay. The Park offers an improved boat launch, refuge harbor and transient mooring for boaters as well as year-round camping and playground facilities easily accessible from State Highway 57.

The 2008–2013 recommendations for Cecil Depeau Bay Shore County Park strongly support improving boating and fishing access to the waters of Green Bay through:

- construction of a fish cleaning station

- repair and expansion of the existing harbor breakwater

- improvement of the walkway on the harbor breakwater to improve accessibility for shore fishing

- expansion of the existing boat launch

- addition of restroom buildings

The L.H. Barkhausen County Park/Fort Howard Paper Foundation Wildlife Area and Cecil Depeau Bay Shore County Park are only two of the eighteen county parks and trails considered in the 2008–2013 Brown County Park and Recreation Plan. The Plan details the current needs and future vision for all Brown County Park System facilities and trails. With the assistance of the Wisconsin Coastal Management Program, the completion of the Plan provides eligibility for Brown County to apply for various state and federal grant programs to implement the overall vision through its detailed recommendations.

While in the Greater Green Bay area, Brown County invites you to visit any and all of our parks. Whether you want to stroll through the Northeastern Wisconsin Zoo, fish for world class walleye on the Fox River, golf Brown County Golf Course, bicycle the Mountain-Bay State Recreational Trail or simply relax and enjoy the sunset over the waters of Green Bay, Brown County has a park for you.

In 2009, Aaron Schuette was a Senior Planner with the Brown County Planning Commission.

Disposal of Old Medicines

Steve Brachman

Over the last several years, public attention has increased regarding the improper management of old medicines. Consumers historically have been told to flush their unused and expired medicines when not needed. Broadly known as PPCPs (pharmaceutical and personal care products), these emerging contaminants are increasingly showing up in the waters of Wisconsin.

Many wastewater treatment facilities lack the ability to remove PPCPs prior to returning treated water to lakes and streams. Although PPCP levels found in waterways are very low and do not seem to have an impact upon human health, researchers from the University of Wisconsin-Milwaukee Great Lakes WATER Institute and the US Environmental Protection Agency have found that even low levels alter fish behavior and reproduction. It is now recommended that consumers and health care professionals discontinue flushing or dumping down the drain most old pharmaceuticals and personal care products.

Old and unused medicines pose other risks. Accidental ingestion by children and the elderly is a significant health issue in the United States with over 78,000 children less than five years of age treated each year for medicine poisoning. Illegal use or theft is an ongoing problem since prescription drugs now account for the second most commonly abused category of drugs behind marijuana and ahead of cocaine, heroin and methamphetamine. Finally, unnecessary accumulation of unneeded medicines in health care facilities is both wasteful and costly.

As a result, there has been a great deal of activity to develop innovative programs to educate the public regarding alternative methods of disposal of old medicines. For example, communities are organizing one-day collection programs similar to Clean Sweeps that collect hazardous household wastes. Typically operated by local governments, wastewater treatment plant operators, neighborhood pharmacies or local police, these events have grown in Wisconsin from only six in 2006 to over sixty in 2008.

Although consumer response has been very strong, one-day events have serious limitations. For example, many consumers find the events inconvenient due to sometimes long traffic lines and infrequent availability. Law enforcement agencies must attend the events—usually at significant cost—to manage controlled substances according to US Drug Enforcement Agency standards. Finally, considerable mobilization time and resources are required to publicize, market, locate and provide safe disposal for one-day collection events.

In 2007, the University of Wisconsin-Extension and the Wisconsin Department of Natural Resources formed a pharmaceutical waste working group to begin addressing these issues. Made up of local government officials, state agency representatives and pharmacists, this group recommended exploring new methods of collecting old medicines. Two potential models have emerged as a result—permanent collection drop-offs at household hazardous waste centers or police departments, and a pilot mail back program.

La Crosse County, for example, now operates a medicine collection program that utilizes deputized County staff to receive and dispose of unwanted medicines. Similarly, police and sheriff departments in Columbia County and Marshfield place secure drop boxes at their locations for ongoing disposal.

An old medicine mail back pilot program has served as perhaps the most convenient collection program to date. For many years, pharmacies, hospitals and drug manufacturers have utilized reverse distributors to manage expired or recalled pharmaceuticals by simply shipping them back to a centralized facility for safe disposal. Capitalizing upon Wisconsin's existing pharmaceutical return infrastructure, the mail back pilot used Capital Returns in Milwaukee to operate a hotline and mail back service for consumers in Waukesha and Winnebago Counties.

The program's kick off in May 2008 utilized over one hundred pharmacies to post notices and distribute package inserts notifying residents in the two counties of the toll-free call center for old medicines. By contracting the call center, consumers were instructed which types of medicines could be accepted and provided a shipping container for return shipment. As a result, over 1,700 households were able to conveniently ship back their old medicines during the eight-month pilot period.

But have these innovative efforts encouraged significant consumer behavior change? A recent survey of participants in the mail-back pilot indicated that consumer participation may lead to real modifications in disposal practices. For example, eighteen percent of randomly sampled residents of Winnebago and Waukesha Counties either poured down the sink or flushed their old medicines, while only two percent of the mail back program participants continued this practice. Thirty-six percent of the random sample indicated that they stored old medicines in their home indefinitely or placed them in the trash as is, while less than five percent of the mail back program participants practiced similar behaviors.

Other steps are under consideration in Wisconsin's pursuit of safe alternatives for old medicine disposal. One option would continue the mail back pilot program should the US Drug Enforcement Agency ease the ability of reverse distributors to accept and manage consumer medications. There also exists great interest in exploring product stewardship approaches to unwanted pharmaceutical disposal. For instance, model legislation in the State of Washington provides for industry-funded disposal at pharmacies. In addition, the state pharmaceutical society and others are exploring approaches to change prescribing practices allowing smaller quantities to be more effectively utilized.

Regardless of the approach chosen, it is essential that Wisconsin's Great Lakes be protected from contamination by old medications.

In 2009, Steve Brachman was a Solid and Hazardous Waste Specialist at the UW-Extension Solid and Hazardous Waste Education Center.

SMALL COMMUNITY STORMWATER MANAGEMENT

Sandra Dee Schultz-Naas

Madeline Island—located in Lake Superior along the Bayfield Peninsula—is among the 22 Apostle Islands and home to La Pointe, one of Wisconsin's oldest communities. La Pointe was established as a French trading post as early as 1693 but was home to the Ojibwe people long before.

Today, about 250 people reside year-round in La Pointe. During summer months, history, nostalgia and the promise of a unique island experience draw as many as 2,500 visitors per day to this small unincorporated community.

This large influx of people and the town's proximity to Lake Superior create significant natural resource management issues. Of the most serious issues, runoff events are aggravated by the fact that most visitors enter and exit the Island by ferry at a single point.

Runoff from storm and snow melt negatively impact water quality if not properly treated. In 1990, the International Joint Commission recommended the designation of Lake Superior as a demonstration area for zero discharge of persistent toxins. To carry forward the demonstration, Wisconsin, Minnesota, Michigan and Ontario entered into an agreement to form the Lake Superior Binational Forum.

The Binational Forum set about to assess urban stormwater impacts on the Lake Superior basin. Thirteen municipalities were studied and yearly averages determined for pollutants entering the basin through storm drain systems. The study found that thousands of pounds of phosphorus, nitrates, lead, chlorides and other oxygen consuming materials annually ended up in wetlands and ultimately Lake Superior. In addition, almost 34 billion pounds of solids found their way to the Lake through storm drains.

The Town of La Pointe fully realized that a clean Lake Superior was vital to its economy and quality of life. While not a large community, La Pointe wanted to be part of the Binational Forum's noble effort to reduce stormwater impacts on the lake.

La Pointe's Town Road Foreman Keith Sowl knew firsthand how tourism activity could aggravate runoff events. After hearing about the Binational Forum goals and research in 2000, Mr. Sowl and former Town Chairman Burke Henry discussed how stormwater runoff from their community impacted Lake Superior and how best La Pointe could help reduce that impact.

Armed with research and a plan, Mr. Sowl and Mr. Henry worked with the Town Board to begin a comprehensive upgrade of the stormwater management program in La Pointe and at strategic locations around the Island where heavy traffic was an issue. The Town placed a strong emphasis on improving public access while insuring that stormwater best management practices were included in all designs. Partnership funding from agencies including the Wisconsin Coastal Management Program, the Wisconsin Department of Natural Resources, the US Army Corp of Engineers Section 154 Program, the Ashland County Land & Water Conservation Department and neighboring communities helped make these plans reality.

Stormwater Management Upgrades and Demonstration Project. The absence of sidewalks, curb and gutter, and limited space for parking contributed to a runoff management problem in the commercial area of La Pointe. Water ran quickly through the drainage system due to the lack of retention areas. Heavy foot and car traffic denuded vegetation resulting in sediment and pollutant transport through eroding ditches and over unpaved parking lots. Gas, oil and other nonpoint pollutants were picked up by runoff and deposited directly into coastal wetlands and eventually into Lake Superior.

The Town road crew addressed these issues by constructing stormwater collection and transport systems, curb and gutter, sidewalks and outfall protection as part of a major upgrade nearest coastal wetlands. At the same time, they solicited Laurie's Store for a stormwater best management practice demonstration project. Here they collected roof water and directed it to a rain garden, added green space to provide for infiltration of runoff, and used oil, debris and sediment collectors in the stormwater intake drains.

Winter Public Access and Stormwater Management. A 2.5-mile ice road connects La Pointe and Bayfield during the winter. With an estimated use of about 600 cars per day, Island and mainland approaches contributed much sediment to the Lake and became dangerous to navigate. La Pointe and Bayfield improved their respective winter approaches to Lake Superior by incorporating sediment and erosion control measures and rerouting runoff from the long, steep slopes that provide access from land to ice.

Public Access for Recreation and Emergency Services. La Pointe is currently working on developing a trail and boat dock at North Shore Park on the north end of the Island. This new access will not only improve public access to Lake Superior, but also provide a path for improved emergency services to assist boaters, ice fishers and campers.

While some of the faces and names have changed, the tiny community of La Pointe continues to do its part to curb pollutants from entering Lake Superior. At just fourteen miles long and three miles wide, Madeline Island is having a big impact on Lake Superior's future. With the help of many funding agencies, La Pointe has taken a proactive role in meeting the Binational Forum's zero discharge goals for Lake Superior, the greatest of the Great Lakes.

In 2009, Sandra Dee Schultz-Naas, CPESC, was a Soil Scientist at Stable Solutions LLC.

WIND ON THE WATER

Timothy Le Monds

Wisconsin has three primary native options for producing electricity from renewable sources: wind, hydroelectric and biofuels. Exploring these renewable energy sources has become increasingly important given heightened concerns about global warming, the availability of fuel supplies and price volatility.

The use of renewable energy in Wisconsin has grown in recent years due in large part to the establishment of a renewable portfolio standard (RPS). This standard requires that ten percent of the state's electricity be produced from renewable sources by 2015. Recently, Governor Jim Doyle and the Governor's Task Force on Global Warming (Task Force) recommended expanding the RPS to twenty-five percent by the year 2025, with ten percent of total retail electric sales coming from renewable resources within the state.

Due to its availability, wind generation is expected to become a large component of Wisconsin's renewable energy portfolio. Meeting the state's energy needs by generating electricity from wind provides significant environmental benefits compared to the use of fossil fuels. These benefits include reduced dependence on nonnative energy sources, reduced emissions of air pollutants and greenhouse gases, reductions in the generation of solid wastes, and little or no water consumption. Despite these benefits, there exist concerns about using on-land wind resources for power including reliability, relative costs, effects on wildlife and impacts on existing land uses.

Harnessing Wisconsin's Great Lakes wind resources offers several potential advantages over on-land wind projects. First, offshore wind projects have the potential to produce power on a large scale that may be more economical than terrestrial wind projects due to the presence of more robust and consistent winds. Second, these same winds allow offshore projects to use larger turbines with a higher potential output than could be used on land. In addition, offshore projects may produce fewer concerns about interfering with existing land uses. Taken as a whole, these advantages have the potential to offset the challenges, risks and higher initial costs that might be expected with developing and operating an offshore wind project.

In recognition of these benefits and the need to identify potential concerns, the Task Force recommended that the Public Service Commission of Wisconsin lead a study group to investigate the feasibility of generating electricity from offshore wind resources on the Great Lakes. The study group found that offshore wind projects are technically feasible and represent one potential approach to meeting a portion of the state's long-term energy needs. Other major findings in the study include:

- The development of wind projects in the Great Lakes will require a coordinated effort by state and federal agencies, local government, affected Indian Tribes and possibly the Wisconsin Legislature.

- In the near term, the cost of energy generated from offshore wind will likely exceed the cost of energy generated from terrestrial wind projects. As offshore wind technology and operational experience improve, the cost of energy from offshore wind may decrease.

- Offshore wind projects are technically feasible in the near-shore areas of the Great Lakes with present day technology. There exist significant technological challenges with the development of wind projects in deeper water locations where the best project sites may be located based on wind resources and other considerations.

- Wisconsin's existing transmission system could—without substantial upgrades—support the development of smaller-scale offshore wind projects of less than 600 MW that are located near a city. Projects larger than 600 MW may require more substantial upgrades to the existing transmission system including developing new transmission lines.

The study also found that of the two lakes, Lake Michigan likely offers greater opportunities for development of offshore wind projects and should be the focus of any future efforts by the State. Wisconsin's waters in Lake Superior are not extensive and a substantial portion is subject to development or use restriction.

Any offshore wind project in the Great Lakes will need to be large enough to take advantage of economies of scale, and obviously larger projects will require larger expanses of water. European experience with offshore wind projects has demonstrated that such projects typically require more area than comparable land-based wind projects due to the wind disturbance caused by multiple rows of turbines. For example, the proposed Cape Wind project near Cape Cod, Massachusetts—with a proposed capacity of 468 MW—would require 26 square miles to accommodate 130 turbines.

The Public Service Commission of Wisconsin will continue its investigation of offshore wind development in the Great Lakes. Next steps will include collection of wind resource, wildlife and other ecological data, further research on the development of deep water foundations, and discussions with other states and Canada on procuring a construction vessel for the Great Lakes.

Work will also begin with the Wisconsin Legislature to consider statutory changes to facilitate the development of offshore wind generation on the Great Lakes.

While tapping the vast wind resources of the Great Lakes has the potential to create significant quantities of renewable energy for Wisconsin, further investigation is required before moving forward with a large scale project that harnesses wind on the water.

In 2009, Timothy Le Monds was Director of Governmental and Public Affairs with the Public Service Commission of Wisconsin.

2010

FOREWORD

Governor Jim Doyle

Dear Friends of Wisconsin's Great Lakes,

In Wisconsin, the Great Lakes are fundamental to our identity and way of life. Lake Michigan and Lake Superior's natural resources, transportation routes and abundant beauty have enriched our lives for generations. The generations of Wisconsin's citizens that follow will continue to rely on the Great Lakes for recreation and as a gateway to national and global markets.

Because of their importance to the state, the region and the nation, one of my highest priorities as Governor has been to protect and enhance the Great Lakes. During the last eight years, it has been an honor to work with many talented and dedicated individuals to preserve the future of the Lakes. Together with many local and tribal governments, community organizations and citizens, we have achieved much since 2003.

Coastal Nonpoint Pollution Protection. In 2003, the National Oceanic and Atmospheric Administration and the US Environmental Protection Agency approved the Wisconsin Coastal Nonpoint Pollution Control Program. Wisconsin's program, among the first such programs in the nation, serves as a model that addresses nonpoint source pollution from urban impacts, marinas, forestry, agriculture and hydromodification.

Regional Collaboration. As co-chair of the Council of Great Lakes Governors, I worked with other state and provincial leaders to develop and implement regional policies to restore and protect the Great Lakes. Together, the Council established nine priorities benefiting the basin. These priorities were codified in 2004 by Presidential Executive Order 13340 to become the Great Lakes Regional Collaboration.

Great Lakes Compact. Wisconsin worked with the other seven Great Lakes states, two Canadian provinces and the US government to develop landmark legislation creating unprecedented protections for the Lakes. In 2008, I signed legislation approving Wisconsin's participation in the Great Lakes Compact. The Compact became federal law later that year.

The protections contained the Compact will ensure the environmental sustainability and economic viability of the Great Lakes for years to come.

Lake Superior National Estuarine Research Reserve (NERR). In 2008, I nominated the St. Louis River as the Lake Superior National Estuarine Research Reserve. As the largest US tributary to Lake Superior and the headwaters of the entire Great Lakes system, the St. Louis River basin is a nationally significant region providing critical habitat for birds, fish and plants. Federal designation of the Lake Superior NERR is expected in 2010 when it will join a national system of twenty-seven other reserves. The Lake Superior NERR will further enhance Wisconsin's reputation as a national leader in research and educational outreach related to freshwater studies.

Coastal Management. The Department of Administration's Wisconsin Coastal Management Program continues to work cooperatively with federal, state, local and tribal governments, universities, non-profit organizations and citizens to protect the Great Lakes as a natural, commercial and recreational resource.

As we look toward the future, this partnership remains strong. The federal government has committed an unprecedented $475 million in the first of a five-year investment to clean up contaminated sites, protect critical habitats and control aquatic invasive species and nonpoint pollution in the Great Lakes. Wisconsin has received notice that fifty proposals totaling nearly $30 million have been initially approved. This federal commitment will have a tremendous impact on the health of the Great Lakes well into the future.

The Great Lakes will continue to grow in importance as a vital natural resource and economic engine. I am proud of the work we have accomplished to preserve the Lakes for generations to come.

Jim Doyle served as Wisconsin's 44th Governor from 2003 to 2011.

NEW LIFE FOR AN OLD COAL DOCK

Rob Vanden Noven

Historic Port Washington, established as a city in 1835, is located on Lake Michigan's western shore just 25 miles north of downtown Milwaukee. The heart of the city is its marina dredged in 1870 to become the first man-made harbor in North America. Adjacent to the marina, the historic downtown boasts the largest collection of antebellum architecture in the entire state, highlighted by several self-guided walking tours.

Hikers, bikers, bird-watchers, sailors, beach-goers and tourists from all over the Midwest come to Port Washington for the beauty and tranquility it has to offer. St. Mary's Catholic Church prominently watches over the downtown while the historic light station attracts tour groups from all over the world. The art deco lighthouse at the end of the break wall has guided boaters and attracted scores of people daily since the 1930s.

The Port Washington Generating Station—constructed by Wisconsin Electric in 1935—has stood on the city's Lake Michigan shoreline where the lakebed was filled to provide an area for coal deliveries and storage. In 2003, We Energies began a five-year project to convert the existing coal fired power plant into a state-of-the-art facility burning only natural gas. The conversion process resulted in the availability of nearly twenty acres of lakefront property formerly used for coal storage to become available for public use and a natural habitat for migrating birds.

At the same time We Energies began planning improvements to the power generating station, the City of Port Washington began planning improvements to convert the environmentally challenged and restricted coal dock into a recreational jewel, all adjacent to Port Washington's picturesque downtown and marina. In 2008, a Wisconsin Coastal Management Program grant funded the hiring of planners, landscape architects and engineers to move forward with ideas gathered by a citizens' committee in the years prior.

The first step taken by the City was the creation of the Coal Dock Committee comprised of stakeholders representing the marina, the parks system, tourism, the downtown business district, elected officials and citizens. Eight firms were interviewed by the Committee and the team of Hitchcock Design Group/Crispell-Snyder was ultimately selected to perform design work.

Hitchcock interviewed all stakeholders individually, met with the committee regularly, conducted a programming workshop open to all residents, facilitated a charrette, prepared alternative strategies, worked with various regulatory agencies and prepared a final concept design and implementation plan for approval by the City's Common Council. Crispell-Snyder then worked with City staff to create engineering plans and specifications based on the approved concept for construction in the following years.

Components of the project include accessible recreational trails, fishing areas, docking for visiting tall ships and other Great Lakes craft, an access roadway, parking lots, lighting, sewer and water, landscaping and other amenities that will enhance the natural beauty of the scenic shoreline. A footbridge will connect the north and south docks that are separated by the power plant's intake channel.

The south dock will feature a naturalized area providing a stopover point for migratory birds while maintaining waterfront access to boaters and fishermen around the perimeter of the dock. South of the migratory area, the path will continue to a newly developed beach served by a parking lot that will facilitate non-motorized small craft—canoes, kayaks, sailboards—launching and retrieval. The launching area will be the first of its kind in all of Ozaukee County.

The Wisconsin Coastal Management Program has assisted with the funding of previous portions of the City's Harborwalk between Upper Lake Park, Veteran's Memorial Park, Rotary Park and Fisherman's Park along the Lake Michigan shoreline. This project will double the length of the existing Harborwalk connecting the City's four lakefront parks to the north beach, marina, the historic downtown and the Ozaukee County Interurban Bike Trail.

The potential impact of the proposed improvements is limitless. The City of Port Washington enjoys large tourist traffic that visits from all over Wisconsin and the Midwest during the summer and fall seasons. In addition to the tens of thousands of people that use the marina each summer for pleasure boating and charter fishing, it is estimated that over

100,000 visitors come each year to Port Washington's lakefront for popular festivals such as Fish Day, Pirate Festival, Maritime Heritage Festival, farmers markets and other events. Additionally, nearly 100,000 users of the Ozaukee County Interurban Bike Trail pass through the community on a yearly basis.

The City is working on grant writing and budgeting for the construction of the proposed improvements. The current plan would build the majority of the park and infrastructure improvements over a four-year period while entering a second phase of planning to construct a building to serve the public as a community center, museum and/or park facility. Upon completion of these improvements, the City of Port Washington is sure to have a one-of-a-kind, four season attraction for its residents and a destination for visitors of which it can be proud.

In 2010, Rob Vanden Noven was City Engineer/Public Works Director with the City of Port Washington.

A View of Wisconsin's Coast from Washington

Donna Wieting

The Coastal Zone Management Act (CZMA) helps bridge the miles between Wisconsin's beautiful Great Lakes coasts and Washington D.C. The National Oceanic and Atmospheric Administration's (NOAA), Office of Ocean and Coastal Resource Management (OCRM) partners directly with the Wisconsin Coastal Management Program (WCMP) to assist with work on the Great Lakes coasts. The CZMA takes a comprehensive approach to coastal resource management—balancing the often competing and occasionally conflicting demands of coastal resource use, economic development and conservation—while helping states address their own coastal priorities.

OCRM has had a productive and dynamic relationship with the WCMP since the program's approval in 1978. The WCMP uses federal CZMA resources to fund an impressive array of projects along both Wisconsin's coasts. These projects address a number of coastal issues including public access, stormwater management, wetland preservation and Great Lakes education. The WCMP has been a leader in creating a National Estuarine Research Reserve on Lake Superior and has successfully competed for additional NOAA funds for land conservation.

On the national front, there is good news for this federal and state government partnership. Following the lead of the President's Ocean Policy Task Force, NOAA is making sustainable coastal and Great Lakes communities a long-term priority goal in its Next Generation Strategic Plan. Shortly after President Obama appointed Dr. Jane Lubchenco to head NOAA in 2008, she gathered staff and stakeholders to develop a strategy for the future of the nation's coastal, Great Lakes and ocean resources, and the role NOAA should play in the next generation of coastal and ocean science and management. The resulting plan will be the basis of NOAA's corporate planning, performance management and stakeholder engagement over the next five years.

Sustainable Coastal Communities is of one of the Plan's four major goals. It will strive for coastal and Great Lakes communities that are environmentally and economically sustainable. Some important elements of the goal are climate change and weather adaptation, already a primary issue for Wisconsin and other Great Lakes states. Comprehensive marine spatial planning also promises to figure prominently in the goal. Other objectives revolve around marine transportation, improved water quality and human health.

Coastal managers, stakeholders and citizens weighed in on where and how NOAA directs its energies on the coastal goal and the other priority goals—climate adaptation and mitigation, weather-ready nation and sustainable ocean ecosystems. The Next Generation Strategic Plan is posted at the NOAA Office of Program Planning and Integration Web site at www .ppi.noaa.gov.

OCRM's interest in Wisconsin's coasts goes beyond national policy. We are working with Wisconsin toward common objectives that enhance and preserve the state's coasts and coastal communities. Two recent Wisconsin initiatives are particularly noteworthy.

Preserving Wisconsin's Coastal Treasures. One of the OCRM programs that best exemplifies the value of the partnership between NOAA and the WCMP is the Coastal and Estuarine Land Conservation Program (CELCP). CELCP is a competitive program that helps communities purchase valuable coastal land to preserve in perpetuity. CELCP saves habitat threatened with development and keeps coastal space available for people to hike, bike, bird watch or just see the sun go down over the lake. Moreover, it is a matching program that makes federal and local dollars go further to save land that otherwise might not be affordable.

Three Wisconsin projects were recently named to be funded through CELCP. The Nemadji River project—to be supported with regular CELCP funding—will save almost 4,000 acres in the Nemadji River watershed including six miles of river frontage. CELCP will also fund two projects through the Great Lakes Restoration Initiative. The Houghton Falls Nature Preserve project encompasses 77 acres of the Bayfield peninsula on the south shore of Lake Superior for nature-based recreation. The Mashek Creek project—just north of Kewaunee on Lake Michigan—will protect about 27 acres for recreation and education. These joint local and federal efforts will allow three Wisconsin treasures to be enjoyed for generations to come.

Lake Superior Reserve. Another success of the partnership between NOAA and the Wisconsin Coastal Management Program will soon become official. OCRM staff has been working with the WCMP, the University of Wisconsin Cooperative Extension and local partners for several years to bring Lake Superior into the National Estuarine Research Reserve (NERR) System. Located where the St. Louis River flows into Lake Superior, the proposed Lake Superior NERR will include 16,697 acres of wetlands, hardwood forests and sandy beach. By October 2010, this beautiful area will likely become the twenty-eighth member of the NERR System.

The CECLP projects and the Reserve are living examples of how Wisconsin and Washington can be closer than they seem. NOAA's Next Generation Strategic Plan will help map a future for an even stronger partnership with shared goals for America and Wisconsin's coasts.

In 2010, Donna Wieting was Acting Director of NOAA's Office of Ocean and Coastal Resource Management.

Real-Time Wave Information System at the Apostle Islands Mainland Sea Caves

Gene Clark, PE, and Dr. Chin Wu

The sea caves at the Apostle Islands National Lakeshore are unique and spectacular natural rock formations. These eroded sandstone formations were formed when lake water and waves eroded the soft sandstone near the water edge, yielding a series of caves carved out of the exposed sandstone cliffs.

In Lake Superior, many sea caves are located on two of the islands—Devils Island and Sand Island—as well as on a relatively remote area on the mainland near Meyers Beach. The mainland sea caves can be viewed from above on land by a rugged two-mile hike along the bluff top trail from the Meyers Beach parking lot, but the best way to see these rock formations is on the water. The sea caves have become a world-class destination for kayaking, luring paddlers with their natural beauty and scenic wilderness. However, the sea caves can also be very dangerous.

Wave conditions in Lake Superior are dynamic and complex. Relatively moderate waves—in comparison with ocean waves—can be generated in open water in the Great Lakes. Waves diffract, refract and reflect when they encounter the twenty-one islands and twelve-mile mainland shoreline that make up the Apostle Islands National Lakeshore. Occasionally, unexpected and extremely high waves—sometimes called freak waves— occur when wave groups resonate together to create a singular wave that is two to five times larger than the incident wave heights. This problem is compounded at the vertical walls and scooped-out hollows in the sea cave areas.

Kayakers are well warned to avoid the cave area during rough seas. However, during periods of marginal waves, kayakers may see comfortable boating, but be unaware of the amplified waves near the sea caves. Due to the combination of wave focusing processes and shifting wind directions, freak waves can form suddenly and then disappear in several seconds. Unexpected freak waves can capsize boats or kayaks leaving little opportunity for kayakers to respond to this type of emergency. It is believed that two fatalities (*Duluth News Tribune*, 8/24/2004 and 6/26/2007) were experienced by kayakers who may have been knocked out of their kayaks by freak waves near the popular sea caves. Future fatalities may be prevented if real-time wave conditions at the caves can be provided at the Meyers Beach launching area over a mile away.

The immediate safety concern to collect and provide real-time wave climate information at the Sea Cave was taken on by a team including members from UW-Madison, UW-Sea Grant, the Apostle Islands National Lakeshore, the City of Bayfield, the Inland Sea Society, the Friends of the Apostle Islands and Wisconsin Coastal Management Program.

A real-time wave observation system (RTWOS) was designed and tested in 2009. The RTWOS consists of the following components—an immersed water pressure sensor, a marine grade underwater submerged buoy, anchored cable, a waterproof box on land with an on-demand Campbell Scientific data acquisition system that can save the real-time data and transmit data through wireless modem, a 12-volt battery supply fed with a solar panel power charging system, and a main site with a PC that can retrieve, displace and save real-time data.

Using wireless cellular technology, the system successfully sampled and transmitted wave data to a host computer at UW-Madison, 350 miles away from the remote sea cave site. In addition, a real-time monitor control software was employed to display the processed data to a Web page being developed at the UW-Madison campus.

During the summer and fall of 2010, the team will add on-line and off-line digital image cameras (DIC) to the RTWOS system and a water temperature gauge. Making visual images with real-time wave height information from this remote sea cave location accessible anywhere via a public Web page, sea cave visitors and kayakers will be better informed about potentially dangerous wave conditions at the sea caves.

In addition, Lake Superior is well known for its cold temperatures, even in the middle of summer. Average water temperatures in May and June are only in the 40s while even in late summer, typical surface water temperatures rarely exceed 60°F. Therefore, the real-time water temperature is also valuable to warn kayakers to wear wet suits or dry suits and pay very close attention to varying weather and wave conditions.

The web hosting software and public website will continue to update its visual photo display and post results to the Internet in real-time. The Web site will be easily accessible and readable for persons using mobile internet devices such as BlackBerry, iPhone and PDA. It is anticipated that many users may access the Web page from remote locations such as Meyers Beach or the Apostle Islands National Lakeshore headquarters—therefore, the page will be optimized so that information can be downloaded quickly.

Finally, the project management plan includes safety education and outreach, Web access training and informational meetings by creating public awareness of the potentially dangerous wave conditions at the sea caves and how to access the real-time information about the conditions via the project Web site.

In 2010, Gene Clark was a Coastal Engineering Specialist with the University of Wisconsin Sea Grant Institute. Dr. Chin Wu was a Professor with the Department of Civil and Environmental Engineering at the University of Wisconsin-Madison.

THE WISCONSIN COASTAL MANAGEMENT COUNCIL

Mayor Larry MacDonald

Of the many challenges facing Wisconsin's coastal communities, a lack of good ideas is not among them. Citizens, local governments, Native American tribes and nonprofit organizations along our shores have a long history of overcoming obstacles by combining home-grown innovation, people and resources.

For more than three decades, the Wisconsin Coastal Management Program (WCMP) has played a critical role in enhancing our communities by providing technical assistance and funding to assist countless local projects including land use planning, nonpoint source pollution abatement, public access and Great Lakes education. A critical part of the WCMP's success is the participation of a citizen-based council that guides the program by providing perspective on local and statewide coastal issues.

The Wisconsin Coastal Management Council (Council) is a fourteen-member body appointed by the Governor to provide advice and assistance to the WCMP staff and partners. Council membership includes public and local government representatives from the Lake Superior region, the Green Bay and upper Lake Michigan region, the southern Lake Michigan region and City of Milwaukee. Council members also represent tribal government, academia, the State Senate, the State Assembly and the Departments of Administration, Transportation and Natural Resources.

The Council brings together diverse perspectives to advise the WCMP on policy matters involving Wisconsin's coastal management efforts. For instance, the Council annually considers program priorities used to guide the allocation of resources through the program. The Council may also provide policy advice to the Governor and federal partners on matters involving Wisconsin's coasts. In addition, Council members use their broad knowledge of coastal issues to make strong connections with key decision-makers—state legislators, local government officials, Native

American tribal representatives and state agency officials—and the general public.

The Council is most active in its work involving local projects in need of WCMP financial resources. Our successful grant program is often considered to be the main part of what we accomplish, and has been a critical component for hundreds of coastal projects through the decades.

Serving on the Council since 2002 (Chairman since 2009) and as Mayor of the City of Bayfield (population 627) since 1994 has provided me an interesting view of coastal issues and solutions. Prior to serving on the Council, I represented the City of Bayfield as a WCMP grant applicant for a wide variety of projects. Some were funded and some were not. However, with each grant application we received sound, practical input and advice from the WCMP. It was not always what we wanted to hear, but always worth hearing.

Local applicants frequently have several good ideas for WCMP-funded projects. However, ranking those ideas needs to be a key initial element of their planning. Normally, only one grant per funding cycle will be awarded to an applicant, although they may apply for additional projects provided their list is prioritized.

My advice is to think big during the early stages of a project idea and focus on program requirements as the plan matures. Contact with WCMP staff is essential so the grantee's application is written to have the best chances of success. Grant guidelines are well detailed and must be followed. Good project planning will minimize obstacles to a successful application.

For example, the City of Bayfield in 1994 applied for a WCMP grant to renovate the historic Bayfield Lakeside Pavilion, a structure owned by the City since 1938. The grant application required proof of ownership. However, we learned just before the application was due that the transfer of title had never been completed. We were fortunate to find the daughter of the former owner who actually remembered the day in 1938 when the City paid her father for the structure. We obtained title shortly before the grant was due.

Grant applicants can take several preliminary steps to increase their chances of success:

- Contact the WCMP staff to review successful grant applications that relate to their ideas.

- Participate in WCMP grant workshops to ask questions of program staff.

- Attend a Council meeting to get a better understanding of the decision-making process.

- Contact a former grant recipient, a current Council member who lives in your area or the local regional planning commission to get perspective on a proposed project.

In 2010, the WCMP awarded 39 grants totaling $1.6 million. These awards leveraged other funds to generate aggregate project value of nearly $5.4 million. Grant recipients range from the very small Town of La Pointe on Madeline Island to the City of Milwaukee. All communities are welcome to participate in the program.

In past years, grants have been provided for projects as diverse as waterfront planning, community playgrounds, storm water runoff solutions and healthy beaches. Grant recipients are generally pleased to share their knowledge with new applicants. Communities that participate in the program become strong supporters of the broad spectrum of help and ideas provided by the WCMP.

Each of our coastal communities, tribes and non-profits has different needs, talents and skills. However, we all share the same goal of protecting two of the greatest resources on Earth, the Great Lakes named Superior and Michigan.

In 2010, Larry MacDonald was Mayor of the City of Bayfield.

WETLAND GEMS: RECASTING THE IMAGE OF WETLANDS

Katie Beilfuss, Becky Abel and Laura England

No matter who you are or where you live, wetlands affect your life.

From clean water to flood attenuation, shoreline protection to fish and wildlife habitat, wetlands provide important natural benefits as well as recreational and educational opportunities that enrich the lives of the people of Wisconsin and our state's economy.

But a history of negative and erroneous stereotypes of wetlands—they are wastelands, they breed mosquitoes and other pests, they stand in the way of development—has contributed to the destruction of nearly half of Wisconsin's wetlands as well as pervasive misunderstandings about the value of wetlands. People who value Wisconsin's lakes, rivers and streams are often unaware of the role that wetlands play in keeping our beloved waterways healthy. Some of this lack of understanding may stem from the fact that wetlands as a natural community type are confusing and not always readily recognizable.

Just what are wetlands? Can they be dry? (Yes) Must they have cattails or pond lilies? (No) Can they be wooded? (Yes) Many of Wisconsin's citizens do not understand what wetlands are or the ways in which wetlands affect their lives. The Wetland Gems program aims to change all that.

In 2009, the Wisconsin Wetlands Association (WWA) announced 100 Wetland Gems, high quality habitats that represent the wetland riches—marshes, swamps, bogs, fens and more—that historically made up nearly a quarter of Wisconsin's land area. They are landscapes that both preserve the past and inspire for the future.

The Wetland Gems program was designed to raise the profile and elevate public awareness of wetlands, their importance and value. It also aimed to motivate Wisconsin families and citizens to explore and enjoy wetlands, generate community pride about local wetland treasures, and catalyze community involvement in stewardship of local wetland treasures.

WWA has set a goal that citizens of Wisconsin will value all wetlands as natural treasures, and that increased public understanding and recognition of the value of wetlands will ultimately mean greater protection of Wetland Gems and other Wisconsin wetlands over the long-term.

The Wetland Gems list built upon the results of extensive conservation planning efforts that identified critical habitats, threats and conservation actions to protect the state's natural communities, species and special places, including coastal habitats. These include The Nature Conservancy's Ecoregional Plans, the Wisconsin Important Bird Areas Project, and the Wisconsin Department of Natural Resources' Land Legacy Report, Wildlife Action Plan, State Natural Areas Program and Coastal Wetlands Assessment Report.

Following consultation with wetland experts, WWA selected ninety-three sites that collectively represent the diversity of wetland community types present in each of eight geographic regions. Wherever possible, WWA chose Wetland Gems containing multiple wetland and upland community types and representing fully functioning ecological systems. WWA selected an additional seven Workhorse Wetland Gems, sites that illustrate how wetlands deliver priceless services including flood attenuation, water quality protection, fish and wildlife habitat, shoreline protection, groundwater connections, and recreation and educational opportunities.

The announcement of Wisconsin's Wetland Gems included a series of public events held in communities around the state. The events celebrated Wetland Gems sites, recognized the landowners of these sites, and promoted the value and importance of wetlands.

These Wetland Gems celebrations paid many dividends. They forged connections between individuals and groups that could prove critical for future wetlands outreach programs. They provided mutually-beneficial opportunities to connect with legislators who were invited to make comments about the importance of wetlands during the event programs. They attracted new audiences including members of local convention and visitors bureaus, chambers of commerce and county and town boards. And they garnered media coverage that spread the message of the importance of wetlands to broader local, regional and statewide audiences through Web, print and television stories.

The announcement of Wisconsin's Wetland Gems was just the start of efforts to recognize and promote these sites that together represent

Wisconsin's wetland heritage. Popular demand led to the publication of a beautiful full-color book featuring all of the Wetland Gems materials—maps, fact sheets and more—compiled in a convenient, spiral-bound collection. This book—a travel guide to Wisconsin's wetlands—is sold through WWA, nature centers and gifts shops.

The Wisconsin Wetlands Association is also working with Wetland Gems site landowners and managers to help them promote the designation to increase community awareness of and appreciation for these special places. And WWA is working to bring formal worldwide recognition to a select few of these Wetlands Gems that are of international importance through the Ramsar Convention on Wetlands (www.ramsar.org).

We can change people's minds about wetlands, and must do so if we are to protect these beautiful and critical resources. Change can be motivated in small ways—an expedition to hear spring frogs with neighborhood children, an outing to witness sandhill cranes congregating at sunset, or a quiet float through a local floodplain forest. Our hope is the Wetland Gems program will inspire thousands of these visits that will in turn collectively inspire a casting change for wetlands from obstacles to treasures.

In 2010, Katie Beilfuss (Outreach Programs Director), Becky Abel (Executive Director) and Laura England (Special Projects) worked for the Wisconsin Wetlands Association.

DUCK CREEK FISH PASSAGE

Stacy Gilmore

Duck Creek is a 42-mile stream that originates in central Outagamie County and winds northeast where it empties into the bay of Green Bay, just north of the city of Green Bay. More than 100 miles of Duck Creek and its tributaries lie within the Oneida Indian Reservation. During the last fifteen years, the Oneida Tribe of Indians of Wisconsin (Oneida Tribe) has partnered with the Wisconsin Department of Natural Resources (WDNR), the US Fish and Wildlife Service (USFWS), Brown County and others to restore stream habitat and water quality in the Duck Creek system.

Duck Creek and its tributaries have been a major focus of hydrologic and habitat restoration efforts in recent years. Past land use practices caused changes in hydrology leading to alterations in channel morphology, stream bank erosion and loss of critical habitat. Agricultural land use is still prevalent in the watershed, and the WDNR, Brown County and the Oneida Tribe are all active in addressing agricultural impacts to surface waters. The Duck Creek Watershed has also been considered a priority watershed under the Wisconsin Nonpoint Source Water Pollution Abatement Program. This designation has strengthened collaboration and cooperation around the vision of restoring health to the Duck Creek system.

In January 2008, representatives from the WDNR, USFWS, Brown County and the Oneida Tribe met to identify issues and evaluate stream data associated with an initiative to enhance fish passage in Duck Creek. Of particular concern, several low-head dams in Duck Creek pose significant obstacles to fish passage.

Two large structures on Duck Creek at Pamperin Park are in need of major repairs. They also pose potential liability risks to Brown County because of their location on public land and use for public access. The Pamperin Park structures have created slow, warm, low-quality water impoundments that contain degraded natural habitat. Each spring, migrating fish congregate in these impoundments because the structures restrict the distribution of many fish species upstream to better feeding, spawning and nursery habitat.

Extensive fishery surveys have been conducted throughout the Duck Creek system by WDNR, USFWS and the Oneida Tribe over the last two decades. Assessment of watershed-wide fishery impacts of dam removal included compiling species and distribution lists and identification of invasives, exotics and any species of concern. Water quality and habitat data were evaluated with fishery data to make ecologically-based recommendations regarding the structures in Duck Creek.

The project team drafted a plan that included removal of the Pamperin Park structures and proposed modifications to another structure upstream at the Oneida Golf and Country Club (OGCC) to act as a barrier to invasive fish species. The proposed plan was approved by Brown County and supported by the Oneida Environmental Resource Board and Oneida Land Commission.

Pamperin Park Barrier Removal. Proposed work will consist primarily of removing two concrete dams—low-head structures about 100 feet long and two to three feet high—with heavy equipment. In-stream fish habitat restoration and streambank stabilization will also be included as part of the project. With the fish impoundment removed, fish refuge status can be lifted and the fishery may be opened to park visitors. In the near future, tribal fishing areas will be enhanced upstream to provide more fishing opportunities to Oneida Tribe members.

OGCC Barrier Modification. OGCC is located directly upstream from Pamperin Park. The lowhead dam on this property is in good repair and more conducive to fish passage than the structures at Pamperin Park. Some modifications at the waterline are necessary to improve the upper OGCC structure as a more effective barrier to invasive sea lamprey and round goby. Modifications to this structure may include the addition of a lip to prevent sea lampreys from using their suction-cup mouths to climb over the barrier, or creating areas of high velocity to exploit the sea lampreys' poor swimming ability. The result will be a fish pass through which fish can swim, but through which sea lampreys cannot.

Natural Streambank Re-Establishment. The southern streambank of Duck Creek in Pamperin Park has been armored in concrete, presumably for protection from spring ice jams. Runoff from an adjacent parking lot travels down this concrete slope and directly into Duck Creek. The volume and speed of this runoff further degrades the water quality of the

Creek. Removal of the in-stream structures will allow ice floes to proceed downstream without jamming in this area. Re-establishment of native vegetation along the streambank will improve water quality and provide habitat for fish and other aquatic species.

The cooperative efforts of this project team will not only facilitate a sound ecological recommendation based on years of data, but also provide for monitoring long after the project is completed. Funding for the project has been secured through the Fox River Natural Resource Damage Assessment, the USFWS National Fish Passage Program, the Wisconsin Coastal Management Program and the Great Lakes Restoration Initiative (Bureau of Indian Affairs).

Removal of the structures will build on years of previous efforts within the basin, and is an essential step toward restoring the ecological balance of the Duck Creek watershed.

In 2010, Stacy Gilmore was a Water Resources Specialist with the Oneida Tribe of Indians of Wisconsin.

LIGHT DETECTION AND RANGING (LiDAR) DATA

Scott M. Galetka

Bayfield County has a wealth of natural features and amenities that attract people from around the world. The County offers varied water resources including warm sand beaches, rushing waterfalls and cold, crystal clear water flowing in artesian wells. Several of Wisconsin's national treasures are found in Bayfield County, such as the Apostle Islands National Lakeshore, Chequamegon Nicolet National Forest and Whittlesey Creek National Wildlife Refuge.

The County's location on Lake Superior makes it a true getaway for people to become inspired, learn, teach, relax and talk with a great mix of people from all walks of life. Our community appreciates its many environmental resources and their importance on local economy. We, like many people on the Lake, benefit from tourism and work hard to ensure our resources are protected for residents and visitors alike.

The Bayfield County Land Records Department and its partners believe one of the best ways of ensuring the resource is enjoyed and protected is by acquiring Light Detection and Ranging (LiDAR) data on the coastline. LiDAR is a remote sensing system used to collect elevation measurements. Data is acquired by scanning the Earth with a laser mounted on an aircraft to acquire x, y and z coordinates on the landscape to inventory land use.

Bayfield County uses LiDAR data for many purposes, including zoning for building setbacks on the shoreline, conservation efforts and tourism. Several County departments—Health, Land Records, Administration, the County Board, Forestry, Highways, UW-Extension and Sheriff—are finding LiDAR data useful in carrying out their functions.

We are excited about the possibilities of using LiDAR data for tourism and physical health. For instance, the County is in the process of collecting trail data and overlaying it with elevation data taken from the LiDAR flight. This combination of information will allow the County to assign different skill levels to individual trails. When made available to the public, outdoor enthusiasts will be able to make smart decisions when they choose to hike or bike a trail that may be above their skill level. This information will also be placed in our dispatch center for Wireless E-911 calls to better define the origin of calls made from cell phones. The trail project is one example of how LiDAR data will be used by the County to promote public safety and health.

LiDAR data has been used for preliminary work on the recently built rain garden on the County Courthouse lawn. The rain gardens have visually improved the Courthouse grounds, but also have the ability to capture eighty percent of the annual runoff and put it back into the groundwater. This provides the benefit of limiting the amount of runoff that would otherwise flow directly into the cool lake bringing its contaminants and raised temperature along with it.

The County's most ambitious use of LiDAR data was on a one-mile buffer of shoreline including a project area around the Cities of Bayfield and Washburn. Original proposals to collect the data came back over budget. Instead, we worked with the Department of Administration to expand the project to neighboring communities and thereby identify economies of scale to bring costs down.

The project was ultimately expanded to include the entire south shore and four miles up the St. Louis River at Superior. The project was successful because of help from many public and private partners including the National Oceanic and Atmospheric Administration, the United States Geological Survey, the National Parks Service, the Red Cliff Band of Chippewa Indians, the cities of Ashland and Superior, the Wisconsin Coastal Management Program, the Wisconsin Land Information Program and Impact Seven, Inc.

The contract with LiDAR consultants Laser Mapping Specialist and Allied Information Solutions provided that the County and its partners—including Ashland and Superior—would conduct ground control work to bring down project costs. The willingness of the contractor to find savings and the assistance of our partners made this project happen.

Through this project, we have developed a geographic information systems user group to build on additional partnerships. These partnerships will help capture common goals and develop our skills as a region.

The success of this project is creating potential opportunities for

Bayfield County. For example, Bayfield County has moved to next in line on the list of Federal Emergency Management Agency re-mapping projects—Bayfield County was not previously on the list. In addition, the US Fish and Wildlife Service is also considering moving Bayfield County up on its priority list for certain projects and we are combining these projects into existing goals of the community.

Bayfield County has acquired skills to help neighboring communities that may want to expand on our LiDAR work. We are looking into the feasibility of processing LiDAR data in-house to help support our neighbors in their ventures.

Bayfield County thanks its partners for being part of this project, and we welcome future opportunities to work with anyone to accomplish common goals for the region.

In 2010, Scott M. Galetka was the Land Records Administrator/Land Information Officer for Bayfield County.

2011

FOREWORD

Governor Scott Walker

Dear Friends of the Great Lakes,

Promoting economic development and jobs is a top priority for my administration. Our Great Lakes are a tremendous natural resource that gives people reason to live in, visit and do business in our state. As such, Lakes Michigan and Superior are economic and job drivers for Wisconsin.

Tourism. Wisconsin's $13 billion annual tourism industry is a significant part of our state's economic foundation. Tourism supports nearly 300,000 jobs and generates hundreds of millions of dollars in tax revenues for needed public services. Beaches, water recreation and related water activities contribute to $5 billion of tourism spending in coastal counties. We must ensure that travelers and recreational tourists choose Wisconsin for fun and relaxation. To that end, we will continue to market and invest in the health of our coastal resources.

Fishing. Whether for sport or commercial, fishing is big business in Wisconsin. With 1.4 million licenses issued annually, sport fishing generates $2.75 billion in economic impact and 30,000 jobs. The approximately 70 licensed commercial fishers on Lake Michigan and Lake Superior recently took in harvests with a wholesale value of around $5 million. Clean and healthy waters for fish habitat are good business. We are improving our fish habitats and further promoting sport fishing.

Marinas. Over 240 marinas and hundreds of boat dealerships in Wisconsin generate thousands of jobs and millions of dollars of economic activity annually. Designated "Clean Marinas" attract boaters who prefer businesses that protect the environment. Participating marinas benefit from cost savings from reduced hazardous waste disposal, fewer pollutant clean-ups, lower insurance rates and reduced potential for violations and fines.

Beaches. Each beach visitor can bring up to $50 per person per day to the local economy. Therefore, one beach closure can cause thousands in lost revenue. Beach health is critical for our economy, and during my tenure as Milwaukee County Executive Milwaukee's Bradford Beach—and three Apostle Islands beaches on Lake Superior—joined Racine's North Beach as Blue Wave certified, the national environmental certification for beaches.

Commerce and Shipping. Great Lakes shipping connects Wisconsin and interior United States companies to world markets. More than $8 billion of commerce move through Wisconsin's Great Lakes and Mississippi River ports. In 2010, US flag shipping on the Great Lakes rebounded 35% over 2009 levels, a trend that will continue to support thousands of port related jobs in Wisconsin.

Shipbuilding. Wisconsin is home to world famous ship builders and dozens of smaller builders that contribute over $1 billion in economic output and 3,500 maritime jobs. Two large projects underway in Marinette include the building of the *Sikuliaq* for the National Science Foundation and two US Navy combat ships. Wisconsin companies will continue to be leaders in commercial and military ship building.

The Great Lakes are central to our social and economic development and are a natural resource of irreplaceable value. Wisconsin continues to enhance the natural and economic potential of its coastal resources through local, state, federal and private organizations and resources. This year's *Wisconsin Great Lakes Chronicle* details projects that benefited from the collaborative efforts of numerous partners dedicated to Lake Michigan and Lake Superior.

Scott Walker was elected Wisconsin's 45th Governor in 2010.

WISCONSIN PORTS ARE STRONG ECONOMIC ENGINES

Jason Serck

A 2007 report issued by the US Army Corps of Engineers estimates that over $8 billion of cargo pass annually through Wisconsin's Great Lakes and Mississippi River ports. Wisconsin's commercial ports are economic engines that move commerce from the United States to world markets and support thousands of jobs for Wisconsin families.

The Wisconsin Department of Transportation (WisDOT) cites industry data demonstrating the efficiency of maritime commerce. A barge uses a single gallon of fuel to move one ton of freight 576 miles. In contrast, railroads can transport at a rate of only 413 ton-miles per gallon; trucks are estimated at 155 ton-miles per gallon.

Wisconsin's location on two Great Lakes provides significant advantages that have structured our history and economy. The same WisDOT report estimates that Wisconsin commercial ports in 2008 supported nearly 10,000 jobs and $462 million in wages and salaries. In total, Wisconsin ports created over $1.6 billion of economic activity in 2008.

In addition to scores of small marinas and harbors, Wisconsin's Great Lakes infrastructure is based on six major ports on Lake Michigan and Superior: Milwaukee, Manitowoc, Sturgeon Bay, Green Bay, Marinette and Superior.

Milwaukee. The Port of Milwaukee handles an average of 3.64 million tons of cargo annually. The Port connects two railroads, the Interstate highway system, over 300,000 square feet of warehouse space and acres of storage areas with domestic and international shipping. Milwaukee handles the third largest volume of grain on the Great Lakes, and also moves coal, general cargo, iron, cement, sand, salt and limestone.

The Port of Milwaukee offers more than general cargo handling. The Port is emerging as a major transport point for high-tech wind energy equipment. In addition, the *Lake Express* high speed ferry makes seasonal trips between Milwaukee and Muskegon, Michigan. The *Lake Express* offers two-and-one-half-hour trips for passengers and automobiles across Lake Michigan.

Manitowoc. The Port of Manitowoc plays a smaller, but critical, role for Great Lakes commerce. Manitowoc handles more than 350,000 tons of cement, rock, stone, coal and wood annually, and provides 91,000 square feet of warehouse space.

Manitowoc is home to Burger Boat Company, a manufacturer of custom yachts serving customers around the world. Burger is the oldest yacht builder in America with a history dating back to 1863. Manitowoc is also the home port of the S.S. *Badger,* a 410-foot passenger and car ferry that makes seasonal trips to Ludington, Michigan. The S.S. *Badger* is the only coal-fired steamship operating in the United States.

Sturgeon Bay. The Port of Sturgeon Bay is known worldwide for its ship building and ship repair facilities. Bay Shipbuilding is a leading manufacturer of Great Lakes bulk and cargo ships; many of the 1,000 self-unloading carriers in operation on the Lakes were constructed by Bay Shipbuilding at its Sturgeon Bay yards.

Palmer Johnson builds luxury yachts in Sturgeon Bay for domestic and international customers. The company—which began as a builder of wooden fishing boats—has been in operation for more than ninety years.

Green Bay. The Port of Green Bay connects domestic and international markets through maritime, rail and highway shipping. Several major trucking firms are located in the Green Bay area and offer direct links to the Port for the movement of regional commerce.

The Port annually handles more than 2.5 million tons of cargo including coal, limestone, iron, cement salt and bulk liquids. In addition, Green Bay operates 400,000 square feet of warehouse space and 100 acres for the storage of general and bulk shipments. The Port can also handle 30,000 tons of agricultural commodities in its silo facilities.

Marinette. The Port of Marinette provides both cargo handling and ship building operations. The Port annually handles 350,000 tons of cargo including iron, salt, coal, limestone and wood pulp. The Port is also home to Marinette Marine Corporation, a manufacturer of large, customized ships used around the world. Marinette Marine builds high-tech ships for government customers including the US Navy and US Coast Guard. The Navy Littoral Combat Ship, Coast Guard Great Lakes Icebreaker *Mackinaw* and Staten Island ferries were all built in Marinette.

Superior. The Port of Duluth-Superior is the largest port on the Great Lakes. The Port annually handles more than 45 million tons of cargo including iron ore, coal, grain, cement, limestone and salt. More than 1,100 ships annually make port in Duluth-Superior to transport goods and commodities around the world.

The Port is connected to the Interstate highway system, four major railroads and two shipyards. Duluth-Superior is a regular port of call for foreign and domestic cruise ships. Duluth-Superior is among the 20 largest cargo handling ports in the United States, and more than 2,000 jobs in the region are tied to Port operations.

Wisconsin's economy has developed since before statehood because of its abundant natural resources and commercial routes. The state's commercial ports remain economic engines that serve not only Wisconsin communities, but also the iron mines of Minnesota, coal fields of Montana and wheat farmers of the Great Plains and Canada.

In 2011, Jason Serck was Planning Director for the City of Superior and Immediate Past President of the Wisconsin Commercial Ports Association.

WISCONSIN'S COASTAL COUNTIES:
DEMOGRAPHIC TRENDS

David Egan-Robertson

Like the entire state, Wisconsin's coastal counties experienced a slowing of population growth during the 2000–2010 period. Overall, the fifteen counties that abut Lakes Superior and Michigan grew by 57,500 residents, or 2.9%, from 2000–2010, while these counties gained 4.4% in the prior ten years. In comparison, Wisconsin grew by 6.0% during the 2000s and by 9.6% during the 1990s.

Clearly, the coastal counties are not a homogeneous grouping. Four counties have a preponderance of seasonal-use housing, smaller average household sizes and older populations dominated by relocated retirees. A second group of four counties represent a composite of seasonal housing and smaller-sized cities. Finally, seven counties are characterized by large cities and denser development.

Recreational/Seasonal-Use Counties: Natural Decrease, Out-Migration. In a reversal of the 1990s, the total population for Bayfield, Door, Iron and Marinette Counties declined in the 2000s. Perhaps most strikingly, the net migration was negative last decade after a period of strong in-migration in the 1990s.

Collectively, these four counties lost three percent of their population, declining from 93,219 to 90,464, with a range from 0% (Bayfield) to -14% (Iron). The pattern of natural decrease common to recreational/seasonal counties continued with all four counties having more deaths than births, accounting for 2% of the population loss. In addition, all four counties had decadal birth rates under 10 per 1,000, well below the state rate of 12.8.

Both Bayfield and Door Counties experienced positive migration in the 2000s (each +1.4%), but Iron and Marinette experienced net outmigration (-2.2% and -8.7%, respectively) in numbers large enough to more than offset Bayfield and Door's gains. In the 1990s, all four counties gained population through migration, ranging from 8% to 17%.

These reductions and reversals in migration beg two questions: First, who left and/or who didn't move in? The percentage of children in these counties declined by -3.6%, more than the state decline (-2.0%) and that for all coastal counties (-1.8%), indicating that some net out-migration of families with children occurred.

Second, was there an alteration in migration flow among retirees? Typically, recreational/seasonal use counties gain "young" retirees (ages 55–74), then lose "old" retirees who either move to Sunbelt states or Wisconsin's metropolitan areas, usually due to family ties and increasing health care needs. Is it probable that fewer retirees—than in the previous decade—decided not to move on a permanent basis to these counties? Planners should pay attention to more refined Census data that becomes available in the next two years to examine the age-specific migration patterns in these four counties.

Small Cities/Transitioning Counties: A Mix of Demographic Results. Four coastal counties—Ashland, Douglas, Kewaunee, and Oconto—have a mix of seasonal-use housing and year-round residents; the occupancy rates range from 65% in Oconto to 87% in Kewaunee. In addition, the percentages of population under 18 ranged from 21.4% to 23.6%.

Collectively, these four counties gained slightly more than 2% in population, increasing from 115,992 to 118,550, although this growth represented less than one-quarter of the percentage change of the 1990s. All four counties had gains in natural increase, and all had decadal birth rates over 10 per 1,000.

Regarding migration, Ashland County experienced net out-migration of -4.7% of its population. Kewanuee had a slight loss, and Douglas and Oconto posted positive migration gains. Comparatively, in the 1990s all four counties gained population through migration, ranging from 3% to 16%.

It is somewhat surprising that Kewaunee County did not post a migration gain as it did in the 1990s (4.8%). Following the 2000 Census, Kewaunee and Oconto Counties were added to the Green Bay metropolitan area because of increased commuting ties. In contrast, Oconto County's growth both in natural increase and migration remained steady, almost equaling the state's percentage increase.

Large City/Densely Settled Counties: Continued Growth. The seven most populous coastal counties—Brown, Kenosha, Manitowoc, Milwaukee,

Ozaukee, Racine and Sheboygan—all with densities well above the state average of 105 persons per square mile and occupancy rates over 90%, generally saw increases in population in the 2000s. With the exception of Manitowoc County (-1.8%), these counties grew from 0.8% (Milwaukee) to 11.3% (Kenosha).

As a group, these counties added 58,000 residents, or 3.2%. This rate was only slightly below the 4% growth of the 1990s. Nearly one-fourth of the population is under age 18, and birth rates were higher than the state average in Brown, Kenosha, Milwaukee and Racine counties.

All of the counties exhibited strong gains in natural increase during the 2000s. However, migration in the most recent decade was a mixed situation. Four of the seven counties—Manitowoc, Sheboygan, Milwaukee and Racine—experienced net out-migration. In the 1990s, only Milwaukee did.

After three decades of losses, it is interesting to note greater stabilization in Milwaukee County's population. The county lost a net 150,000 people from 1980 until 2000 due to migration. In the past decade, about 57,000 more people moved out than moved in, but the excess of births over deaths compensated for this loss.

In 2011, David Egan-Robertson was a Demographer at the Wisconsin Demographic Services Center, Department of Administration.

Wisconsin's Clean Marina Program

Victoria Harris and Jon Kukuk

Wisconsin is home to over 240 marinas, including more than 140 located in Great Lakes coastal waters and tributaries. Over 635,000 boats are registered in Wisconsin and the state boasted the highest growth in the number of registered boats in the nation between 1999 and 2007.

Marinas, yacht clubs and boat yards that provide recreational boating services are important assets of most waterfront communities. These facilities offer public access to the water, harbors of refuge for vessels in distress and substantial recreational and economic benefits.

Spending on boats and boating activities in the Great Lakes states totaled nearly $16 billion in 2003 and directly generated 107,000 jobs. Taking secondary effects into account, recreational boating supported 244,000 jobs, $19 billion in sales, $6.4 billion in personal income and $9.2 billion in value added revenues. Benefiting businesses include marine manufacturers, retailers, marinas, boatyards, restaurants, lodging accommodations and charter boat operators. (*Great Lakes Recreational Boating's Economic Punch*, Great Lakes Commission, 2003)

Coastal communities and marine related businesses depend on clean waters and a healthy coastal environment for their continued prosperity. Clean water is as essential for a quality boating experience as it is for other human and aquatic life uses. And marina operators recognize that good stewardship and environmental protection are in their best interest.

While marinas contribute many millions of dollars to Wisconsin coastal community economies, the waters surrounding them can become contaminated with pollutants derived from boating activities. Chemical runoff from boatyards, toxic metals from anti-fouling paints, petroleum from fuel docks, solvents, anti-freeze, sewage, fish waste and litter can all be released into the water. Even small releases from the growing number of marinas and boats can add up to serious pollution potential. This is especially true when large numbers of boats congregate in small embayments and harbors.

Marina construction and maintenance dredging can destroy or degrade important aquatic habitat. In addition, boaters may advance the spread of aquatic invasive species and diseases via boat trailers, live wells or bait buckets.

The Wisconsin Marina Association (WMA) and University of Wisconsin (UW) Sea Grant are helping marinas around the state stay shipshape while protecting the water resources that their customers enjoy. In July 2008, the Wisconsin Coastal Management Program funded two projects to organize a Wisconsin Marina Association and develop a Wisconsin Clean Marina Program. These concurrent projects were intentionally intertwined to advance Wisconsin's marine industry and improve Wisconsin's valuable Great Lakes.

The WMA is the voice of its members in working with government agencies and affiliated national and local organizations on issues affecting recreational boating. The Clean Marina Program encourages marine businesses and recreational boaters to protect coastal water quality by engaging in environmentally sound operating and maintenance procedures. The program provides guidance, training and technical assistance to marina and boatyard operators on best management practices (BMPs) that prevent or reduce pollution. The voluntary program aims to be a win-win for marine businesses, boaters and the environment.

UW Sea Grant worked with a steering committee representing seven marinas, the Wisconsin Coastal Management Program, the Wisconsin Department of Natural Resources, the UW-Extension Solid and Hazardous Waste Education Center, the US Coast Guard and leaders from other Clean Marina programs to develop criteria for Clean Marina certification. The partners also produced outreach and education materials including a Clean Marina best management practices guidebook and Clean Boater tip sheets. These materials are available on the program's Web site at www .wiscosnincleanmarin.org.

The guidebook outlines practices required by law as well as additional BMPs for siting new and expanding marinas, marina design, stormwater management, vessel maintenance, petroleum control, sewage handling, waste disposal and marina management. Facilities that follow the recommended practices and pass onsite inspections may become certified as Clean Marinas in recognition of their environmental stewardship, and they are encouraged to use the designation to promote their businesses.

In July 2010, the newly formed Wisconsin Marina Association received an additional grant from the Wisconsin Coastal Management Program to manage the Wisconsin Clean Marina program and launch the Clean Marina certification process with technical support from UW Sea Grant. As of May 2011, nearly fifty-five marine businesses have joined the WMA, five Clean Marina training workshops have been attended by more than sixty marina managers, eleven marinas have become certified "Clean Marinas" and more than 240 BMPs have been adopted collectively by the certified marinas. We anticipate certifying an additional six marinas by July 2011. Seventeen marinas have also signed pledges and are taking steps toward certification.

Surveys of marinas participating in other state Clean Marina programs show clear benefits to certified marinas. Marinas can improve their bottom line by reducing hazardous and solid waste generation and disposal, recycling shrink wrap and antifreeze, minimizing spill clean-up costs, increasing marina occupancy and slip fees for boaters who prefer to patronize Clean Marinas, and qualifying for reduced insurance premiums. Additionally, boaters appreciate the efforts and results of these environmentally-friendly marinas.

The commitment by the Wisconsin Marina Association and marine businesses to Wisconsin's Great Lakes waterways—with support of the partners of the Wisconsin Clean Marina Program—shows great promise for sustaining the recreational boating industry, improving Great Lakes water resources and helping in the recovery of Wisconsin's economy.

In 2011, Victoria Harris was a Water Quality Specialist with UW Sea Grant Institute. Jon Kukuk was President of the Wisconsin Marina Association and Owner of Nestegg Marine in Marinette.

Milwaukee's Second Shoreline: The Milwaukee River Greenway

Ann Brummitt

The Milwaukee River Greenway is a seven-mile section of the Milwaukee River that has shaped much of Milwaukee's development. Home to Native Americans followed by European settlers, the river has supported diverse communities with sustenance, industrial power and recreation. Unfortunately, industrialization took its toll and the Milwaukee River—like so many urban rivers in North America—became a trash river unsuitable for most types of recreation or enjoyment.

The removal of the North Avenue Dam in 1997 sparked a turnaround in the river's fortunes as urban dwellers and wildlife returned to this resilient shoreline in the most densely populated municipality in the state. Water quality improved and fish diversity jumped sixfold. The river became a destination for anglers from around the Midwest, and a flyway and home for over 200 species of birds, numerous mammals, amphibians, reptiles and unique flora, including several threatened species.

In 2006, a grass-roots collaborative called the Milwaukee River Work Group (MRWG) formed to protect 878 acres along the Milwaukee River within the City of Milwaukee and nearby suburbs. The initial gathering was in response to development pressure, clear-cutting and a lack of protective shoreline regulation. MRWG grew to include citizens and riparian owners, over twenty non-profits, neighborhood associations, businesses and government agencies all dedicated to improving this resource.

With Wisconsin Coastal Management Program funding, MRWG worked with the Village of Shorewood and the City of Milwaukee to craft protective ordinances that passed in 2006 and 2010, respectively. These ordinances resulted in permanent protection of river natural areas including building height restrictions and setbacks to preserve scenic beauty and protect wildlife habitat, strict standards for stormwater management, noise and light pollution guidelines and landscaping provisions for native plants.

The University of Wisconsin-Milwaukee Foundation was the first to put these measures into practice with the design of the Cambridge Commons dorms. Project architects re-oriented the building to the river, lowered its front to protect the river's scenic beauty, and added two green roofs and a 20,000 gallon rain water collection tank under the building's courtyard. Seven hundred students now live trailside to the river in a LEED Gold certified building and can join a Living Learning Community dedicated to sustainability and the environment.

The Wisconsin Coastal Management Program also funded the Milwaukee River Greenway Master Plan: A Vision for Recreation and Restoration, released in May 2010. The plan provides a comprehensive vision for a restored urban wilderness and shared recreational opportunities in three communities. The plan recommends the formation of the self-funded Milwaukee River Greenway Coalition to implement a work plan that features a thirteen mile trail for non-motorized recreational users.

The plan prioritizes a branding and signage program for the Greenway at four gateway entrances and eleven access points. Trailheads will be marked with maps and interpretive signage. Trails will be designed to protect wildlife habitat and provide stronger links to the surrounding neighborhoods.

Hundreds of stakeholders provided input to the plan through public meetings and committee work. The plan spells out a habitat framework for restoration and preservation of the natural resources within the Greenway and recommends a complete biotic inventory to inform decisions about recreational improvements, habitat restoration and species management. The Milwaukee River Greenway Plan is already producing important projects.

Rotary Centennial Arboretum. The prime gateway to the Greenway, the region's first Arboretum has been envisioned by Rotary Club of Milwaukee on donated industrial lands. The Club, in partnership with the River Revitalization Foundation, the Milwaukee Urban Rivers Foundation and the Urban Ecology Center, broke ground and planted the first tree last summer. The Arboretum will feature 1,000 trees native to southeastern Wisconsin, universally accessible trails and outdoor learning areas for children.

Thirteen Miles of Trails. A branding and signage campaign is underway with a goal of opening a thirteen-mile trail system simultaneously with the Rotary Centennial Arboretum in September 2013. The first ever sustainable trails workshop was held and crews began working on trail improvements. Trail acquisition, building and improvements will continue through 2013 to close gaps, avoid sensitive plant locations and improve sustainability.

Cambridge Woods Nature Sanctuary. A plant inventory is underway throughout the Greenway and signs of Emerald Ash Borer are being monitored. The Wisconsin Coastal Management Program is funding work that will formally designate Cambridge Woods a nature sanctuary with vegetative screening to route bicyclists to the Oak Leaf Trail and improved access routes to the river.

Greenway Gateway. MRGC's partner, the River Revitalization Foundation, has begun work on another former industrial site to develop the southern gateway featuring native plants, a children's play area, and a canoe and kayak launch.

PCB Removal. At the northern end in Lincoln Park, the Wisconsin Department of Natural Resources, the US Environmental Protection Agency, Milwaukee County and the Milwaukee Metropolitan Sanitary District are continuing removal of mud containing PCBs in the Lincoln Park lagoon and channel. The project is expected to be complete in 2012 and is an important step to improving recreation and fish health in the river.

The Milwaukee River Greenway is shaping up to be an exceptional place to play, learn and recreate within a renewed urban wilderness that will serve Milwaukeeans and visitors alike for generations to come.

In 2011, Ann Brummitt was Director of the Milwaukee River Greenway Coalition.

CHEQUAMEGON BAY AREA PARTNERSHIP

Ed Morales

From her office in the Larson-Juhl Center for Science and the Environment at Northland College in Ashland, Dr. Wendy Gorman, Professor of Biology, is coordinating an ambitious new effort to establish baseline data on the health of the Cheuqamegon Bay shoreline. Throughout the summer, a team of student researchers will survey previously unmonitored beaches in the Bay region. Samples collected by researches will return to Northland's state-certified lab where students working under the direction of Dr. Gorman will analyze the results for evidence of *E. coli* contamination.

Dr. Gorman says that although many of the region's beaches have been monitored for several years, shorelines on the area's reservations—which are targeted specifically by this new initiative—have been largely overlooked. Using the baseline values Dr. Gorman's team establishes, researchers will then be able to track *E. coli* levels over time and work with local municipalities to create shoreline management plans to mitigate the impact of beach contaminants and reduce the frequency of beach closures.

The project is an initiative of the Chequamegon Bay Area Partnership (CBAP), a collaboration of fifteen municipalities, tribal governments, non-profit organizations and government agencies formed in 2009 to address environmental issues facing the Bay area. The partnership represents a complex melding of philosophies and politics, with national and regional stakeholders meeting to work toward their mutual benefit.

At the center of the partnership stands the Sigurd Olson Environmental Institute (SOEI), Northland's research and outreach arm and the coordinating partner of CBAP. As the SOEI Program Director, Mike Gardner plays a key role in managing the on-the-ground efforts of the Partnership. This summer, Mr. Gardner is leading a team of students on a mission to clean and protect shoreline across the Chequamegon Bay.

Mr. Gardner says that the general health of regional beaches is closely tied to the overall health of the regional economy. His opinion is backed by an analysis from the University of Michigan suggesting the Great Lakes directly support more than 1.5 million US jobs and generate $62 billion in wages annually.

The link between the health of the Great Lakes and the health of regional economies across the basin was one of the driving forces behind the establishment of the Great Lakes Restoration Initiative (GLRI), a $475 million effort to target the greatest threats facing the Great Lakes basin.

"Lake Superior is the world's largest lake," says Lissa Radke, the United States Coordinator of the Lake Superior Binational Forum, one of the organizations involved in CBAP, "but that doesn't mean you can't topple it."

Ms. Radke's office at the SOEI is bursting at the seams with evidence of a professional career dedicated to advocacy for Lake Superior. Since 2003, Ms. Radke has served as the stateside coordinator for the Binational Forum, a collaboration of Canadian and American stakeholders representing municipalities, governmental agencies, First Nations and nonprofit organizations around Lake Superior. Together with Jim Bailey, her Canadian counterpart, Ms. Radke works to further collaboration among these stakeholders on the restoration and protection of the Lake.

In October 2010, CBAP received word that it secured GLRI funding for the first three of its grant applications. The Binational Forum received funds to develop and distribute new educational materials around the Lake, while a larger group of five CBAP partners received support to restore habitat for fish and other wildlife throughout the Chequamegon Bay. The third grant provided funding to conduct the shoreline health surveys that Dr. Gorman coordinates, helping researchers better understand beach health and areas impacted by nonpoint pollution.

Mr. Gardner says understanding and mitigating the causes of beach closures is central to the long-term economic security of the Bay area and beyond, and emphasizes the importance of tackling environmental issues now.

"The Chequamegon Bay is known for its pristine beaches," he says. "People drive from all over the Midwest to spend time on the Lake, but no one wants to drive 300 miles to find a 'beach closed' sign."

Historically, there has been a clear distinction between protecting the environment and developing local economies, and support for each effort often broke along ideological lines. Today, the link between the environment and regional economies is well established, and there is significant evidence suggesting a modest investment in the restoration of the Great Lakes now can provide tremendous economic benefit in the future. A recent study published by economists at Grand Valley State University in Allendale, Michigan demonstrates that GLRI funding can provide nearly a 6–1 return on the initial investment.

"In the 21st century, the conversation is no longer about jobs or the environment," says Ms. Radke, "but how we protect the environment while providing jobs in our communities."

In 2011, Ed Morales was a Communications Specialist with Northland College.

BRADFORD BEACH: JEWEL OF MILWAUKEE'S EMERALD NECKLACE

Laura Schloesser

On a hot June afternoon in 1931, Milwaukee County Parks' beaches were packed with people trying to escape the summer heat. According to the *Milwaukee Sentinel*, over 4,000 people enjoyed a day along Lake Michigan at Bradford Beach. By this account, Milwaukee's lakefront was a welcoming, vibrant place where people gathered for recreation and relaxation.

Fast forward seventy years to a similar day, but at a very different Bradford Beach. At the end of the century, Bradford was a desolate, wasted half-mile of sand in the heart of downtown Milwaukee used by only few diehard sunbathers and dog walkers. But while the beach saw little activity, there were people working behind the scenes who had a vision of returning the beach to its heyday.

Milwaukee's beaches—and in particular Bradford Beach, the jewel of its Emerald Necklace—became a civic priority for the community. Corporate partners, philanthropists, advocacy groups and the Milwaukee County Parks Department, led by Director Sue Black, shared a common desire to revitalize Bradford Beach by forming a powerful partnership. These likeminded individuals came together to forge a plan to transform the lakefront property under the jurisdiction of Milwaukee County Parks into a regional destination for outdoor recreation.

In 2007, MillerCoors took the lead with a generous five-year, $500,000 donation directed toward improving the environmental health of beaches. One-quarter of the MillerCoors donation was earmarked for the University of Wisconsin-Milwaukee Great Lakes WATER Institute for research on Lake Michigan beach water quality. The Institute's research included water monitoring devices, web cams and an assessment of stormwater management.

The WATER Institute's timely research on beach *E. coli* contamination and its mission to support sustainable activities were critical to the long-term health and preservation of the beach and near shore Lake

Michigan. The Institute played a critical role in developing the scientific data needed to restore Bradford Beach.

MillerCoors presented the remaining $375,000 of its grant to the Milwaukee County Parks Department to apply the WATER Institute's research findings to Bradford Beach and integrate recommendations into daily operational plans. Migratory Bird Management, Inc. of Brookfield was hired to patrol the beaches daily with Border Collies to help reduce *E. coli* in the sand from gull droppings. In addition, local at-risk youth were hired through the Milwaukee Community Service Corps to remove *Cladophora* from the beach. Each activity dramatically improved the health and aesthetics of the beach.

Other key components of the Bradford revitalization plan improved beach and water safety and beach cleaning:

- Private donations were given for the first two years to cover additional lifeguard staffing at the beach.

- Local philanthropic foundations donated funds to procure a jet ski and sled for water rescue and patrol.

- A local energy company purchased a beach cleaner used daily to groom and clean the sand.

- A local waste hauler donated 40 enclosed garbage containers and 20 enclosed recycling containers for use along the lakefront.

- Eight beach rain gardens were constructed by Milwaukee County to direct and naturally filter storm water from the adjacent roadway and parking lots.

- Educational signage was provided by the local sewerage district.

Other Milwaukee corporations and philanthropic groups joined in the commitment to revitalize Bradford Beach with the goal of achieving national Blue Wave certification. The prestigious Blue Wave status is awarded by the Clean Beaches Council based on meeting 28 rigorous criteria for marine and freshwater beaches. Bradford Beach was awarded this certification within one year of implementing the revitalization plan.

In addition to Blue Wave certification, Bradford Beach, the Milwaukee

County Parks and the numerous partners and friends that restored Bradford Beach to the jewel it once was have been recognized with several awards:

- Bradford Beach received a 2008 Silver Star award for Outstanding Aquatic Facility from the Wisconsin Park and Recreation Association.

- The Milwaukee County Department of Parks, Recreation & Culture received a 2009 Salute to Local Government Public-Private Cooperation Award from the Public Policy Forum for the revitalization of Bradford Beach.

- Bradford's stormwater controls project was recognized by the American Council of Engineering Companies of Wisconsin with a 2009 Engineering Excellence Award.

- The Bradford Beach Stormwater Treatment Project was awarded the 2009 Public Works Project of the Year award by the American Public Works Association.

The Milwaukee County Parks Department continues to educate visitors to Bradford Beach and its five other Lake Michigan beaches on their personal responsibility to maintain the health and vibrancy of all beaches. Public awareness and support remain the most important tools we have to preserve Bradford and all of Milwaukee's beaches.

Preserving Milwaukee's Emerald Necklace—and Bradford Beach particularly—is a responsibility Sue does not take lightly. Our forefathers such as Charles Whitnall, Alfred Boerner and the famed Frederick Law Olmsted were dedicated to making Milwaukee great by designing and developing vast recreational spaces for the community. Today's generation will be held accountable by tomorrow's. We are therefore committed to leaving this great parks system better than we found it.

In 2011, Laura Schloesser was the Safety, Security and Training Manager with the Milwaukee County Department of Parks, Recreation and Culture.

Restoring Wild Rice in Allouez Bay

Amy Eliot

My dad, Frank Gotelaere, and his thirteen siblings grew up on Allouez Bay in Superior where they hunted, fished and no doubt got into other quagmires. Dad said the ducks tasted great then because they fed on wild rice, which he remembers was thick all across Allouez Bay.

Northern wild rice (*Zizania palustris*) is an aquatic grass that has tremendous wildlife value because of its nutritious seed; an acre of good rice bed can yield well over 500 pounds of seed. Dad also recalls that the wild rice seemed to disappear many years ago when the bay was dredged for fill for the re-construction of the US 2/53 road bed. After that, he said the wild rice never came back.

Many historic rice beds have been lost in the western Great Lakes region over the decades, although no one is certain how many acres have vanished or what caused the disappearance. Wild rice beds can be destroyed by grazing geese or they can be out-competed by exotic species or opportunistic native plants.

In addition, large wakes can destroy beds when the ribbons of leaves laying flat on the water are buoyant and easily uprooted. Particularly damaging are changes in hydrology—such as reduced flows and increased water levels—where even small increases in depth can destroy wild rice habitat. It is estimated that the St. Louis River has lost 7,700 acres of wetland and open water habitat since settlement.

The loss of wild rice beds in Allouez Bay started a turn-around in 2009 when the Douglas County Land and Water Conservation Department—under the supervision of Christine Ostern—joined with the National Oceanic and Atmospheric Administration (NOAA) and the Great Lakes Commission Habitat Restoration Partnership (GLC HRP) to restore fish and wildlife habitat in the lower St. Louis River estuary.

Because wild rice requires the right conditions, we sought the expert advice of Peter David, a wildlife biologist with the Great Lakes Indian Fish and Wildlife Commission (GLIFWC) and wild rice restoration expert. During a boat tour, we showed Mr. David patches of wild rice growing near the mouths of Bear Creek and an unnamed creek; he was able to locate single stems of wild rice that were in rough shape but present.

Mr. David thought the creek mouths would be good places to put in test plots since the conditions that wild rice prefer were present: clear water so sunlight can reach the young plant, flowing water, soft organic muck with optimal depths of 1–2 feet and other marsh vegetation to mitigate water level fluctuations caused by boats and high winds.

The team selected two sites approximately 1.5 acres in size. Mr. David helped us obtain the wild rice seed from a local harvester. Financial support from GLIFWC, NOAA and GLC HRP made it possible to purchase three hundred pounds of wild rice in the late summer of 2010. However, to minimize loss to waterfowl, the team waited until after the fall migration and just before iceup to seed the plots.

The rice had to be stored in running water to keep it from drying out and spoiling. We worked with Bill Gobin at the WDNR Brule River Fish Hatchery to put the 50-pound bags of wild rice in the Little Brule River. The flowing water of the Little Brule kept the rice from freezing.

With the help of resilient volunteers—including my dad, Mike Savage, Valerie Kozlovsky and Philip Anderson—we located the restoration areas with GPS units and started to broadcast the seed. We mastered the technique of tossing the seed into the strong wind where it separated and drifted onto the water.

We will fence off four small areas in the spring to keep geese and carp from the seeded plots. Anthony Havranek, Water Resources Manager at the St. Croix Tribal Environmental Department, provided the design for the exclosures that were used in a similar project. This extra step may help us determine if water conditions or grazing are causing a problem for wild rice regeneration.

We will monitor progress over the growing season, although it may take longer than one year to evaluate the project since wild rice seed can remain dormant for five or more years after seeding. This adaptation allows rice to survive an occasional crop failure. If the wild rice grows, we will spread seed again this fall. For now, all we can do is wait to see if wild rice reaches the surface sometime in mid-June.

Native Americans consider wild rice or *manoomin* a gift from the Great Spirit; wild rice has been central to their culture for hundreds of years.

Our team is very pleased to be part of a growing interagency effort to restore this important cultural and ecological species in the western Great Lakes. It is especially gratifying to me that my father is participating as well, and that the restoration project is taking place where my own family grew up.

In 2011, Amy Eliot was an Associate Researcher at the Lake Superior Research Institute, University of Wisconsin-Superior.

2012

Foreword

Governor Scott Walker

Dear Friends of the Great Lakes,

My administration continues to promote economic development and jobs as a top priority. Our Great Lakes are a magnetic natural resource that gives people reason to live in, visit and do business in our state. Wisconsin's stewardship of the Great Lakes is demonstrated by example and initiative.

Tourism. Wisconsin's $13 billion annual tourism industry supports nearly 300,000 jobs and generates hundreds of millions of dollars in tax revenues. Beaches, water recreation and related water activities contribute $5 billion of tourism spending alone. The Department of Tourism initiated Travel Green Wisconsin to promote smart, environmentally friendly business practices. Wisconsin will continue to market and invest in the health of our coastal resources including our growing and competitive Travel Green businesses.

Fishing. Fishing is big business in Wisconsin. With 1.4 million licenses issued annually, sport fishing generates $2.75 billion of economic activity and supports 30,000 jobs statewide. Approximately 70 licensed commercial fishers take annual harvests of around $5 million wholesale. We will continue to improve fish habitats and promote sport fishing.

Marinas. The nearly 300 marinas and hundreds of boat dealerships in Wisconsin generate thousands of jobs and millions of dollars of economic activity. Designated "Clean Marinas" attract boaters who prefer businesses that protect the environment. Participating marinas benefit from cost savings from reduced hazardous waste disposal, fewer pollutant clean-ups, lower insurance rates and reduced potential for violations and fines. Minnesota is implementing and Illinois developing programs based on Wisconsin initiatives.

Beaches. Each beach visitor can bring up to $50 per day to the local economy; therefore, a beach closure can cause thousands of dollars of lost revenue. Wisconsin communities regularly monitor and test water quality to ensure beachgoers have a healthy, enjoyable experience. The City of

Racine piloted a rapid method of testing for *E. coli* levels in water providing same day decisions to open or close a beach. Milwaukee's Bradford Beach, Racine's North Beach and three Apostle Islands beaches on Lake Superior have attained "Blue Wave" status, the national environmental certification for beaches.

Commerce and Shipping. Great Lakes shipping connects Wisconsin and the interior United States companies to world markets. More than $8 billion of commerce moves through Wisconsin's Great Lakes and Mississippi River ports annually. In 2012, US flag dry bulk shipping on the Great Lakes increased 3.1 percent over 2011 to 9,811,289 net tons, a trend that will continue to support port related jobs in Wisconsin.

Shipbuilding. Wisconsin is home to world famous shipbuilders and dozens of smaller builders that contribute over $1 billion of economic output and 3,500 maritime jobs. In Marinette, the US Navy combat ship USS *Fort Worth* was officially accepted in June 2012 and two more Navy combat ships are set for construction. The National Science Foundation research vessel *Sikuliaq* is scheduled for January 2013 delivery. Wisconsin companies will continue to be leaders in commercial and military shipbuilding.

The Great Lakes are a cornerstone of Wisconsin's continued economic, social and educational development. Wisconsin continues to enhance the economic and natural potential of its coastal resources through local, state, federal and private organizations. This year's *Wisconsin Great Lakes Chronicle* showcases a few of the many economic success stories and future challenges the Great Lakes corridor faces.

Scott Walker was elected Wisconsin's 45th Governor in 2010.

ASIAN CARP: A CALL TO ACTION

Attorney General J.B. Van Hollen

Bordered by the beautiful waters of Lake Michigan, Lake Superior and the great Mississippi River, Wisconsin faces one of the most serious economic and environmental threats in recent years: an Asian carp invasion into Lake Michigan that would threaten ecosystems and Wisconsin industry.

The non-native Asian carp, which also are known as bighead and silver carp, consume up to 40% of their weight in food per day and compete directly with commercial and sport fish for sustenance. In some stretches of waters they inhabit, up to 97% of the biomass consists of Asian carp.

Anyone who has ever seen video of leaping silver carp also knows that fishing, boating, water skiing and other recreational pursuits become dangerous around these large fish. The carp—some of which grow to 100 pounds—literally vault through the air after being startled by motors.

An Asian carp invasion into Lake Michigan would significantly affect Wisconsin's and the region's commercial and recreational industries that depend on a healthy lake. The Great Lakes fishery is valued at $7 billion annually. In Wisconsin, sport fishing alone in Lake Michigan and Lake Superior is estimated to generate 5,000 jobs and $419 million annually. This does not include the Great Lakes' considerable value to other industries or other states, and it does not account for the loss of recreational opportunities that will diminish if Asian carp invade the Great Lakes.

The US Army Corps of Engineers has assured Great Lakes states that monitoring, electrical barriers, netting, application of pesticides and reduction in commercial river lock operations would keep the carp from getting too close to Lake Michigan. These measures, we were told, would protect the Great Lakes while the Corps and other federal agencies continue to "study" solutions.

However, in December 2009 a bighead carp was recovered from the canal north of Illinois' Lockport Lock, and continuing eDNA sampling indicates that Asian carp are present at multiple locations lakeward of the electric barrier system. In June 2010, a bighead carp was recovered from Lake Calumet approximately six miles from Lake Michigan. Nothing stands as a barrier between Lake Calumet and Lake Michigan.

According to the Mississippi Interstate Cooperative Resource Association (MICRA), Asian carp also are marching up the Mississippi River. In April, the Minnesota Department of Natural Resources reported that "commercial fishermen working near Prescott, Wis., netted a 30-pound bighead carp from the St. Croix River where it flows into the Mississippi." It was "the second time this year Asian carp have been found by commercial fishermen in Minnesota waters."

In other words, the measures employed by the Army Corps of Engineers are not able to keep Asian carp from invading the Great Lakes and more needs to be done if we are to avert tragedy. Before the turn of the twentieth century, an artificial door to the Great Lakes was created when Lake Michigan was linked with the Mississippi River system to allow Chicago to send its sewage west and south. It is time to shut this door.

On behalf of the State of Wisconsin, I filed a lawsuit with the Great Lakes States of Michigan, Minnesota, Ohio and Pennsylvania asking the federal district court in Chicago to reestablish the physical separation between the Great Lakes basin and the Mississippi River systems and order other immediate preventive and long-term solutions.

The separation we request is no pipe dream. The Great Lakes Commission and the Great Lakes and St. Lawrence Cities Initiative led a project to develop and evaluate alternatives for physically separating the Great Lakes and Mississippi River basins in the Chicago Area Waterway System to prevent the movement of Asian carp and other aquatic invasive species (AIS). In January 2012, the Commission and Initiative published its report indicating that "separation can be achieved while also maintaining or enhancing water quality, flood management and transportation."

Meanwhile, the economic benefits of separation would be tremendous. The report states, "[s]eparation could generate significant benefits for the Chicago region and the Great Lakes and Mississippi River basins as a whole, with the potential for between $1.4 billion to $9.5 billion in long-term savings from avoided AIS control costs and damages alone, as well as improved water quality, strengthened flood protection and modernized shipping facilities. While the separation costs will be incurred over a limited timeframe, the benefits will be enjoyed indefinitely. The project's technical report concludes that 'stopping a single AIS from transferring between basins could avoid billions of dollars in economic loss.'"

If we want to save the Great Lakes, we need to move the United States government from short-term, inadequate solutions and studies to prompt and effective action. While I have joined attorneys general of other Great Lakes states to seek a judicial solution, I encourage those who share my concerns to contact their elected representatives at the federal level and let them know that we need action, not studies, if we are going to save the Great Lakes.

In 2012, J.B. Van Hollen was Attorney General of the State of Wisconsin.

Wisconsin Great Lakes Shoreline Analysis

Dr. David Mickelson and Jeff Stone

In the past thirty years, parts of Wisconsin's shoreline have changed dramatically. Consider how Sheboygan's waterfront has evolved from a fuel dock to a vacation resort. Changes such as those in Sheboygan are documented in over 10,000 oblique air photos now available for viewing.

This photo collection results from discussions of the Wisconsin Coastal Hazards Work Group including the Wisconsin Coastal Management Program (WCMP), Department of Natural Resources, Wisconsin Emergency Management, University of Wisconsin Sea Grant Institute, the University of Wisconsin-Madison and the Association of State Floodplain Managers (ASFPM). The Group wondered about the condition of our Great Lakes shorelines after two decades of relatively low lake level, and what changes had taken place since an extensive survey of shoreline conditions during high water levels of the mid-1970s.

Beginning in 2008, ASFPM and Dr. Mickelson partnered to map and evaluate changes in Wisconsin's Lake Michigan and Lake Superior shoreline between the mid-1970s and late-2000s. Funded by the WCMP, the project was conducted in three phases with the final phase completed in March 2012.

The overall goal of the shoreline evaluation centered on a qualitative analysis of shore erosion hazards and bluff stability between the two time periods. The shoreline mapping and evaluation was accomplished by using oblique aerial photos of the shoreline for both time periods along with current aerial imagery and base maps.

In 2007, ASFPM and Dr. Mickelson submitted a proposal to WCMP that included acquiring new oblique aerial imagery for the entire Wisconsin shoreline, qualitatively mapping within a Geographic Information System (GIS) the shoreline characteristics for both time periods, and developing a web-based mapping tool that allowed easy access and viewing of the photos and shoreline characteristics. Jeff Stone and his ASFPM associates spent considerable effort converting, capturing, analyzing and storing the oblique photos and all the associated GIS datasets required for the shoreline mapping effort.

In 1976, black-and-white oblique air photos of Wisconsin's Great Lakes shoreline were taken by the Department of Natural Resources as part of a major bluff erosion project. The 1970s oblique photos were scanned, converted to digital images and manually geo-located—a process used to locate the approximate location of where the photo was taken—allowing the digital image to be linked to a specific map location. Approximately 3,000 photos were processed for the 1970s time period.

In 2007 and 2008, oblique digital photos were taken of all of Wisconsin's Lake Superior and Lake Michigan shorelines. The 2007/08 photographs were geo-located automatically and the GIS datasets were generated with minimal processing. Over 7,800 photos were processed for the 2000s time period.

Next the shoreline characteristics were mapped for each time period using three classification components: beach description, backshore description and structure type. A standardized data model was developed within the GIS database to allow consistent data entry of the shoreline characteristics.

For the most part, shoreline classification work was done mile by mile, with all six classifications—three for each time period—completed for a single reach before moving down the shoreline. Shoreline characteristics were explored and/or evaluated for approximately 575 miles of shoreline for Lake Michigan, including Door County Peninsula and Green Bay, and approximately 237 miles of shoreline for Lake Superior, including Madeline Island.

Preliminary analysis of the shoreline conditions between both time periods was supported by the original funding. Among the most important results are changes in the stability of bluffs along the shore. For the counties along Lake Michigan where comparative analysis is possible, the shoreline mapped as having unstable and failing bluffs dropped from about 63 miles to 26 miles between the two time periods. On Lake Superior, the drop was from over 35 miles to about 30 miles classified as unstable and failing.

About thirty percent of the evaluated Lake Michigan shoreline had some type of shore protection in 2007/2008. This compares to about nine percent in 1976. The length of shore protected by some kind of structure increased in nearly every county. Kenosha County showed the greatest increase with Milwaukee County a close second. About nine percent of Wisconsin's Lake Superior shoreline had some type of shore protection in 2007/2008, compared to less than six percent in 1976/1978. In the near future, the project team plans to submit a proposal to perform a more comprehensive analysis of shoreline changes and why they have or have not taken place.

Finally, the last major component of the project was the development of the web-based mapping tool known as the *Shoreline Classification and Oblique Photo Viewer* (*Shoreline Viewer*) available at www.floodatlas.org/wcmp/obliqueviewer. *Shoreline Viewer* provides the oblique photos from both time periods along with shoreline characteristics in map view.

Public access to the rich collection of historic photos and the mapped datasets was a key component for the project. Web-based mapping applications enhance the ability to communicate to the public the underlying science and risk associated with Great Lakes' coastal hazards such as bluff failure. Through the *Shoreline Viewer*, the public can see what has changed on Wisconsin's shoreline between the late 1970s and the late 2000s.

In 2012, Dr. David Mickelson was an Emeritus Professor at the University of Wisconsin-Madison and owner of Geo-Professional Consultants, LLC. Jeff Stone was Project Manager and Geographic Information System Coordinator at the Association of State Floodplain Managers.

Wisconsin Lake Michigan Water Trail

Angela Pierce

The Wisconsin Lake Michigan Water Trail is a 520-mile network of public access locations used by boaters along Lake Michigan. Water trails are routes along rivers and coastlines that provide recreational users—such as kayakers, sailors, recreational boaters and anglers—with information on access points, safety considerations, activities and points of interest.

Development of the Wisconsin Lake Michigan Water Trail is the result of a multiyear effort between the Wisconsin Coastal Management Program, the Wisconsin Department of Natural Resources, the Bay-Lake Regional Planning Commission and the National Park Service Rivers, Trails and Conservation Assistance Program. The public and the kayaking and boating communities provided valuable feedback throughout the process.

The Wisconsin Lake Michigan Water Trail provides kayakers and boaters with information on public access locations, amenities and safety issues, and identifies gaps where additional public access is needed. The project area covers the entire western Lake Michigan shoreline from the Michigan-Wisconsin border at Marinette to the Illinois-Wisconsin border at Pleasant Prairie. With nearly two million residents and over one-third of Wisconsin's population living within a thirty-minute drive of the Lake Michigan shoreline, this trail has positive impacts for public recreation, public health, environmental stewardship, economic development and tourism.

The development of the Lake Michigan Water Trail was primarily oriented around increasing and improving public access to the shoreline and waters of Lake Michigan. This collaborative project involved acquiring Global Positioning System (GPS) location coordinates, inventorying available amenities and photo-documenting each access location along the lakeshore. Some of the data collected at each site includes access type, fees and the availability of parking, electricity, camping, shelter and restrooms.

Over 360 sites in eleven Wisconsin counties were evaluated for potential

non-motorized water access that could be branded as the Lake Michigan
Water Trail. After review by project partners, kayaking and boating partners and the public during open houses and a public comment period, 191
water trail points were selected to provide a good distribution of sites that
provide safe and easy access and good amenities.

Sites were categorized by access types—carry-in access, developed access, alternate access or emergency access—based on the method by which
the water can be accessed, the ease of accessing the water and the level of
potential user conflict at the site.

Carry-in access is a public site with accessible shoreline that provides
easy kayak access to the water and has little user conflict from adjacent
landowners. *Developed access* is a public site that provides water access via
a public boat ramp or dock.

Alternate access is a non-ideal carry-in access site that may be only a
road that ends at the water. Alternate access sites may have a steep slope
to the water, require wading or paddling through marsh or present some
potential for user conflict from adjacent landowners.

Emergency access is a site to be accessed during extreme situations when
the need to get off the water is immediate. Emergency access sites are
not recommended for non-emergency use because the sites are primarily
road ends where the potential for user conflict is high, little to no parking
is available or an agreement has been made with the site owner to allow
emergency-only egress.

Public access gaps where further access or improvements are needed
were evaluated for future targeted efforts to improve the connectivity of
the water trail network by increasing public land holdings along the shoreline. The gaps in access were identified along stretches where a distance
from one access point to another is greater than five miles, or where camping sites are more than ten miles apart.

These gap areas created "enhancement zones" along the water trail
where future efforts will be aimed at closing the gaps and improving site
amenities. Enhancement zones along the Lake Michigan Water Trail are
eligible for Stewardship grants and communities are encouraged to work
with the Department of Natural Resources to improve or expand access
along the Trail.

On April 25, 2012, the Wisconsin Lake Michigan Water Trail was recognized by the Natural Resources Board as an official state trail. The Lake Michigan Trail is the second longest trail in Wisconsin after only the Ice Age National Scenic Trail. With overwhelming Board, agency and public support, the Wisconsin Lake Michigan Water Trail became the first official State water trail designated by the Natural Resources Board.

Future efforts planned for the Wisconsin Lake Michigan Water Trail include development of a branding strategy and marketing materials, signage, a website where GPS coordinates can be downloaded, integration with the Wisconsin Coastal Atlas and mobile applications. Future efforts will focus on achieving designation as a National Recreation Trail. This designation would add Wisconsin to the Lake Michigan Water Trail National Recreation Trail that will eventually circle Lake Michigan in all four states. Such recognition will require letters of support from each community along the water trail.

A final report for the Wisconsin Lake Michigan Water Trail can be downloaded at www.baylakerpc.org/natural-resources/lakemichigan -water-trail-planning.

In 2012, Angela Pierce was a Natural Resources Planner with the Bay-Lake Regional Planning Commission.

Superior's Shores: Nature, History and Recreation

Mary Morgan

The City of Superior is situated at the western tip of great and majestic Lake Superior. Nestled between the St. Louis River—the largest United States tributary flowing into the Great Lakes—and Superior Bay, the community enjoys 96 miles of coastal shoreline.

Superior's 27,213 residents are deeply connected to Lake Superior and surrounding waters—economically, recreationally, environmentally and psychologically—as a matter of identity. They naturally want to spend both private and public moments near the water. The Wisconsin Coastal Management Program (WCMP) has made it possible for locals and visitors to comfortably enjoy the coast with public access grant projects.

Billings Park, located on the shore of the St. Louis River in the west end of the City, is the community's largest formal park. The 27-acre park was donated to the City by Mr. Frederick Billings of Woodstock, Vermont in 1890 and has been a favorite of residents and visitors for over 120 years.

The park features picnic areas, play equipment, two pavilions, numerous gardens—including a Japanese style garden—and a series of trails that wind through the park's uplands that overlook the river and hills of Minnesota. The shore provides a boat launch, trail system and several small islands that create areas of interest for park users.

WCMP funds assisted in establishing the boat launch and trail system and strengthening the shoreline surrounding the main upland in the park. Graduation parties, corporate picnics and family gatherings take place at this popular venue which draws up to 100 reservations each season.

Located nearby, the *Arrowhead Fishing Pier* is a remnant of a former 1920s-era bridge that led motorists between Wisconsin and Minnesota. The structure was slowly dismantled by the City as it deteriorated due to age and winter ice flow damage from the St. Louis River. In 2010, a WCMP grant rescued the facility by transforming it into a high quality recreational complex whose features were selected by Superior citizens.

A planning grant was secured to undertake a public process in which citizens voted on the configuration of the new facility, the construction materials used and the amenities now available at the pier. WCMP funds complemented other investments to build the complex which features a 200-foot fishing pier, boat launch, restroom and attractive picnic pavilion. This successful project drew donations from four separate St. Louis River user groups.

Barker's Island, located along the waterfront corridor, is a man-made jewel formed by the dredging of Superior Bay in the late 1800s by Captain Charles Barker. The island supports mixed use facilities including a municipally-owned 420-slip marina, public boat launch, hotel, residential neighborhood, the S.S. *Meteor* Museum, Barker's Island Festival Park and the Lake Superior National Estuarine Research Reserve.

Festival Park is scheduled for twenty-five events during the summer of 2012 including the Lake Superior Dragon Boat Festival, Superior's signature summer event. Eleven brides will say "I do" under the Park's pavilion on the shore of Superior Bay. For two decades, WCMP funds have been used to improve access to Lake Superior beginning with the boat launch on Barker's Island and the popular Osaugie Trail along Superior's waterfront.

The *Osaugie Trail* offers multi-use access and connects to the Tri-County Recreational Corridor leading sixty-two miles to Ashland. Named after Chief Osaugie of the Anishinabe Band, the trail spans five miles from Barker's Island to Bear Creek Park. Chief Osaugie was a leader in the Superior area circa 1800 and was reputed to be an excellent provider and expert hunter and trapper. He was described as friendly and intelligent and many of his ancestors remain Superior residents.

The trail is unique in that users can routinely see wildlife as well as the Great Lakes' largest working port as they travel the route. Two museums, Fairlawn and the Richard I. Bong Veterans Historical Center, grace the waterfront corridor near the trail. Fairlawn consists of a forty-two-room mansion built in the popular Queen Anne Victorian style architecture of 1891, and the Veterans Center exhibits a World War II P-38 Lightning fighter aircraft.

Finally, WCMP dollars provided the City's first outdoor classroom and interpretive trail located in the *Superior Municipal Forest*. With 4,428 acres of woodlands and wetlands located in the southwest corner of the City along the St. Louis River, the Superior Municipal Forest is the third largest municipally-owned forest in the nation.

Forest pursuits include hiking, biking, hunting, fishing, boating, skiing and ecology. The Outdoor Classroom is positioned under a towering white pine and offers seating for sixty students. It is located on the popular Millennium Trail with six interpretive pedestals displaying coastal resource and stewardship messages. Most of the pedestals present original local art or photos. Teachers use the site for environmental education and nature appreciation.

Whether enjoying the St. Louis River, Superior Bay or Lake Superior, residents and visitors stand in awe of the magnificent waters of Superior. Public access has never been more available or more enjoyable than it is today. The City of Superior continues to benefit from its partnership with the Wisconsin Coastal Management Program.

In 2012, Mary Morgan was the Administrator of the City of Superior Department of Parks and Recreation.

Redeveloping the Lower Fox River and Green Bay Waterfront

Aaron Schuette

Harbors have historically been the starting point for exploration of the land that lies beyond the shoreline. Forts were developed to protect these strategic locations that subsequently became ports and centers of commerce.

The Green Bay-area waterfront fostered growth of the lumber and the paper industries. These businesses benefited from Wisconsin's nearby vast woodlands and the low flat banks of the Fox River that enabled the horizontal placement of industrial machinery. The waterfront also became the focal point of activity in the region as downtown commercial areas developed in the cities of Green Bay and De Pere.

These areas were important not only economically and socially, but also as centers for ideas and information. They became the hubs of local government, civil society and commercial business. By the 1840s, a lock and canal system was developed along the Fox River to expand waterborn traffic to inland Wisconsin communities.

Green Bay has enjoyed its status as a Great Lakes port and an international seaport following completion of the St. Lawrence Seaway in 1959. However, an unfortunate side effect of the rapid industrialization of the Fox River was a legacy of pollution in the river and disinvestment on its shores.

That legacy is changing. With the advent of the Clean Water Act, environmental awareness and improved public understanding of the connections between land use and impacts on the river, the Fox River and Green Bay shoreline today is a dynamic, diverse area.

The remediation of river sediments contaminated with polychlorinated biphenyls (PCBs) is underway throughout the river corridor. The impact of this work is promising. Voyageur Park in De Pere has been transformed from a landfill and bulk storage site for coal and salt to a destination that now hosts thousands of early spring anglers from its shores and boats launched from nearby docks during the annual walleye run.

Leicht Park and The CityDeck in downtown Green Bay are becoming focal points for festivals and concerts with the Fox River as their backdrop. Multiple port operators take advantage of the economies of scale associated with waterborne shipping of bulk commodities through the Port of Green Bay by Great Lakes ore carriers and saltwater freighters. Ashwaubenon has reactivated its waterfront through redevelopment of a former brownfield site north of the STH 172 bridge.

Through the Fox River Navigational Authority, plans are underway to reconnect the upper and lower parts of the Fox River to recreational boating. The Fox-Wisconsin Heritage Parkway is being developed to promote the unique history of the rivers and communities along them.

The Lower Fox River and Green Bay Shoreline Waterfront Redevelopment Plan was developed to build on this momentum. The plan creates communication and coordination among the multiple stakeholders within the study area and provides specific recommendations throughout the corridor to balance economic development, environmental restoration and cultural opportunities.

The plan identifies twelve unique opportunity areas with similar land uses within the overall study area to create more manageable, localized recommendations. Within each opportunity area, the existing land uses, current assessed valuations and waterfront public access sites were inventoried and analyzed.

The plan identifies specific opportunity area recommendations that would enable multi-modal connections to and from the river and bay shore to other nearby attractions such as the East River Trail, Lambeau Field and Bay Beach Amusement Park. The goal is creation of a waterfront district with consistent streetscaping and wayfinding.

Additionally, the plan identifies existing underutilized waterfront locations that could be potentially redeveloped with uses that are dependent on waterfront locations. The plan contemplates additional port operations, public waterfront access, water-related businesses or natural shoreline restoration efforts.

For the plan to succeed, the waterfront needs to have a well-balanced 24/7 activity base. When considering the Fox River and Green Bay shorelines, this means an appropriate mixture of port, commercial, recreational, residential and institutional uses that each contribute to the overall activity level along the shoreline that spills over to adjacent areas. In order for this to happen, the waterfront needs to be woven into adjacent neighborhoods and nearby attractions.

A community should celebrate what makes its waterfront district unique. In the case of the Fox River and Green Bay shoreline, distinctive features include its rich history, multiple recreational uses, business opportunities and connections to the larger community. As is the case in all successful waterfront communities, daily activities associated with diverse neighborhoods and exciting downtowns extend the urban waterfront beyond the water's edge.

The recommendations contained within the plan are intended to start a conversation among Brown County's residents, municipalities, agencies and private-sector partners about how the Fox River and Green Bay shorelines can enhance our quality of life. As local planning and development continues, it is hoped that this effort will produce a higher level of communication and coordination among various interests to create a unified waterfront district. Therefore, the completion of this plan is not an end to the waterfront planning process in Brown County, but rather a beginning.

In 2012, Aaron Schuette was a Principal Planner with the Brown County Planning Commission.

MILWAUKEE'S MENOMONEE VALLEY

Laura Bray

Four miles long and a half-mile wide, the Menomonee River Valley extends from the confluence of the Menomonee and Milwaukee Rivers to Miller Park Stadium. For hundreds of years, the 1,200-acre Menomonee Valley was a wild rice marsh and home to Native Americans who gathered for fishing, hunting and the rice harvest.

As Milwaukee developed, the Menomonee River was channelized, its banks armored and its marshes filled with contaminated material to make new land for industry. When Milwaukee became known as the "Machine Shop of the World," the Menomonee Valley was its engine. The Valley has long been the state's center of industry and home to thousands of jobs.

Characteristic of many industrial cities, Milwaukee's economic conditions changed in recent years and many manufacturing companies moved or closed their doors. By the latter half of the twentieth century, the Valley had become Wisconsin's most visible eyesore with hundreds of acres of abandoned, contaminated land and a forgotten, polluted river.

In the late 1990s, the City of Milwaukee, the Milwaukee Metropolitan Sewerage District (MMSD), the State of Wisconsin and Valley businesses came together to develop a plan for the Menomonee Valley. One of the plan's recommendations was the creation of a public-private partnership—Menomonee Valley Partners—to facilitate this effort. Since 1999, a wide array of stakeholders has been working together to revitalize the Menomonee Valley for the benefit of the entire Milwaukee region.

In the past decade, thirty-three companies have moved to or expanded in the Valley resulting in the creation of 4,700 jobs. In addition, fourteen miles of the Hank Aaron State Trail and a nationally recognized shared stormwater treatment system have been developed, and forty-five acres of native plants have been established. More than ten million people visit the Valley's recreation and entertainment destinations each year.

Today, the Valley is a national model of economic and environmental sustainability. Recognized by the Sierra Club as "One of the 10 Best

Developments in the Nation," the Menomonee Valley continues to receive local and national accolades.

During the last decade, the Wisconsin Coastal Management Program has been engaged in nearly a dozen projects that have led to the Menomonee River Valley's reemergence, including:

- Sustainable Design Guidelines for the Menomonee Valley, a project to ensure that redevelopment efforts in the Valley are environmentally sustainable.

- Stormwater Park, an infrastructure project that treats stormwater from seventy acres of redevelopment and creates recreational open space that serves as a public amenity.

- Menomonee Valley Cultural Resources, a project which led to the creation of twelve interpretive signs throughout the Menomonee Valley that explain the unique history of the area from Native Americans to railcars, and immigrant neighborhood life to native plants.

- Airline Yards Design Development, a design for developing a twenty-four-acre park with 2,600 feet of river frontage in a 140-acre former rail yard.

The next phase of the Valley's revitalization—*Menomonee Valley From the Ground Up*—builds upon the area's success to date. From the Ground Up will provide a comprehensive approach to environmental, community and economic development which, when completed, will reach tens of thousands of residents in the region. This phase includes three main projects.

Converting a rail yard into a 24-acre park. Menomonee Valley Partners is working to turn a narrow parcel with a half-mile of river frontage into an ecologically diverse park that will become part of the Hank Aaron State Trail. The plan includes the restoration of several habitat zones native to southeast Wisconsin, stabilization of an eroding riverbank and creation of new public access to the Menomonee River. Neighbors, school groups and other volunteers will be engaged in building the park, planting trees and actively building an amenity in the heart of Milwaukee.

Building new bike and pedestrian infrastructure. This project will weave the Valley back into the fabric of the City through six new miles of the Hank Aaron State Trail and three bike/pedestrian bridges that reconnect city neighborhoods to the Valley. When completed in Spring 2013, the Hank Aaron State Trail will be a fourteen-mile system stretching from Lake Michigan to Waukesha County that offers walk-to-work opportunities and connections to some of the largest tourist attractions in the region including the Lakefront, Milwaukee County Zoo and Summerfest.

Opening a Menomonee Valley branch of the Urban Ecology Center. A third branch of the Urban Ecology Center will be established to serve the Valley and its nearby neighborhoods. Through its Neighborhood Environmental Education Program, the Center provides K-12 schools with programs to strengthen their science curriculum using hands-on outdoor learning experiences. The curriculum is developed with participating schools and aligned with local and federal science, literacy and math standards. In addition, the Center offers after-school, weekend and summer programs for youth, families and adults.

Through the efforts of many, many partnerships, the Menomonee Valley is connecting people to jobs, environmental education, restored natural resources and new recreational opportunities. The revitalized Menomonee Valley will be a place to work, play and learn for generations to come.

In 2012, Laura Bray was the Executive Director of Menomonee Valley Partners, Inc.

A COASTAL FELLOW'S
WISCONSIN ADVENTURE

Kathy Johnson

If anyone said ten years ago I would someday live in Wisconsin, I would not have believed it. However, that is exactly what happened after I became a Coastal Management Fellow in 2010.

Growing up as a young child along Winyah Bay in South Carolina, I developed a passion for the coastal environment. Some of my most enjoyable moments were spent along the beach or in a boat exploring the many marshes and waterways in Georgetown County. These experiences and my formal education in Environmental Planning led to me to apply for a NOAA Coastal Management Fellowship.

The Coastal Management Fellowship Program began in 1996 and is sponsored by the National Oceanic and Atmospheric Administration (NOAA) in conjunction with the coastal states. The program has two main objectives. First, the program offers coastal resource management and policy experience to postgraduate students seeking careers in coastal management. Second, the program provides project assistance to state coastal management programs.

States interested in hosting a Fellow for two years submit potential projects to the NOAA Coastal Services Center. Students in turn apply through their own state's Sea Grant Program and go through a competitive process to be nominated as a fellowship finalist. Twelve finalists are invited to a matching workshop hosted by the NOAA Coastal Services Center in Charleston. Ultimately, six Fellows are selected and placed in each of the host states.

As the first NOAA Fellow assigned to Wisconsin, I have been able to learn first-hand about coastal policy and proper management to ensure protection of the Great Lakes. My fellowship project involves assisting the University of Wisconsin Sea Grant Institute in the construction of the Wisconsin Coastal Atlas (www.wicoastalatlas.net). In addition, I recommended and developed spatial decision support tools which will be used to aid planners and coastal managers in implementing local comprehensive and hazard mitigation plans.

My fellowship in Wisconsin has provided many memorable and interesting experiences that have developed my career as a coastal manager. (Note: My first impression of Wisconsin was not of Lakes Michigan or Superior, but of how pretty and green the cornfields are!)

For example, I participated in a tour of St. Louis Bay on the research vessel *L.L. Smith, Jr.* where I learned about a corrosion problem that has caused deterioration of steel pilings in the Duluth-Superior Harbor. In Cornucopia, I observed a different coastal hazard: erosion along the coastline which has resulted in bluff failure in locations along Lake Superior. Although different from the hurricanes to which I am accustomed, exposure to these hazards is nonetheless a real threat to life and property in the Great Lakes region. To address the erosion threat, the Wisconsin Coastal Management Program (WCMP) has helped finance a project by Bayfield County to develop safer setbacks for new construction.

In the lovely City of Bayfield along Lake Superior and Washington Island and Door County on Lake Michigan, I examined locations where Coastal Zone Management Act (CZMA) funds have been used to implement public access projects along the coasts. I soon realized the major impact CZMA and WCMP have in preserving and protecting Wisconsin's Great Lakes.

Although living in the Low Country of South Carolina had given me significant exposure to wetlands, I had no idea that Wisconsin also has vast areas of wetlands. I have studied wetlands throughout Wisconsin's coastal zone and come to a greater appreciation of their importance. However, I am not alone in appreciating Wisconsin's wetlands.

At a recent Wisconsin wetlands conference, the Ramsar Convention on Wetlands honored the Bad River Band of Lake Superior Chippewa Tribe with the treasured Wetland of International Importance award. In addition, the Wisconsin Wetlands Association received a Wetland Conservation Award from the Ramsar Convention.

I was pleased to celebrate such high honors and found myself taking pride in my new state for leading the nation in wetlands protection. That feeling of pride grew when I joined a group touring wetland sites in Wisconsin and Illinois that hopefully will become part of the proposed Hackmatack National Wildlife Refuge.

Moving to Wisconsin has necessitated a major adjustment to the climate. Upon recommendation of a former colleague, I decided to try to "embrace" the cold weather. Early in 2011, I walked on Madison's frozen Lake Monona with colleagues from my office! I have enjoyed snowshoeing and tubing, but my favorite winter activity was a trip to Cable, Wisconsin where my son joined me for our first ever snowmobile trip. It was less than ten degrees and sooooo cold, but we had an awesome adventure!

I consider myself very fortunate to have been selected as a NOAA Fellow to study and contribute to the nation's critical Great Lakes system. I am perhaps even more fortunate to have served as a Fellow in Wisconsin where folks made me feel welcome and even seemed to appreciate my Southern accent.

I can truly say that Wisconsin has become my second home state and the Great Lakes are my second coast. For my friends down South, don't worry, I still say *y'all*.

In 2012, Kathy Johnson, employed by The Baldwin Group, was the NOAA Coastal Management Fellow with the Wisconsin Coastal Management Program and the University of Wisconsin Sea Grant Institute.

2013

FOREWORD

Governor Scott Walker

Dear Friends of the Great Lakes,

Wisconsin is emerging as a world leader in freshwater economic development, research and tourism. Several projects along our Great Lakes coasts
highlight collaborative initiatives among state and local governments,
higher education, community leaders and business associations.

Wisconsin's ports and waterways are economic lifelines for the transport of commodities and products to global markets. The Wisconsin
Coastal Management Program (WCMP) is funding a Wisconsin Commercial Ports Master Plan to document the flow of waterway commodities and
examine ways to increase waterborne freight transportation.

In 2012, the Wisconsin Housing and Economic Development Authority provided $20 million in New Markets Tax Credits to Milwaukee's
Global Water Center. The financing will redevelop a vacant seven-story
building into office and research space for business, government and academic tenants specializing in water products, technology and economic
development.

In Racine, a WCMP grant supported Back to the Root: An Urban River
Revitalization Plan. The plan sets the stage for business and community
development along this important Lake Michigan tributary.

The Wisconsin Harbor Towns Association (WHTA) represents nine-
teen coastal communities along Wisconsin's scenic coastline. With WCMP
funding, the WHTA updated the Wisconsin Harbor Towns Travel Guide
to assist visitors search among the many amenities along our shores. The
Guide is available online at www.wisconsinharbortowns.net.

A WCMP and Department of Tourism partnership produced new Lake
Superior and Michigan episodes of the popular *Discover Wisconsin* trav-
elogue. The shows promote the importance of Wisconsin's Great Lakes as
natural resources and tourist destinations. The episodes will be televised
through 2015.

Wisconsin universities are leaders in freshwater education. Graduate students at the University of Wisconsin-Milwaukee School of Freshwater Sciences are at the forefront of research that will lead to improved policies and management of freshwater resources around the world.

The Institute for Water Business at the University of Wisconsin-Whitewater is preparing students with the knowledge needed to wisely manage water resources as future business leaders. The UW-W program includes a water business minor and water emphasis.

Marquette University Law School offers its students an innovative water law curriculum. These courses prepare future attorneys to specialize in matters involving water rights, environmental policy and natural resources law.

Under the leadership and vision of its citizens, Wisconsin is moving forward to protect its water resources, offer world-class tourism amenities and enhance water-related business opportunities. Enjoy this year's *Wisconsin Great Lakes Chronicle* showcasing emerging trends and success stories along our coasts.

Scott Walker was elected Wisconsin's 45th Governor in 2010.

Low Water, High Challenge

Dave Knight and Gene Clark, PE

Of the physical variables that affect Wisconsin's coastal communities, Great Lakes water levels may be the most impactful. They dictate how waterfront property is used and managed, and to what degree commercial and recreational navigation access is available. Water levels also impact how well coastal infrastructure—such as piers, breakwaters and bulkheads—protect valuable assets from storm and flood damage.

Periods of high water present obvious challenges for coastal protection as demonstrated by scenes during the mid-1980s of waves rolling over piers, houses falling off eroding bluffs and harbor waters lapping onto parks and sidewalks. But the extremely low water regime now underway presents its own challenges by necessitating more navigational dredging and exposing sections of aging piers and breakwaters that are ill-designed for such conditions.

Compounding the low lake level issue is another unfolding reality—a longstanding federal commitment to small harbor dredging and upkeep of harbor infrastructure may be coming to an end. Budgetary constraints and questions as to federal interest in maintaining once commercial—but now largely recreational—harbors have virtually deprioritized them out of the federal harbor maintenance program.

Convergence of these climatic and budgetary events could redefine the roles of state and local governments in Great Lakes harbor maintenance. But could opportunities for a more nimble and cost effective adaptive management style also emerge in the process?

It would be much easier for all concerned if Great Lakes water levels were stable, predictable or completely manageable. But they are none of the above and this year's extremes stand as yet another testament to the lakes' capriciousness.

An exceedingly warm and dry 2012 drove water levels that were already on an approximately fifteen-year downward trend to near or record setting lows in early 2013. All three of the primary drivers of Great Lakes water levels—less precipitation, more lake surface evaporation and less basin runoff—contributed to the current condition. Other hydrological factors remain in play—such as diversions into and out of the basin and flows between the lakes—but the main determiners of water levels remain climate-related.

Looking ahead, basin climate models do not project much likelihood for change in the near term. Two particularly significant trends—warming water temperatures (Lake Superior recorded the warmest water temperatures in over a century during 2012) and steadily diminishing winter ice cover—contribute to more evaporation and the potential for even lower water levels.

Another aspect of the climate model impacting coastal protection is an expectation of increased storm volatility. The US Army Corps of Engineers noted that over half of the coastal structures on the Great Lakes were built prior to World War I and 80 percent are older than their typical 50-year lifespan. Many of these structures were not designed to be exposed to the open air and low water levels may accelerate deterioration and cause actual failures.

For boaters and cargo carriers, a dredging crisis was shaping up long before current water levels exacerbated the problem. Inadequate funding of the Corps' Great Lakes dredging program for over a decade has created a backlog of over eighteen million tons of sediment in Great Lakes harbors and channels. Some 36 of 60 federally-authorized commercial harbors—seven in Wisconsin—and 46 of 80 recreational harbors—nine in Wisconsin—were in need of dredging at the start of 2013.

Despite all these needs, the federal administration's budget allowed the Corps to dredge only fifteen Great Lakes harbors in 2013, including only two in Wisconsin—Green Bay and Superior. The Corps has identified $64 million in Wisconsin port dredging, operations and maintenance needs for FY14, but only $12 million is provided in the President's budget.

With the Corps of Engineers withdrawing from all but the busiest Great Lakes commercial ports and not withstanding Congressional reform of the Harbor Maintenance Trust Fund which could restore a significant amount of available federal dollars, the responsibility for maintaining safe navigation access and reliable coastal protection structures may have to tilt further toward state and local entities.

According to the Wisconsin Department of Transportation, the Harbor

Assistance Program (HAP) grant cycle recently drew dredging applications totaling about $7.45 million. A project to dredge the federal navigation channel between Washington Island and the mainland is particularly critical because the island ferry must light load and switch docks due to shallow conditions.

Harbors that do not qualify for the HAP can apply to the Wisconsin Department of Natural Resources Recreational Boating Facilities grant program. In addition, almost all dredging activity in Door County was being privately financed with over 60 permits filed during a recent seven-month period.

At least one other state, Michigan, has stepped up in 2013 with a $21 million emergency dredging program that will assist 49 harbors impaired by low water levels. For Wisconsin and all other Great Lakes states, harbor maintenance and coastal protection are two functions that will only grow in importance, even as they may grow in difficulty to address.

With less reliance on federal resources and more dramatic lake level swings in store, state agencies and local governments are facing a literal future of uncharted waters.

In 2013, Dave Knight was a Great Lakes Port and Navigation Specialist at David Larkin Knight LLC. Gene Clark, PE, was a Coastal Engineering Specialist at the University of Wisconsin Sea Grant Institute.

WASHINGTON ISLAND:
A UNIQUE WAY OF LIVING

Joel Gunnlaugsson

I am a ferry captain for the Washington Island Ferry Line, the only way of getting to and from the island on a year-round daily basis. An Islander, I was born here and have called the island home ever since.

There are no fast food restaurants, chain motels, big box stores or movie theaters, so people make their own entertainment. People come to relax and commune with nature. Outdoor activities abound from hunting and fishing to kayaking and swimming.

The island—rich in Scandinavian tradition—has historical museums, churches and public parks to visit. Historical and cultural attractions are spread out over 36 square miles that are also good for hiking, biking and driving excursions.

Washington Island is the largest of Door County's 30 islands and located five miles northeast of the Door Peninsula tip. It is one of a string of islands that are outcroppings of the Niagara Escarpment, which runs east-west from New York State through Ontario, Michigan, Wisconsin and Illinois. The escarpment is most famous as the cliff over which the Niagara River plunges at Niagara Falls.

Washington Island consists of rock formations and in places its sides are rugged and precipitous. Between West and Washington Harbors, high rising rocky bluffs—filled with nooks and caves and covered with evergreen trees—are picturesquely imposing. Around Detroit and Jackson Harbors, the beach is more sloping.

About 1641, the Potawatomi Indians came to the island; in the mid-1800s they greeted the first immigrants from Norway, Sweden, Denmark, Iceland, Finland and Ireland. Washington Island is today the second largest Icelandic community in North America. Trinity Lutheran Church is an authentic Norwegian stave church with acanthus carvings and hand crafted shingles.

The Town of Washington Island, established in 1850, includes five other islands: Plum, Detroit, Hog, Pilot and Rock. Only accessible by ferry, the 900-acre Rock Island State Park is Wisconsin's only state park that constitutes an entire island. Rock Island is home to the first United States commissioned lighthouse on Lake Michigan. The refurbished Potawatomi Lighthouse is open for public tours from May to October.

Washington Island has year round residents and its own economy. A winter population of 700 grows to 3,500 in the summer. A self-sufficient community, the island has over 100 miles of paved roads, fire and EMS personnel, a medical clinic, the state's smallest K-12 school, an electric power company, a grocery store, gas stations, taverns, restaurants and motels, an airport and a helicopter pad.

The economy includes hospitality, retail, construction, farming, logging and commercial fishing. However, tourism is the island's largest industry. The ferry carries 200,000 passengers and 70,000 vehicles each year. About 65 percent of the passengers are visitors and the remainder are Islanders.

Forests originally covered the island. Predominantly evergreen, these trees are still found in uncleared areas. Lake proximity makes the climate mild and equable. In the spring, fruit and vegetation are comparatively safe from the late frosts. Combined with soil that seems peculiarly adapted to fruit, the island is an excellent orchard region. Apples grow well and acres of cherry trees are cultivated. Small fruits abound.

The soil gives a unique flavor to peas and other vegetables that make them much sought by canneries. Potatoes are extensively raised. Crops are harvested under contract at profitable prices.

An island industry to note is *place based marketing* that has grown out of the high quality local agriculture. Local produce is prominently featured at local restaurants and enjoyed by Islanders and visitors alike.

Finding a use for Washington Island's natural wheat—certified organic in 2008—allowed local farmers to participate competitively in commercial agriculture and benefit the regional economy. Capital Brewery's Island Wheat Ale increased the two primary growers' wheat harvests to more than half a million pounds—all herbicide and pesticide-free—spanning 800 acres.

The island's narrow six-mile passage connecting Lake Michigan and

Green Bay has turbulent currents and strong sudden winds that the local Indians called *Door to Death*. The Death Door's Spirits vodka, white whiskey and gin distillers are committed to working with local farmers to increase the use and fame of the island's wheat. All of these unique commodities help to diversify the island's economy.

As a ferry captain, I find the Great Lakes' low water level of particular concern. Year-round ferry access generates $16 million of annual economic activity through transportation of passengers, vehicles and cargo. In January 2013, a record drop in lake level made it impossible to run the icebreaking ferry and Detroit Harbor was unusable for non-icebreaking vessels. This necessitated a $750,000 dredging project at Potato Dock and the State has allocated $5.2 million to dredge the Detroit Harbor channel.

Washington Island continues to work on geographic constraints—insularity of island life, diversifying the economy and preserving natural features and biodiversity. By their very nature, islands are isolated and sensitive to change. These attributes make them refuges for natural heritage and biological diversity and thus have high conservation value. While the island's features are subject to threats from human activity, we view these challenges as opportunities.

Spend time on Washington Island, the best island life Wisconsin has to offer!

In 2013, Joel Gunnlaugsson was a Ferry Captain, the Island Town Chairman, a Door County Board Supervisor, a Lions Club member and the 2nd Assistant Fire Chief. He acknowledged the following sources: washingtonisland.com, washingtonisland-wi.com, ediblechicago.com and Islands of Life: A Biodiversity and Conservation Atlas of the Great Lakes Islands.

RED CLIFF BAND RECLAIMS FROG BAY

Dennis McCann

When David Johnson bought a prime piece of Lake Superior frontage at
public auction in 1980, he learned that the Red Cliff Band of Lake Superior Chippewa also wanted the land but could not afford to place a bid.
He would recall years later that it made him feel a bit awkward to obtain
one-time tribal land in such a way, but not so uncomfortable that he considered turning the land—which he knew would someday have much
greater value—back to the Tribe.

Yet when that same parcel and adjacent land owned by Mr. Johnson
were dedicated as the new Frog Bay Tribal National Park in late 2012, he
attended as the man of honor. The park became possible because Mr.
Johnson and his wife, Marjorie—working through the Bayfield Regional
Conservancy—sold the 87-acre property to the Red Cliff people at half its
appraised value.

The Johnsons' act of goodwill guarantees the site's towering canopy
and pebbled beach will remain in its pristine state. Following a pipe ceremony, the event moved to speeches—including one by Mr. Johnson who
dedicated the park to his recently deceased wife.

The new park is a victory for conservation, but also a triumph for the
Red Cliff Band because it marks the return of land that had historically
been located within tribal boundaries and carried great cultural and spiritual significance. And by creating the nation's first tribally-owned national
park open to the public, *this gem*—as Tribal Chair Rose Gurnoe-Soulier
called it—will be enjoyed by more than just tribal members.

Tribal Vice-Chair Marvin Defoe, whose inspiration it was to declare
the land a tribal national park, credited Mr. Johnson for seeing the value
of working with the Tribe and the Conservancy to permanently protect
a special place.

"I would like to acknowledge him for the generosity," said Mr. Defoe.
The Chippewa's very identity is indelibly tied to the land and the water
and the Johnsons' actions will allow them to "make sure the land is held
in reverence again."

It was Mr. Johnson's own reverence for the land that allowed the property to maintain so much of its natural beauty. He preferred to keep the property—with its diverse boreal forest community of hemlock, white pine, spruce and other species—in its pristine state.

He declined the financial benefits of placing the land into the state's Managed Forest Law program because doing so would have required occasional logging. For the same reason, the Johnsons did not put the land on the market for fear that any interested developer would carve it into 150-foot lots.

Instead, the land was conserved to create a park for all to enjoy. The Conservancy will hold a conservation easement on the entire property to preserve its beaches, forest and ravines against any development.

How the transfer came about involved more than a bit of serendipity. The Johnsons had been long-time neighbors of and close friends with former Sen. Gaylord Nelson and his family. Sen. Nelson is deemed the father of the Apostle Islands National Lakeshore, and the view from the Johnsons' Frog Bay property is of islands managed as part of the Gaylord Nelson Wilderness.

It was Sen. Nelson's daughter, Tia—who said Marjorie Johnson was "like a second mother to me"—who put the Johnsons in contact with Ellen Kwiatkowski, then executive director of the Conservancy, and initiated discussions that led to tribal acquisition. At the time, Ms. Kwiatowski said, "The thing I like about this project is it brings so many groups together."

Under the purchase agreement, a committee of elders, natural resource professionals, tribal government representatives and Bayfield Regional Conservancy staff will oversee management of the park. Tribal crews and volunteers will maintain trails and access roads, tribal wardens will enforce game regulations, and tribal police will enforce park hours.

Almost as soon as the acquisition was completed, Red Cliff natural resources employees began establishing new trails. A bathroom was built at the small parking area at the park entrance, and in 2013 the Tribe plans to build a footbridge over a steep ravine to link the parking area with the new trail loop.

However, Chad Abel, Red Cliff Natural Resources Administrator, said visitors were not waiting for the improvements to be completed before visiting the long off-limits site. Every morning, Mr. Abel said, five or six cars were already in the parking area and some visitors even came in winter to snowshoe down to the beach.

Looking ahead, the Tribe's goal is to acquire adjacent parcels to protect even more of the Frog Bay watershed. First, though, the Tribe is enjoying its unique accomplishment.

Mr. Defoe said a tribal national park—a name that reflects the sovereignty of the Red Cliff people—will allow members to share more of their reservation, culture and traditions with the larger world. That, he said, is possible only through public access to Frog Bay, access that would not be available if the land was privately owned.

"It's kind of like you own a home, [but] you can't go in that one bedroom there."

Now, he said, the home is open to all.

In 2013, Dennis McCann was a Bayfield writer and author whose latest book was This Superior Place: Stories of Bayfield and the Apostle Islands.

Protecting Wisconsin's Great Lakes Beaches

Todd Breiby

Many Wisconsin coastal communities are premier tourist destinations that offer diverse water-related recreational opportunities. World-renowned natural resources and thousands of Great Lakes-based businesses enhance the quality of life for residents and have a direct impact on the state's economy, job market and tourism industry.

Great Lakes beaches—found in many of Wisconsin's harbor towns and coastal communities—are integral to the vitality of local economies. Beaches are anchors for recreational, economic and waterfront development activities and provide access for individuals to connect with the Great Lakes. In addition, beaches are seen as indicators of the health of the Great Lakes and its watersheds.

With more than 190 public beaches along Wisconsin's Lake Michigan and Lake Superior coastlines, harbor towns and local tourism associations are increasingly promoting their Great Lakes beaches to statewide, regional and national audiences. It is estimated that $3–5 billion of tourism activity is directly connected to water-related recreation in Wisconsin's Great Lakes counties with each beachgoer bringing $35-$50 per day to the local economy. Therefore, excellent beach health and water quality leads to increased visitation and usage, which in turn has a positive economic impact on the state.

Bacterial contamination, *Cladophora*, toxic algal blooms and outbreaks of Type E botulism in fish and birds are examples of health concerns that can result in poor quality beach and water resources. Elevated fecal indicator bacteria such as *E. coli* in recreational waters pose a public health risk and directly impact the local economy due to swim advisories and beach closures.

In addition, other issues—some originating far inland—are putting stress on the Great Lakes. Nonpoint and point source pollution, land use practices and invasive species are impacting water quality at beaches in Wisconsin and throughout the Great Lakes.

Over the last decade, the commitment of local governments and beach managers, state programs, a robust research community and collaboration at all levels have placed Wisconsin at the national forefront for beach research, management and education. Several examples of Wisconsin's leadership are particularly notable.

In 2012, the *City of Racine* became the first municipality on the Great Lakes to receive permission from the US Environmental Protection Agency to use qPCR (quantitative polymerase chain reaction) to produce a more rapid response in monitoring recreational waters. This process means that decisions to open or close beaches can be made the same day on which samples are collected. Traditional methods are culture-based with results not available for 18–24 hours. That means swimmers would not know until the next day if they swam in contaminated water.

Early successes from the City of Racine rapid testing process led to collaborative efforts with the University of Wisconsin-Oshkosh on the establishment of *regional rapid method testing facilities* funded by the Great Lakes Restoration Initiative (GLRI). In addition, the Wisconsin Coastal Management Program (WCMP) funded two Wisconsin Department of Natural Resources (DNR) projects: one to develop a decision support tool to predict *E. coli* levels in real-time, and a second to develop operational nowcasts—real-time predictive models—at high priority beaches.

Local governments continue to seek cost effective ways to monitor recreational water quality and provide the necessary notifications to protect public health, particularly in light of the potential absence of federal Beaches Environmental Assessment and Coastal Health Act (BEACH Act) funding. With 2013 funding from the WCMP, *Ozaukee and Sheboygan County Health Departments*—in coordination with the Wisconsin DNR—will test a two-tiered nowcast system. This project will run a standard Tier I nowcast model on days when beach monitoring is conducted, plus an automated Tier II nowcast using only web-accessible data on other days when samples cannot be taken.

Through funding from the WCMP and the GLRI, *beach re-engineering projects* on Lake Michigan and Lake Superior have addressed issues of contamination. These stewardship projects—including the identification of contamination sources, the development of design plans and the implementation of best management practices—have greatly assisted in resurrecting beaches as coastal gems. Mitigated beaches have shown substantial increases in usage. Successful examples include North Beach in Racine, Bradford Beach in Milwaukee and Egg Harbor Beach in Door County.

Racine's North Beach is one of five *Blue Wave* beaches in Wisconsin. Certified in 2004, North Beach was the first in Wisconsin and the second on the Great Lakes to receive this unique national designation for outstanding environmental stewardship. Designations such as Blue Wave certification reflect the dedicated efforts of local communities and stakeholders who have worked diligently to improve and maintain the health of these coastal resources.

Wisconsin has made substantial progress over the last decade in restoring and enhancing its Great Lakes beaches, but more work is on the horizon. Continued efforts include the active monitoring of beaches and recreational waters following the implementation of best management practices, economic analyses of the effects of beach mitigation on local communities, and the development of cost-effective means to sustainably monitor Wisconsin's Great Lakes recreational waters.

Looking ahead, Wisconsin is committed to ensuring its Great Lakes beaches play a vibrant role in the quality of life of its coastal communities and in the economy for us all.

In 2013, Todd Breiby was the Coastal Nonpoint Control and Education Coordinator at the Wisconsin Coastal Management Program.

COMMUNITY INVOLVEMENT IMPROVES AREAS OF CONCERN

Gail Epping Overholt

The natural harbors and tributaries along the Great Lakes have long been important industrial and recreational centers. In Wisconsin's early days when transportation by water was common, shoreline communities grew into hubs of shipping, commerce and industry. Rivers were dammed, dredged, straightened, widened and often lined with concrete to accommodate needed economic growth.

Over time, the waters became heavily polluted by industrial, agricultural and urban use. This pollution eventually compromised or eliminated many of the important environmental functions that human and natural communities depend upon. The loss of these functions—or beneficial uses—was the principal reason that five Wisconsin waterways became listed as Areas of Concern (AOCs).

The US-Canada Great Lakes Water Quality Agreement identifies fourteen beneficial uses that are used in designating AOCs, including healthy fisheries, clean beaches, safe drinking water and suitable habitat for wildlife. Thanks to support from the Great Lakes Restoration Initiative and a resurgence of local interest, Wisconsin is now poised to take giant leaps toward restoring many of these beneficial uses and even delisting these waterways as Areas of Concern.

The road to delisting can be long and complicated. At each step of the way, local experts pinpoint and evaluate existing problems and identify causes. They then develop corrective actions and strategies to achieve desired results. With community support, work proceeds to meet restoration goals for each beneficial use.

In Wisconsin, officials recognize that cleaning up an AOC must be community-driven to be successful. Persons directly affected by the AOC lead efforts to achieve cleaner water, stronger local economies and revitalized communities. Citizens are encouraged to voice their expectations and contribute their knowledge to produce solutions based on the complexities of their communities. Both large and small Wisconsin AOC projects demonstrate the wisdom of the community-based approach.

The *Sheboygan River AOC* has made impressive progress and creates a path for other Wisconsin AOCs to follow. From dredging toxic sediment to evaluating river-bottom plants and animals, the work seems endless. However, the Sheboygan River project proves the old saying, "many hands make light work."

This tremendous effort is due to collaboration and partnership across a spectrum of interests. The US Environmental Protection Agency, the Wisconsin Department of Natural Resources, the City of Sheboygan, Sheboygan County, Pollution Risk Services (Tecumseh Corporation) and Wisconsin Public Service have established a foundation of institutional cooperation.

Local governments serve a critical role by contributing the matching funds required to complete the work that will take this AOC to the third stage of the cleanup plan. During this last stage, monitoring will show whether conditions have improved sufficiently to allow the Sheboygan River AOC to be delisted.

At the citizen level, people from all walks of life are involved in data collection through science programs provided by UW-Extension. For example, training sessions and hikes allow residents to contribute knowledge about Wisconsin bats, freshwater mussels and birds. The success of the Sheboygan River restoration is due to the dedication of countless people from different agencies, organizations and backgrounds who have contributed their energy and expertise to this large, coordinated effort.

Over 200 people make up the citizen Stakeholder Input Group (SIG) involved in the *Milwaukee Estuary AOC*. A key feature of the SIG is a twelve-member stakeholder delegation team representing public, private and nonprofit interests in the Milwaukee area formed to improve public input and act as an idea incubator for public engagement. In addition, a technical team developed a Fish and Wildlife Habitat Plan that identifies a broad range of restoration projects. Each technical team member brings unique expertise to the table for an ecosystem-based, multi-pronged approach.

An important component of the Milwaukee AOC project is an education, information and outreach campaign led by the SIG. The campaign will increase public involvement through interpretive signage, live video of underwater habitats, canoe and kayak expeditions, workshops and cleanup events. The SIG approach embodies Milwaukee's commitment to community engagement.

Smaller—but no less important—projects are at work at AOC's along Wisconsin's coasts. For instance, high school students in the Lower Fox-Green Bay AOC are serving as citizen scientists by creating videos that illustrate the complexities of the river system. Similarly, students in Sheboygan are gaining hands-on experience by assessing the health of the river ecosystem as they monitor a variety of water parameters alongside experts and their teachers at Camp Y-Koda.

Milwaukee's River Ambassadors—citizens versed in the history of the city and local restoration projects—are volunteers who educate citizens and visitors along the Riverwalk about interesting river characteristics. It is not uncommon to engage an Ambassador on a bustling summer evening about floating islands that provide resting places for migrating fish.

In Sheboygan, families volunteer to cut invasive brush, pick up litter and monitor frog and toad populations in wetlands. Birders along both the Sheboygan and Menominee Rivers enter their observations into the Cornell Lab of Ornithology's eBird web-based database.

No matter the scope of the effort, it is important that citizen voices are included in the process of cleaning Wisconsin's Areas of Concern. All who love our Great Lakes region—its woods, lakes, rivers and prairies—should feel welcome to participate in the care and preservation of our precious waters and lands.

In 2013, Gail Epping Overholt was a Natural Resources Educator at the University of Wisconsin-Extension.

Ozaukee County Fish Passage Program

Andrew Struck and Matt Aho

Fish and other aquatic life require access to various habitats as well as Lake Michigan to reproduce, grow, feed and survive. In a productive ecological system, fish and aquatic life can move freely up and down rivers and streams from Lake Michigan to wetlands and floodplains to fulfill critical life cycle needs. This freedom of movement is critically important on watersheds connected to Wisconsin's Great Lakes.

For instance, native northern pike are weak swimmers and jumpers and very susceptible to impediments. They can only jump eight inches, have difficulty with velocities greater than two feet per second and require frequent rest areas when traveling through streams. Passage for adults moving upstream and young-of-the-year moving downstream are equally crucial.

In 2006, the Ozaukee County Planning and Parks Department received Wisconsin Coastal Management Program (WCMP) funding to identify high quality habitats and aquatic life passage impediments on eleven major tributaries to the Milwaukee River and Lake Michigan. This initial inventory was the impetus for a $5.2 million National Oceanic and Atmospheric Administration (NOAA) grant in 2009 to establish a countywide Ozaukee Fish Passage Program (Program). The Department has since leveraged an additional $3.5 million of federal, state, local and private grants to further develop and implement the Program.

Many native species spend much of their adult lives in Lake Michigan, but migrate many miles to spawn in high quality riparian habitats in the upper Milwaukee River watershed. The watershed downstream of Ozaukee County is highly urbanized and little of the formerly-abundant wetland and riparian habitat remains in its natural state. In-stream habitat has also been significantly altered in many locations for navigation and development. Therefore, the lower river and estuary have experienced reduced native species abundance and diversity.

In contrast, the upper watershed in Ozaukee County has significant areas of relatively high quality native species' spawning habitat. Until recently, access to these areas was fragmented by large dams and other impediments. Since many freshwater fish move long distances for life-cycle functions, these areas can provide habitat suitable for spawning and juvenile development if hydrologically connected.

The Program addresses impediments that fragment aquatic connectivity and inhibit access to these high quality habitats. Impediments include dams, improperly placed or sized culverts, invasive vegetation, log and debris jams, pervious fill deposits, and straightened, incised and disconnected stream channels.

To date, the Program has removed or remediated 195 impediments to fish and aquatic life passage on the mainstem Milwaukee River and 30 tributary streams reconnecting over 100 stream miles to hundreds of acres of wetlands and floodplain for spawning habitat.

Major projects include construction of a nature-like fishway at the Mequon-Thiensville Dam, designing a fishway for the Grafton Bridge Street Dam, and the Lime Kiln Dam and Newburg Dam removals. In addition, the Program has remediated 45 large road/stream crossing impediments and removed 144 small-scale impediments.

The Program has also produced economic benefits for the County. The Department has invested in failing local transportation infrastructure without significant local tax investment, created jobs by generating over 62,000 paid labor hours—including job training opportunities to at-risk inner city youth, provided over 3,000 volunteer hours to 300 individual volunteers, and supported education and outreach to over 7,800 individuals.

In 2010, the Department received additional WCMP funding to improve conservation planning for coastal fish and wildlife resources by developing a Fish and Wildlife GIS-based Decision Support Tool. The tool identifies target species for conservation focus and critical habitats important to ensure their survival. Planners and decision makers use the tool to prioritize areas where limited conservation dollars may produce the maximum benefits for habitat restoration and improvement projects.

Preliminary tool outputs are guiding multiple large scale habitat improvement and restoration projects including a pilot wetland restoration on Sandhill Creek to improve lateral hydrologic connectivity to the flood-plain. Two other large scale projects with multiple partners will address stream re-meandering, restoration of hydrologically and biologically functional floodplains, bank and in-stream structure restoration and wetland enhancements on one mile of both Mole Creek and Ulao Creek.

The Program has also implemented comprehensive environmental monitoring to document baseline and trend data and gauge environmental response to impediment removals and habitat improvement projects. The Program monitors fisheries—including mainstem and tributary waterways—through electro-fishing, tributary larval fish trapping, tagging and tracking of fish, and an underwater camera located in the nature-like fishway at the Mequon-Thiensville dam. The camera has documented the passage of 36 fish species and six wildlife species including the rare softshell turtle. A live streaming video of the fishway is available online at www.ozaukeefishway.org.

Larval fish trapping has documented the rare Iowa darter and the least darter, a species of concern in Wisconsin. Additional environmental monitoring includes continuous and discrete water quality sampling and sediment contaminant characterization sampling to better understand the ecological health of local rivers and streams.

Through the support of the WCMP, NOAA and numerous federal, state, local and private partners, the Ozaukee County Planning and Parks Department's Fish Passage Program has significantly improved the ecological function and productivity of the region's natural resources by making connections across our watersheds.

In 2013, Andrew Struck was the Director of the Ozaukee County Planning and Parks Department. Matt Aho was the Program Manager for the Department's Ozaukee Fish Passage Program.

Two Rivers Plans for the Future

Peter Herreid

As waves tumble onto shore before the picture windows of the Water's Edge Restaurant, it is not uncommon to hear Italian, German or other European languages drift over from a neighboring table. Travelers from as far away as the land of Gutenberg are frequently attracted to the City of Two Rivers to see rare pieces of wood type at the Hamilton Museum.

Another European draw—particularly among immigrants from Eastern Europe—is Carp Fest, the City's annual carp fishing tournament. Carp is a popular sport fish in Europe and anyone who has accidentally hooked one while fishing for a game fish understands the thrill of landing a large specimen. The East and West Twin Rivers converging downtown are excellent carp habitat and give the City one of its nicknames, Carptown.

The City's other, more appealing nickname to marketers—the Cool City—is also rooted in its geographical position on a node of land jutting out several miles into Lake Michigan. This feature produces a cooling lake effect in the summer that makes Two Rivers the coolest spot in Wisconsin. That is not a bad reputation to have following Wisconsin's record heat in 2012! Neshotah Beach, the Kites over Lake Michigan Festival, Point Beach State Forest and other nearby natural amenities draw visitors to Two Rivers during the summer months as well.

Despite all of these natural and cultural advantages, the City's once vibrant manufacturing base is shrinking and its population declining. The closure of the Thermo Fischer Plant and the Kewaunee Power Station are recent contributors to job losses. But while the City may be transitioning from its industrial past, it is working toward a future with new plans to drive economic growth.

The *City of Two Rivers 20-Year Comprehensive Plan* provides the sort of predictability sought by investors because it states the City's intentions for future development and guides its land use decisions. Adopted in 2010, the Comprehensive Plan's recommendations have rung through subsequent planning efforts and discussions at city hall.

City staff point to poster-size maps displaying smart growth areas identified as opportunities for redevelopment. The City welcomes new strategies for lands where factories once produced wood type and other goods, where commercial fleets brought back hulls full of fish, and where coal was once offloaded and stockpiled. As recommended by the Comprehensive Plan, the City recently adopted a detailed bicycle and pedestrian plan and harbor plan as additional strategies for economic development.

The *Harbor Master Plan*—developed with a 2011 Wisconsin Coastal Management Program (WCMP) grant—identifies engineering alternatives to calm the waters within the harbor and other ways to make the harbor more welcoming to visiting boaters. A 2012 WCMP grant funded a design plan to repair failing seawalls and add more transient docking within the harbor. Furthermore, the Harbor Master Plan prioritizes public projects that could serve as catalysts for private redevelopment in the harbor area, such as city-owned shoreland with a trail connection from the South Pier to the Mariners Trail.

The *Mariners Trail* runs six miles along the lakefront between Two Rivers and Manitowoc and has the longest continuous view of Lake Michigan in Wisconsin. Since completed in 2002, the trail has been wildly popular for strolling, bicycling, dog-walking and in-line skating. Much credit for the success of the Mariners Trail goes to an active friends group that beautifies the trail with artwork, gardens and landscaping. The Friends of Mariners Trail has also advocated for trail upgrades and organized supporting infrastructure such as benches, bike racks and a bike repair stand.

While the Mariners Trail leads into downtown Two Rivers from the south, the Rawley Point Trail leads north through the Point Beach State Forest to the Rawley Point Lighthouse. The City touts both recreational trails as among its most attractive assets for economic development.

The ambitious *City of Two Rivers Bicycle and Pedestrian Plan*, adopted in May 2013, identifies specific ways in which to build upon the popularity of the Mariners and Rawley Point trails. The plan recommends incremental measures to improve the link between the trails with a long-term vision to build shared-use paths running along the waterfront downtown. The 17th St. Bridge—a key connection between the trails—has already been reconstructed with an expanded sidewalk and bike lanes, the first on-street bike facilities in Two Rivers.

Funding has been secured for the construction of trails to the high school and site planning is underway. The Bicycle and Pedestrian Plan contends that by continuing the construction of more off-street shared use paths and making streets and intersections more bike and pedestrian friendly, Two Rivers could define itself as one of the most livable communities along the lake—an affordable town where it is easy and convenient to walk or bike to parks, beaches, schools, stores and other daily destinations.

Two Rivers is mindful of the natural and community assets that improve the quality of life for its citizens and visitors. Nurturing these resources will help retain and attract the entrepreneurial talent and educated workforce needed to drive Two Rivers' economic transformation.

In 2013, Peter Herreid was the Grant Administrator for the Wisconsin Land Information Program and the Comprehensive Planning Grant Program. He prepared the City of Two Rivers Bicycle and Pedestrian Plan under the direction of the City's Bicycle Committee.

2014

Foreword

Governor Scott Walker

Dear Friends of the Great Lakes,

Wisconsin's coastal communities have responded to their unique Great Lakes location with innovative initiatives. Residents benefit from cleaner beaches, better lake access, and increased commercial and tourism activity. Many communities have received special recognition for their forward-looking coastal projects.

The National Association of Counties recognized Ozaukee County with an Achievement Award for its Fish Passage in the Milwaukee River Watershed Program. Since 2007, the program has removed over 233 barriers to fish movement, reconnected 129 stream miles, increased fish reproduction, improved water quality and increased countywide tourism. The program received over $8.4 million in grants with most going into the local economy through contracts.

The Gikinoo'wizhiwe Onji Waaban (Guiding for Tomorrow) Changing Climate, Changing Culture Initiative (G-WOW) received the prestigious 2011–2012 Eastern Region Honor Award from the US Forest Service for "Courageous Conservation." The project developed school curriculum and a 200-square-foot interactive exhibit at the Northern Great Lakes Visitor Center near Ashland. It is at the forefront of indigenous education on climate change and cultural life. Funding partners include the Great Lakes Restoration Initiative and the Wisconsin Coastal Management Program (WCMP).

American City and County magazine recognized Port Washington's Coal Dock Park with a 2013 Crown Communities Award, a national honor based on uniqueness, short- and long-term community value and innovative financing. The park was planned and designed utilizing a 2007–08 WCMP Grant. In 2002, seventeen acres on Lake Michigan previously used for coal storage became available due to We Energies' move to gas power. The City partnered with We Energies, the Wisconsin Board of Commissioners of Public Lands, the Wisconsin Department of Natural Resources, the US

Army Corps of Engineers and the US Fish and Wildlife Service to bring residents their newest public access to Lake Michigan. A 1,500-foot promenade and 80-foot pedestrian bridge link four parks, the marina, downtown and North Beach.

Milwaukee's Menomonee Valley is a national model of economic and environmental sustainability, recognized by the Sierra Club as "One of the 10 Best Developments in the Nation," and the American Society of Landscape Architects for urban land restoration. In the past ten years, results include 39 companies moving to the Valley, 5,200 jobs, 45 acres of native plants, seven miles of trails and a nationally recognized shared stormwater treatment system. Annually, ten million people visit the Valley's recreation and entertainment destinations which include the Harley Davidson Museum, Miller Park and the Hank Aaron State Trail. More than 250 organizations and 450 individuals have served on boards, committees and working teams. Thousands more have volunteered.

Wisconsin has fourteen commercial ports situated on the commercially navigable Mississippi River and Great Lakes-St. Lawrence Seaway, giving Wisconsin access to international markets. The ports provide a transportation alternative that many states cannot offer their manufacturers and suppliers. The first phase of the Wisconsin Commercial Ports Master Plan is underway and includes a comprehensive background and status inventory of Wisconsin Great Lakes ports. The planning process is examining port interaction with other freight movement forms and will recommend transportation system changes for long-term, efficient materials movement through the state.

Enjoy this year's *Wisconsin Great Lakes Chronicle* highlighting successful projects and current issues on our coasts.

Scott Walker was elected Wisconsin's 45th Governor in 2010.

Apostle Islands Ice Caves Go Viral

Bob Krumenaker and Neil Howk

The mainland sea caves of northern Wisconsin's Apostle Islands National Lakeshore are the park's most popular summer kayaking destination. Most of the year, the National Park Service (NPS) refers to these formations as the sea caves, but in early winter they transform into the ice caves.

The ice caves form when spray from crashing waves freezes to the rock cliffs just above the surface of Lake Superior. In addition, groundwater seeps and flowing water from the land surface above the caves freeze on the cave walls and ceilings creating formations that look similar to those found in underground limestone caves. The ice formations build over the course of weeks, change rapidly and disappear in spring as quickly as they form.

While other ice caves exist, there may be no better place on the planet where these remarkable structures are so variable, so protected and often so accessible.

Access to the caves depends on whether this portion of western Lake Superior freezes. Solid ice is influenced by more than low temperatures—this part of the lake is vulnerable to big winds and waves which can break up ice quickly. NPS staff monitor ice conditions and require that the ice pack be stable and at least eight inches thick for two weeks before the ice is deemed low risk.

The webcam (wavesatseacaves.cee.wisc.edu) from the park's Real-Time Wave Observation System—developed in cooperation with the University of Wisconsin-Madison, University of Wisconsin Sea Grant, the Wisconsin Coastal Management Program and the Friends of the Apostle Islands—is vital to monitoring ice conditions. However, there is no substitute for the skill and local knowledge of park rangers who measure ice thickness directly.

The deep cold of the winter of 2013–14 arrived in December and intensified in January. The first ice started forming on the lake near the caves early in the calendar year and soon was more than a foot thick. The NPS announced the caves were open on January 15, at least a month earlier than usual.

Park staff anticipated visitation similar to previous *good ice years*—up to 12,000 people over a six-week period. However, each of the first weekend days the caves were open saw the largest daily crowds the park had ever seen—winter or summer.

The ice formations were spectacular as a result of the deep, deep cold. Thousands of people ventured out despite extraordinarily cold conditions. In the first several weeks, steady winds from the west and southwest combined with single digit—or lower—temperatures to create wind chills in the minus 25 to minus 35 degree range on most days. It was brutal! Yet the people kept coming.

In just two months, more than 138,000 intrepid people made their way north to experience the ice caves for themselves. In 2013, the 21-island, 69,000-acre national park counted 150,000 visitors for the entire year!

The 2014 ice cave visitors hiked five miles or more across the frozen lake during some of the coldest days of the year. Some referred to their journey as a *pilgrimage*. This unprecedented popularity speaks to our basic need for a connection to nature and demonstrates a hunger to experience beauty in the world.

There are numerous reasons why the ice cave story went viral. Five years of pent up desire to see the caves had many people adding them to their bucket list. The last time the lake was sufficiently frozen to permit walking over the ice to the mainland caves was 2009. A study of satellite images from 1973 to 2010 showed that ice cover on Lake Superior decreased 79% during that period. A string of relatively mild winters from 2010–2013 featured very little ice cover on the lake. That changed this year with the arrival of the polar vortex.

Word of the caves spread fast. Local media attention was quickly replaced by national coverage. ABC World News, National Public Radio, the CBS Evening News and NBC Nightly News sent crews to produce stories which aired nationally in prime time. *The Wall Street Journal* published a story.

The caves even went international—Australia's 7 Network aired stories on the most watched television news show Down Under. *The London Daily Mail* covered it, as did countless other media outlets across the globe. Al Jazeera even sent a television crew.

Social media also played a huge role in spreading the story. Ice cave visitors shared their pictures and experiences with friends. Postings and photos on the park's Facebook page received three to five times more views than the average posting before the ice caves opened.

Impacts of the 2014 ice cave season may be long lasting. The Bayfield Chamber of Commerce and Visitor Bureau (bayfield.org) estimated that the regional economy received a $10–12 million boost from the increased winter traffic. Many ice cave visitors noted their desire to return to the park and Bayfield area during the summer season to experience the beauty of Lake Superior and the Apostle Islands when the water is blue and the trees are green.

The NPS looks forward to helping visitors enhance their intellectual and emotional connections with the national lakeshore on a return pilgrimage.

In 2014, Bob Krumenaker was the Superintendent and Neil Howk was the Assistant Chief of Interpretation and Education with the National Park Service at the Apostle Islands National Lakeshore in Bayfield.

CRUMBLING COASTAL INFRASTRUCTURE: WHAT CAN BE DONE?

Gene Clark, PE

America's failing roads and bridges are receiving attention by legislators and citizens. However, many of the structures that protect Wisconsin's Great Lakes coastal communities, ports and harbors from storm, wave and ice damage are also aging and failing. Lawmakers and the public may want to pay attention since these structures support recreation, commerce and livelihood along Wisconsin's coasts.

Many harbor outer breakwater structures constructed by the US Army Corps of Engineers near the turn of the century were built with either timber crib or timber piling foundations and then capped with rock or massive concrete covers. Maintenance of these structures has lagged behind demand and many are now in poor condition. The Corps can only provide maintenance assistance to the largest Wisconsin commercial ports and harbors, leaving smaller recreational and commercial harbors to seek maintenance or structure replacement funding elsewhere.

Recent near-record-low Great Lakes water levels have increased damage—especially in timber structures—and allow us to see the damage more easily. Failure of these structures would be catastrophic for the valuable coastal communities they protect. This damage to timber structures is not due to wood borers like those in marine harbors because no freshwater wood borers exist. Preserved underwater, timber cribs can last indefinitely. However, when exposed to air, the timber will begin to rot and/or abrade due to ice or impacts from ships.

Recent failures of Wisconsin's Great Lakes timber structures appear to be at or slightly above the long-term water level mark. Failing timber cribs have been observed at many of Wisconsin's older ports and harbors as the timber core sections begin to decay and slump, bringing the superstructure down with them. Several of Wisconsin's Great Lakes harbors have experienced complete failure of the structures due to deteriorating timbers.

The City of Washburn recently rebuilt 575 feet of its failing outer harbor timber bulkhead wall. The project cost approximately $735,000 and was funded with grants from the Wisconsin Department of Commerce, the Wisconsin Department of Natural Resources and other sources.

Other outer harbor entrance structures and many vertical slip dock walls have been constructed with steel sheet pilings. The outer breakwater sections are often built as steel circular cells, while inner walls are straight steel bulkhead designs. Steel has also been used to cover failing timber structures.

On Lake Superior, accelerated freshwater corrosion is causing deep pits on or complete perforations through steel structures. This new phenomenon—rarely seen elsewhere—is compromising the structural integrity of steel wall in many harbors and marinas on the lake. Recent studies have shown that accelerated corrosion is not the result of stray electrical currents, the age or type of steel used or water quality issues. The studies have identified microbes as at least one factor.

To combat this problem, several million dollars have already been spent on many unstable steel structures in the City of Superior harbor. These structures were either coated with corrosion-resistant paint—by use of specially made cofferdams to de-water the region in front of the damaged steel, clean it and then coat it in dry conditions—or completely replaced with new, coated steel sheet pilings.

Corrosion has also been observed on steel pipes and H-pilings. Steel pins are used to keep timber crib structures intact and they have failed as well. Researchers continue to investigate both the cause of this unusual phenomenon and how best to rehabilitate and repair damaged structures. The Wisconsin Coastal Management Program has funded a study to determine successful methods for protecting steel pipes and H-pilings from freshwater corrosion damage.

Many other coastal structures in Wisconsin use rock or concrete for foundations, scour protection or large breakwaters. Depending on their quality—which typically deteriorate with age—rock and concrete structures can also fail. Soft rock or rock with seams or cracks can break apart. Concrete walls can crack due to settlement or poor quality. When this happens, action by waves, ice or floods can easily displace the structure.

The outer breakwater concrete cap at Port Washington has been failing and recently received $950,000 of federal funds to repair 990 feet of the concrete cap which has crumbled and is no longer safe for walking or fishing. Many other breakwaters are experiencing similar problems. Quality control at the source—at the rock quarry or concrete plant—is of utmost importance to obtain rock and concrete suitable for Great Lakes use. For aging concrete, maintenance is the key.

Much more state and national attention is needed to assist the many smaller Wisconsin commercial and recreational harbors with failing coastal infrastructure problems. Our coastal community economy depends upon them!

In 2014, Gene Clark, PE, was a Coastal Engineering Specialist at the University of Wisconsin Sea Grant Institute.

Lake Superior National Estuarine Research Reserve Starts Strong

Becky Sapper

Lake Superior's freshwater estuaries are both nursery and kitchen for diverse populations of aquatic plants, fish, wildlife and waterfowl that rely on them for shelter, food and spawning. Estuaries also benefit people by slowing runoff and acting as filters to reduce erosion and sedimentation and by providing places for hunting, fishing, recreation and tourism activities. In the case of the St. Louis River, estuaries can also be working ports. Lake Superior's freshwater estuaries and coastal wetlands are an important part of what defines the quality of life in the Lake Superior basin.

These realities were the motivation behind designating the St. Louis River Freshwater Estuary as a National Estuarine Research Reserve (NERR) in October 2010. The Lake Superior NERR is the second reserve in the Great Lakes and the 28th in a national network administered by the National Oceanic and Atmospheric Administration (NOAA). The NERR program is a non-regulatory federal and state partnership which provides federal funding and technical support to advance estuary research, education and stewardship. Wisconsin's lead state agency is the University of Wisconsin-Extension (UWEX), which works closely with the University of Wisconsin-Superior (UWS).

The Wisconsin Coastal Management Program (WCMP) has long supported the designation of a Lake Superior NERR. This began with a 2002 grant to UWEX for an initial feasibility study and continued through participation on a multi-agency partnership for the site selection process resulting in the designation of the St. Louis River. WCMP is an active member of the Reserve Advisory Board along with the City of Superior, Douglas County, Fond du Lac Band of Lake Superior Chippewa, UWS, University of Wisconsin Sea Grant Institute and the Wisconsin Department of Natural Resources.

The Lake Superior NERR's mission is to work in partnership to improve the understanding of Lake Superior freshwater estuaries and coastal resources and address issues affecting them through an integrated program of research, education, outreach and stewardship. The Reserve is comprised exclusively of public lands and waters and contains over 16,000 acres of habitat along the St. Louis River freshwater estuary and Lake Superior.

In the four years since its designation, the Lake Superior NERR has realized many accomplishments. Eight new positions were created for oversight, education, monitoring and research. In addition, over a dozen UWS students have engaged in meaningful NERR experiences, as have several community volunteers.

The Reserve received $5.8 million in new resources focused on its mission along with an additional $600,000 in new funds for further research, education and outreach. An example of this additional funding is a Science Collaborative project—funded by a NOAA grant—which brings local stakeholders and scientists together to develop a process for incorporating wetland science, watershed planning and geospatial tools into decision-making.

UWS acquired two buildings on Barkers Island in Superior to house the Lake Superior NERR. An office and laboratory opened in February 2014 that house NERR and UW Sea Grant partners. The laboratory is adding new equipment to make it a fully operational and certified lab. More renovations will create a public Learning Center, classroom and meeting space. In the meantime, temporary exhibits on loan through Great Lakes partners provide interactive opportunities for the NERR's visitors.

Rivers2Lake is the foundational K-12 education program at the Lake Superior NERR and provides extended training, mentoring and resources to teachers throughout the school year. This program supports the creation of interdisciplinary inquiry-based and outdoor experiences for students based on the St. Louis River and the Lake Superior watershed. Through Rivers2Lake, Lake Superior NERR has provided more than 800 contact hours of professional development for K-12 teachers and conducted more than 6,000 student contact hours.

The NERR System Wide Monitoring Program—located at each of the 28 Reserves—provides researchers, resource managers, educators and other coastal decision makers with standardized, quantitative measures to determine how Reserve conditions are changing in both the short-term and the long-term. The Lake Superior NERR water quality monitoring program collects data at fifteen minute intervals with live data links accessible to the community and researchers nation-wide. In addition to this core program, the Lake Superior NERR was selected as one of six national Sentinel Site locations adding to a national network of long-term sites measuring the effects of climate change on estuaries.

The 4th annual St. Louis River Estuary Summit succeeded in bringing the community, students, scientists, industry and natural resource managers together to share information about the St. Louis River estuary. The 2014 Summit was attended by over 200 people and with talks focused on social science, or how people relate to and interact with the environment.

In just four short years, the Lake Superior NERR is well on its way to providing expected benefits to the Twin Ports region and all of Lake Superior. The Lake Superior NERR makes Superior home to an internationally important research program with unique education opportunities and continued focus on a freshwater estuary that is a source of community pride and activity. To learn more, visit the Lake Superior NERR on Facebook and its website at lsnerr.uwex.edu.

In 2014, Becky Sapper was the Assistant Reserve Manager at the Lake Superior National Estuarine Research Reserve.

OAK CREEK REDEVELOPMENT

Mayor Steve Scaffidi

The City of Oak Creek's Lake Michigan waterfront had long been a place that commerce and opportunity call home. For almost a century, this area—eight miles south of downtown Milwaukee—hosted a range of industrial uses that drove the local economy and created a thriving community of factory workers, business owners and their families. Carrollville—the small company town near the waterfront—had been a vibrant neighborhood for nearly 60 years by the time Oak Creek was incorporated in 1955. It was a place that drew immigrants from all over the world to work and start a family by offering stable jobs and a strong community.

For 80 years, the heavy industry located along the Oak Creek lakefront brought prosperity to the region. However, those gated and intense industrial uses stood between the heart of our Oak Creek community and Lake Michigan. For the residents who did not work in industry, Oak Creek's Lake Michigan shoreline was just out of reach and completely inaccessible. With the loss of manufacturing jobs throughout the country in the 1980s and 1990s, Oak Creek's once bustling industrial waterfront was slowly abandoned, leaving the land polluted and unusable.

Yet this was only the beginning of a new chapter in the City's story. From the ruins of the abandoned factories arose a new interest in opening up the Oak Creek lakefront for the enjoyment of the entire community.

Oak Creek—now a city of 35,000—suddenly found itself with the largest section of undeveloped waterfront in southeast Wisconsin. Our residents and leaders understood we had a rare opportunity to completely transform the character of our community while reviving the jobs center and neighborhood that had thrived in decades past.

To jumpstart the redevelopment process, the City in 2009 invited a panel from the Urban Land Institute (ULI) to forge a vision for reconnecting the community with the lakefront through mixed-use development and a network of coastal open spaces. Two years later—with financial assistance from the Wisconsin Coastal Management Program—the City prepared the Lakefront Redevelopment Action Plan. This expanded the

ULI panel's vision and developed more detailed plans for public gathering spaces, ecological restoration areas and tax-generating redevelopment. The action plan identifies durable funding and partnership strategies as well as catalytic priorities that will keep our lakefront redevelopment effort—now called Lake Vista—moving forward.

Bolstered by the support of the Oak Creek community, the City quickly got to work. We leveraged federal and state grant monies and local tax dollars to acquire abandoned properties, demolish the remaining structures, and clean up and cap the site to provide safe access once again.

We are undertaking major infrastructure improvements that will set the stage for the transformation of our section of Lake Michigan. In 2016, the City will start construction on an extension of Highway 100 to serve as the southern gateway into Lake Vista. New internal trails and roads are scheduled for construction in 2015—they will allow for safe and unhindered bicycle and pedestrian access along the bluff top edge, connecting to the recreational and environmental amenities in Milwaukee County's Bender Park to the south. New recreational fields and scenic overlooks will be Oak Creek's first city gathering spaces that feature views of our great lake. Upon completion, residents and visitors will have access to this section of our city's lakefront for the first time in over 80 years.

Oak Creek is also leveraging the scale and timing of this transformative redevelopment to create a comprehensive green infrastructure system throughout the Lake Vista area. Stabilization and environmental remediation of the bluffs will restore land- and water-based native ecological communities and significantly improve the quality of water entering Lake Michigan from the site. On top of the bluff, a network of sustainable stormwater treatment areas will filter pollutants and extend restored native landscape into the redevelopment areas.

Land adjacent to these new public open spaces will eventually be redeveloped as residential, retail, office and light industrial areas. WISPARK—a real estate development company and trusted partner for cities throughout southeast Wisconsin—plans to build a business park in Lake Vista that could house water-based research and businesses. The adjacent Milwaukee Metropolitan Sewer District treatment plant—once seen as a liability—offers a uniquely sustainable opportunity to reuse hot water discharged from the plant to heat new buildings.

Our Oak Creek lakefront—which for so long was inaccessible and underutilized—has now become an incredible opportunity for community access to the lakefront, as well as a catalyst for economic revitalization of the area. With its revitalizing focus on active recreation, ecological restoration and bluff resiliency—along with the redevelopment of the former brownfield areas—Lake Vista will play a dynamic role in forging new jobs and new neighborhood connections.

In 2014, Steve Scaffidi was Mayor of the City of Oak Creek.

G-WOW Changing Climate, Changing Culture, Changing Coasts

Cathy Techtmann

Unprecedented cancellations of the Bad River tribal wild rice harvest. A trend of diminishing ice cover at Bayfield harbor. Greater frequency of storm and flooding events. Place-based evidence is building that climate change is affecting Lake Superior coastal communities, resources and economies.

For federal agencies like the Chequamegon-Nicolet National Forest and the Apostle Islands National Lakeshore, these changes have created new management issues. The Great Lakes Indian Fish and Wildlife Commission viewed climate change as a threat to Ojibwe treaty rights. The University of Wisconsin-Extension (UWEX) realized that traditional science-only climate change education models were not resonating with audiences. A new approach was needed to engage people on this issue.

These state, federal and tribal agencies partnered to develop the *Gikinoo'wizhiwe Onji Waaban* (Guiding for Tomorrow) Changing Climate, Changing Culture Initiative, nicknamed G-WOW. The result is a new model for climate change educational that links culture with science and prompts action to mitigate its impacts.

G-WOW is the first climate literacy model that links culture and science. It is based on understanding how sustainability of key species that support cultural and economic practices important to coastal communities will be affected by climate change.

For generations, the Lake Superior Ojibwe have relied on the sustainability of coastal species—such as fish and wild rice—to support subsistence, cultural and spiritual lifeways. Their long relationship with these natural systems offers culturally relevant place-based insight into how the region's climate is changing.

The G-WOW model integrates place-based evidence of how climate change is affecting traditional Ojibwe lifeways with scientific climate research to provide an indicator of how climate change is affecting people of all cultures.

For example, *manoomin* or wild rice is the key species supporting the Ojibwe lifeway of aquatic harvesting. The sustainability of wild rice depends on shallow water habitats. Since 2007, the unprecedented loss of wild rice due to flooding, high temperatures, drought and disease has disrupted the traditional tribal harvest. This provides culturally relevant, place-based evidence that climate change may be affecting habitat conditions this species needs to survive.

The strategy of using the sustainability of key species to link culture and science makes the G-WOW model transferable to other cultures and locations. Because a key component of G-WOW is engaging people to fight climate change with change, the model includes a service learning component to develop a project or activity to mitigate climate change.

With funding support from the Great Lakes Restoration Initiative and the Wisconsin Coastal Management Program (WCMP), the G-WOW Changing Climate, Changing Culture Discovery Center was developed at the Northern Great Lakes Visitor Center (NGLVC) in Ashland in 2010. This 200 sq. ft. interpretive exhibit explores the impacts of climate change on Ojibwe wild rice harvesting and other coastal resources based on the G-WOW model. The exhibit's authentic birch bark canoe and Ojibwe word sound board offer unique cultural components.

In 2013, WCMP funding completed the G-WOW Discovery Center with the addition of a 32-inch touch screen kiosk featuring the four season G-WOW curriculum in a condensed, interactive format. Approximately 33,000 visitors, community members, and students view the G-WOW Discovery Center annually. It is the focal point for school and teacher education climate change programs.

With WCMP support, the full G-WOW curriculum for middle school to adult learners was created and went live on the G-WOW website (g-wow. org) in 2013. This robust web based curriculum features four seasonal units that explore climate change impacts on Ojibwe lifeways, including maple sugaring, birch bark harvesting, fishing, wild ricing and respecting culture. Learners can test their own climate change hypothesis, create a service learning climate change activity, and share their results via the website's "talking circle" blog.

In 2014, WCMP funding supported a four-day summer G-WOW professional development institute for teachers and community educators with the goal of building capacity to teach about climate change using the G-WOW model. As part of their training, teachers will engage their students in a climate service project, post it to the G-WOW website and participate in a Coastal Climate Camp with the students during the school year. Portions of the institute will be videotaped to create a virtual teacher training resource on the G-WOW website to maximize professional development opportunities.

The G-WOW Initiative is gaining recognition beyond our region. In 2012, the G-WOW team was presented with an Honor Award by the Eastern Region of the US Forest Service. In 2013, the G-WOW curriculum was incorporated into climate change kiosks at the Aldo Leopold Nature Center in Monona, Wisconsin. This year, the Fond du Lac Tribal and Community College in Duluth received a $1.09 million NASA Innovations in Climate Change-Tribal grant that uses the G-WOW model to increase climate literacy through the Ojibwe Ceded Territories of Minnesota, Wisconsin and Michigan.

Do culture and science agree that climate change is affecting the sustainability of Lake Superior coastal resources? You be the judge!

In 2014, Cathy Techtmann was an Environmental Outreach State Specialist at the University of Wisconsin-Extension and a member of the G-WOW Team.

Egg Harbor Beach and Marina Improvements

Josh Van Lieshout

For many years, the Village of Egg Harbor on the west shore of Door County operated a small and underused beach. In 2005, Door County Soil and Water—in partnership with the Wisconsin Coastal Management Program and others—began a comprehensive study to better understand environmental issues that had caused several beach closures on the Door Peninsula. Closures had created some significant press and local concern because much of the northern Door County economy is tied to tourism, and the use and enjoyment of natural resources—including the bay of Green Bay and public beaches—is a critical component of the economy.

About this same time, the Village of Egg Harbor was trying to determine what to do with a failing breakwater at its public marina and boat launch. The marina and boat launch had originally been constructed as a commercial dock for transport and fishing before the turn of century. Through the years, the dock was expanded, rebuilt and upland improvements were added and expanded. As time and weather took their toll, the community determined that the marina facility needed to be reconstructed and made to last another century.

At the time marina issues were beginning to be defined, the Egg Harbor Village Trustees made a commitment to look at the project through the lenses of environmental quality and public access. Given our proximity to the bay of Green Bay and our economic dependence, water quality was of paramount importance.

As the marina site plan began to take hold, the Harbor Committee and engineer realized that with some smart design, we could increase the available parking space, reduce the amount of impervious area and provide parking lot storm water runoff filtration. Placing a biofilter at the end of a parking lot that juts out into the bay may seem like a waste of real estate and money. However, this improvement provided much needed storm water treatment and green space, and softened an otherwise unattractive fuel and pump station area.

At the Egg Harbor Beach, the Village stepped up to be one of the first communities to implement the recommendations of Door County Soil and Water studies. The recommendations included grading, construction of storm water basins and re-vegetation with native grasses. The project originally constructed in 2009 at a cost of $70,000 was an immediate success on all fronts. More people came to the beach, we had fewer to no instances of beach closures and nuisance birds found another place to gather.

With success comes other opportunities. Parking was a major shortcoming at the beach—it was impossible to find a place to park after 10:00 a.m. The success of the first beach improvement project made it palatable to the public to add parking spaces on this property.

Using Great Lakes Restoration Initiative funding, the Village embarked on a new plan to double the available parking spots. Keeping our water quality concerns in mind, the Village used a type of paver brick to pave the newly reconstructed parking stalls. For this work the Village received a Gold Award from the Wisconsin Masonry Alliance. Again, the response from the public was very favorable. Moreover, the Village continues to receive inquiries from other communities three years after completion of the parking lot project.

While a lot of people enjoy Egg Harbor and Door County, it is unlikely anyone comes just for the beach or marina. They come for the Door County experience of being outdoors, shopping, clean water, great boating and fishing, and access to one of the greatest bodies of water in the world. Having top notch facilities has enabled our business community in Egg Harbor to capture more of the Door County visitors and give them a quality, positive experience like no other place.

However, it isn't all about business. Egg Harbor has a very active and thriving summer community of property owners. As we discovered, as much as the business community and visitors benefit, so do residents because they too have more and better access to the bay. Their experience and quality of life in Egg Harbor is enhanced.

The additional benefit of investing in infrastructure focused on water quality and public access has allowed the community to gain other accolades and exposure, which reach well beyond the limits of Egg Harbor and

Door County. As well as being designated a Harbor of Refuge, the improvements at the marina made it possible for the facility to become certified through the Wisconsin Clean Marina Program. And recently, the marina received certification as a bronze level Water Star Community through Water Star Wisconsin. For these efforts, and many others, the Village of Egg Harbor has earned Travel Green Wisconsin certification through the Department of Tourism.

Investing public dollars in infrastructure is a challenge for appointed and elected officials because many worthy projects compete for limited funding. However, projects that enhance quality of life and business climate, provide for sustainability and improve environmental quality are universally good investments. The Egg Harbor Beach and Marina initiatives are such projects.

In 2014, Josh Van Lieshout was Administrator of the Village of Egg Harbor.

DIGITAL COAST

Rebecca Love and Jeff Stone

There are many places to download coastal data and information. So much that at times it can be mind-boggling just trying to find the data needed to address a particular issue.

Enter the Digital Coast. The Digital Coast website (csc.noaa.gov/digitalcoast) is a central place to find information, training and case studies to help turn data into useful information for those who manage the nation's coasts. Launched in 2008, the site provides information to address timely coastal issues, including land use, coastal conservation, hazards, ocean planning, community resilience and healthy coastal economies.

Less visible to users of the Digital Coast is the partnership effort behind the web platform. The Digital Coast partnership has built a strong collaboration of coastal professionals intent on addressing common needs.

The Digital Coast partnership includes the American Planning Association, Association of State Floodplain Managers (ASFPM), Coastal States Organization, National Association of Counties, National Estuarine Research Reserve Association, National States Geographic Information Council, The Nature Conservancy, and Urban Land Institute. The responsiveness of these organizations has proven essential for creating a platform that evolves and adapts to changing needs and priorities.

As a member of the Coastal States Organization, the Wisconsin Coastal Management Program (WCMP) has played an integral role representing the nation's state coastal management programs in the partnership. The WCMP has provided technical assistance and convened local organizations for collaborative projects in the Great Lakes. Over the past two years, coastal watersheds in Wisconsin have also benefited from the work of Laura Flessner, a NOAA Digital Coast Fellow working with the ASFPM and The Nature Conservancy.

The partnership—including the WCMP, the University of Wisconsin Sea Grant and the University of Wisconsin-Extension—worked together to develop the Great Lakes Coastal Resilience Planning Guide. Funded through EPA's Great Lakes Restoration Initiative, both NOAA's Coastal

Services Center and ASFPM played a leadership role in the Planning Guide's creation.

Through peer-reviewed case studies and local stories, the Coastal Resilience Planning Guide shows how coastal communities are using science based information to address coastal hazards such as flooding, shore erosion and lake-level fluctuations. The Planning Guide connects people with tools, data, publications and other stakeholders needed to consider natural hazards and climate change in local planning efforts.

For example, Brown County Zoning shared its challenge in helping property owners see how lake levels and coastal flooding could affect their homes. This became the first case study titled "Visualizing Coastal Flooding and Lake Level Changes." The case study describes the process of using a visualization tool—like CanVis—that can be used to see potential impacts from coastal development or changes in Great Lakes water levels resulting from storms or long-term fluctuations.

In Ozaukee County, a future case study will highlight bluff erosion processes and science-based methods for determining setback ordinances while supporting risk communication. And in Sheboygan County, a future case study will use analytical tools like NOAA's Nonpoint Source Pollution and Erosion Comparison Tool (OpenNSPECT) to prioritize wetland restoration. The case study will investigate potential water quality impacts and flood risk reduction strategies through wetland restoration in a sub-watershed of the Sheboygan River near Plymouth. This work connects agricultural and land-use decisions, conservation and future climate conditions.

The Land Cover Atlas is an easy-to-use web-based viewer for visualizing Coastal Change Analysis Program (C-CAP) regional land cover data and change information for the coastal United States over multiple dates. The tool summarizes general trends in land cover change—such as forest losses or new development—and can highlight specific changes such as marsh losses to open water, or evergreen forest losses to development. This type of information is useful in planning and preparing for Wisconsin's green infrastructure needs to mitigate the impacts of flooding and climate change. The Land Cover Atlas has recently been updated to include data for 2010 and the ability to view change information by watershed.

The Economics: National Ocean Watch (ENOW) data describe six economic sectors that depend on the Great Lakes and oceans including living resources, marine construction, marine transportation, offshore mineral resources, ship and boat building, and tourism and recreation. The ENOW Explorer allows users to view changes over time and from place to place. Users can discover which sectors are the largest contributors to coastal economies in various parts of Wisconsin, which are growing and declining, and which account for the most jobs, wages and gross domestic product. ENOW data are available for counties, states, regions and the nation and can be compared across geographies.

Coming soon, the Lake Level Viewer is a map-based tool that will help people visualize flooding and exposed land caused by variable water levels on the Great Lakes. The tool is scheduled for release later this fall and is a collaborative effort with Wisconsin Sea Grant, the University of Wisconsin-Madison and the NOAA Coastal Services Center.

The Digital Coast partnership is a growing collaboration. If you have suggestions, questions or examples of how you have applied a tool or resource within the Digital Coast, feel free to contact your state's coastal management program or a partnering member, or send us an email at digital.coast@noaa.gov.

In 2014, Rebecca Love was a Marine Scientist with the NOAA Coastal Services Center. Jeff Stone was a Senior Project Manager and GIS Coordinator with the Association of State Floodplain Managers.

2015

FOREWORD

Governor Scott Walker

Dear Friends of the Great Lakes,

Wisconsin Great Lakes Chronicle was created in 2002 to provide citizens and community leaders with insightful articles about economic, environmental and cultural issues impacting Wisconsin's Lake Michigan and Lake Superior coasts. I am pleased that the 2015 edition includes the 100th such article. Progress toward healthier, more vibrant coastal communities is demonstrated in several important areas.

Commerce. State agencies worked with the Wisconsin Commercial Ports Association to create the Wisconsin Commercial Ports Master Plan. This initiative—funded in part by the Wisconsin Coastal Management Program (WCMP)—outlines ways Wisconsin ports can promote domestic and international shipping based on recommendations of the Council of Great Lakes Governors' Great Lakes Maritime Task Force.

Coastal Tourism. WCMP has funded water trails that provide canoe and kayak access to our coastal waterways, such as those on Lake Superior tributaries and the Milwaukee River. These trails encourage active recreationalists to visit coastal communities and contribute to Wisconsin's tourism economy.

Working Together. The Wisconsin Harbor Towns Association (WHTA)—a non-profit organization representing Wisconsin Great Lakes towns—was formed in 2000 with assistance from WCMP and achieved sustainability in cooperation with the Department of Tourism. A recent WCMP grant funded the Wisconsin Harbor Towns Travel Guide available at wisconsin-harbortowns.net.

Promotion. WCMP has funded *Discover Wisconsin* television programs promoting Lake Michigan, Lake Superior, the Apostle Islands and Door County. WCMP worked with Discover Mediaworks, Inc., the Department of Tourism, WHTA and communities to educate viewers on the importance of Great Lakes resources, sustainable travel and premiere tourist destinations. Learn more at discoverwisconsin.com.

Safety. The Apostle Islands National Lakeshore sea caves are a popular—but often hazardous—place for visiting kayakers. Even when conditions appear calm from the shoreline, waves may be higher and more treacherous at the caves. WCMP funding helped create a Real Time Wave Observation System that allows visitors to review conditions before entering the sea caves. Current wave conditions are available online at wavesatseacaves.cee.wisc.edu.

Public Health. Wisconsin is restoring, enhancing and monitoring Great Lakes beaches to improve public health and provide recreational opportunities. WCMP, Great Lakes Restoration Initiative, Department of Natural Resources, Fund for Lake Michigan and communities are funding beach restoration projects at Egg Harbor, Sturgeon Bay, Ellison Bay, Milwaukee, Racine and Washburn.

Community Revitalization. The Menomonee River Valley was declared a brownfield in 1990, but a public-private partnership led efforts to clean up contamination and redevelop the valley with new businesses. Public places like Three Bridges Park and the Hank Aaron State Trail encourage people to bike, fish and kayak in this once neglected stretch of river. WCMP has helped fund this renaissance.

Government Collaboration. The City of Milwaukee, Milwaukee County and the State of Wisconsin are improving public access and increasing connections among the lakefront, downtown and Historic Third Ward. WCMP funded initial planning and design efforts for the Milwaukee Lakefront Gateway Project. The final four entries from the Lakefront Gateway Plaza National Design Competition can be viewed at milwaukee.gov/lakefrontplaza.

Enjoy this year's *Chronicle* celebrating the work and creativity of those who make Wisconsin Great Lakes coasts great.

Scott Walker was elected Wisconsin's 45th Governor in 2010.

Commercial Ports: Wisconsin's Comparative Advantage

Ernie Perry, Ph.D.

A renewed interest in maritime freight movement is underway. State-level marine freight leadership, regional marine freight partnerships and reduced costs to shippers are driving a renaissance in marine freight shipping. And for good reason.

The Federal Highway Administration reports that more than 54 million tons of freight valued at over $48 billion moves across the country every day, and freight tonnage moved is expected to increase by over 40 percent by 2040. With highways at capacity and railroads at similar levels of saturation, marine freight movement is a sensible, economic approach to expanding and managing the transportation system, which in turn supports our economy and port communities.

Increased logistics and transportation activity at Wisconsin ports support quality jobs as well as sustainable community and economic development. The National Oceanic and Atmospheric Administration, Office of Coastal Management estimates that Wisconsin's marine sectors employ more than 38,000 workers. These are well-paying jobs. The US Bureau of Labor Statistics reports median pay of positions classified as water transportation occupations was 29 percent higher than the median for all jobs.

Established freight corridors also provide access to resources and businesses—as well as economic efficiencies—that attract and cluster businesses. Consider that 30 percent of Wisconsin's total businesses and 35 percent of total employment fall within three miles of just three of Wisconsin's major highway freight corridors: Interstates 90, 94 and 43. Freight corridors—highway, marine or rail—benefit and thus attract business and industry.

Wisconsin is naturally endowed with resources and access to marine corridors necessary to leverage marine freight development. Wisconsin ports are transportation and economic engines that support business and industry, moving 30 million tons of freight worth more than $2.4 billion and generating more than $1.6 billion in economic activity annually. With commercial ports on Lake Superior, Lake Michigan and the Upper Mississippi River, Wisconsin enjoys a comparative advantage in business and logistics.

However, after decades of near-exclusive focus on highway infrastructure, the road and rail systems are at capacity and will simply not be able to move the increasing loads of freight. In Wisconsin, only five percent of freight moves on waterways while highway and rail congestion continue to increase.

Wisconsin's Great Lakes ports have only partially taken advantage of opportunities for increasing freight activity and the economic benefits that arise from marine freight development. And only six commodities—wheat, cement, nonmetallic minerals, limestone, iron ore and coal—constitute 96% of the waterways tonnage moved across the state's Great Lake ports.

The Wisconsin Commercial Port Development Initiative (WCPDI) produced a strategic plan for increasing freight movement through Wisconsin ports to stimulate economic activity and create high quality jobs. The Wisconsin Commercial Port Association (WCPA) teamed up with the Wisconsin Economic Development Corporation (WEDC), the Wisconsin Coastal Management Program (WCMP), the Wisconsin Department of Transportation, the Wisconsin Department of Natural Resources, Brown County, the Wisconsin Transportation Development Association and the University of Wisconsin-Madison to conduct the project. The initiative also leveraged funding from the WCMP, WEDC, WCPA and UW-Madison.

Based on the project's infrastructure and market inventories, freight data and stakeholder input, the project team identified four key strategic areas and 22 distinct strategic initiatives to support freight development at Wisconsin ports. The four areas of strategic action are:

- increased awareness and advocacy for port and waterways development,

- increased market share of marine capable commodities,

- increased funding for port and waterway infrastructure,

- increased cooperation, planning and collaboration to further develop Wisconsin's marine presence and network.

The WCPDI represents the first steps in supporting continued advancement of Wisconsin ports as logistics and business hubs. Infrastructure and market inventories provide the baseline for planning and investment. Stakeholder participation and input reflect a more collaborative network of ports and industries working to ensure the marine freight system supports their needs.

Based on these results of the WCPDI, the project team continues to work with ports and industry stakeholders to advance freight development at Wisconsin ports. In addition to continued agency collaboration—and work to increase awareness through presentations at the state and national levels—WCPDI kicked off Phase II in July 2015. Phase II is designed to identify commodities, cargo or other goods that could move more efficiently across Wisconsin's commercial ports—but are not currently doing so. The project team will assess the feasibility and benefits of moving these commodities and cargo through Wisconsin ports.

The WCPDI is a first step toward leveraging transportation infrastructure, burgeoning freight loads and national marine development momentum toward greater freight movement through Wisconsin's commercial ports. With solid community, agency and industry participation, increased freight activity at Wisconsin commercial ports will bring quality jobs and long-term economic stability to port and harbor communities across the state.

For more information or to access the entire WCPDI report, visit cfire. wistrans.org/research/projects/09-02.

In 2015, Ernie Perry, Ph.D., was the Program Manager at the University of Wisconsin-Madison Center for Freight and Infrastructure Research and Education.

NOAA Coastal Storms Program

Julia Noordyk

Intense storms are increasingly having a negative impact on our coastal communities. Flooding, agricultural and urban runoff pollution, coastal erosion and hazardous swimming conditions are all problems associated with greater intensity and more frequent coastal storms in the Great Lakes.

According to research by the Wisconsin Initiative for Climate Change Impacts (2011), Wisconsin may receive two to three more extreme precipitation events—of at least two inches—per decade, or roughly a 25% increase in frequency by the mid-twenty-first century.

Cue the Great Lakes Coastal Storms Program (CSP)—a regional effort led by the National Oceanic and Atmospheric Administration (NOAA)—to make Great Lakes communities safer by reducing the loss of life and negative impacts of coastal storms.

Since 2012, CSP has provided manpower and funding to help the region become more resilient to extreme weather hazards and climate change. In Wisconsin, University of Wisconsin (UW) Sea Grant, University of Wisconsin-Madison and Wisconsin Coastal Management Program (WCMP) have been working with CSP to assist coastal communities in planning for and mitigating the increasing risks associated with coastal storms.

One of the most inspiring projects is spearheaded by UW-Madison coastal engineering scientist Dr. Chin Wu. Dr. Wu sprang into action after the death of a high school student at Port Washington's North Beach in 2012. Since 2005, at least 26 swimmers have died at Wisconsin beaches from dangerous currents, high waves and piers.

Dr. Wu was awarded a $200,000 CSP grant to pilot test innovative, real-time rip current detection technology at North Beach and Bradford Beach in Milwaukee. Video imaging will provide critical information to beach managers and swimmers about current swimming conditions and risk levels. UW Sea Grant and WCMP also serve as project partners and are providing outreach to the communities with the goal of improving public safety management at the beaches.

UW Sea Grant and WCMP also received CSP funds to participate in a regional beach safety collaborative along with Minnesota, Illinois, Indiana and Michigan. The primary mission of the collaborative is to increase public awareness on how to recognize and respond to dangerous currents and waves at Great Lakes beaches. The collaborative is using Great Lakes-specific social science research to create new, consistent messaging about dangerous currents and waves. This includes a new water safety campaign—www.currentsmart.org—and awareness messages like *When the Waves Are High, Stay Dry.*

Along with new messaging, the collaborative is distributing beach safety and emergency rescue equipment—youth life jackets, throw rings, rescue stations, warning signs and others—to local beaches around Lake Michigan and Lake Superior. Working with NOAA's National Weather Service, UW-Oshkosh and the Wisconsin Department of Natural Resources, UW Sea Grant and WCMP distributed much need safety equipment to 41 Wisconsin beaches for the 2015 season.

In addition to beach safety, CSP is supporting efforts in Wisconsin to improve decision making on the design and placement of coastal structures such as offshore breakwaters, retaining walls, piers and docks. Upshore structures can exacerbate shoreline erosion at adjacent, downshore properties by blocking sand from drifting down the coast.

While it has long been known that coastal structures can greatly influence how sand travels along the shoreline, the downdrift impacts of these structures—groins, jetties and solid docks—have not typically been examined when designing, permitting or building them along the shore. The loss of sand that would otherwise be deposited at downshore properties has resulted in conflicts among landowners.

In response, UW Sea Grant is working with a UW-Madison engineering graduate student to develop a web-based decision making tool that will visualize the impacts of placing coastal structures on Wisconsin shorelines. The tool will provide science-based information to property owners and regulatory agencies to improve permitting decisions for the replacement or construction of new shoreline structures leading to fewer delays and faster processing.

CSP is also focused on reducing the negative effects of climate change on Wisconsin coastal communities through hazard mitigation planning.

As average annual temperatures in Wisconsin continue to rise, there will be shorter, warmer winters, decreased lake ice cover and an increased frequency in heat waves, severe rainstorms and drought.

Currently, local hazard mitigation plans—required by FEMA to receive pre- and post-disaster funding—rely on historical hazard occurrence to calculate risk. Climate change may make past trends unreliable sources for predicting future impacts, frequency, probability and vulnerabilities.

In fall 2014, UW Sea Grant partnered with the Bay-Lake Regional Planning Commission to help the Oconto County Hazard Mitigation Planning Committee consider the possible impacts of climate on natural hazards. The County's hazard mitigation plan now includes recommendations for mitigating climate impacts on water resources, tourism and recreation, infrastructure and maintenance activities.

Great Lakes communities are faced with unique challenges under a changing climate. Fluctuating lake levels, more intense storms and increasing development all put Wisconsin's coastal communities at risk for flooding, shoreline erosion and hazardous swimming conditions.

It is often up to local communities to figure out how to identify, prepare for and mitigate these risks. By connecting federal resources to local needs, the NOAA Coastal Storms Program has enabled Great Lakes communities to become safer and more resilient to the negative impacts caused by coastal storms.

In 2015, Julia Noordyk was the NOAA Coastal Storms Program Outreach Coordinator at the University of Wisconsin Sea Grant Institute.

CAT ISLAND CHAIN RESTORATION

Mark A. Walter

The southern edge of Green Bay contains a wetland habitat complex that was once one of the largest and most diverse in the Great Lakes. In the bay, shallow waters and extensive beds of submergent and emergent aquatic vegetation provide a major stopover for waterfowl and other migrating birds—as well as habitat for varied populations of water birds, furbearers, invertebrates and native fishes. Geographically, the west shore of Green Bay also provides a leading line that guides and concentrates migrating birds from a broad northern opening to the southern tip of the bay.

These wetlands were historically protected from high energy wave and storm actions by the Cat Island chain of barrier islands. According to US Fish and Wildlife Service (USFWS) surveys conducted in the 1990s, the Cat Islands provided nesting habitat for thirteen species of colonial nesting water birds—the highest species diversity of any island in the Great Lakes.

During extremely high water levels in the mid1970s, a series of severe storms during ice breakup resulted in catastrophic erosion and ice damage to the islands. While remnant islands and wetland habitat remained, most was lost or degraded due to erosion negatively affecting both habitat and water quality.

Local officials took note of negative impacts of the lost habitat and went to work. In 1988, the Lower Green Bay Remedial Action Plan identified rebuilding the Cat Island chain as the top priority for habitat restoration in the bay. In 2005, Brown County received a Lake Bed Grant (2005 Wisconsin Act 390) from the Wisconsin Legislature to allow for reconstruction of the Cat Islands.

In 2012—after nearly 25 years of planning and searching for funding—the Brown County Port & Resource Recovery Department began reconstruction of the Cat Island chain through funding provided by a $1.5 million US Environmental Protection Agency (EPA) Great Lakes Restoration Initiative (GLRI) grant. Brown County completed the initial phase of the project through construction of a wave barrier extending 3,900 feet into the bay. Additional phases have been funded through a cooperative effort between Brown County and the US Army Corps of Engineers (Corps).

The remainder of the wave barrier—as well as the side dikes for the three islands and an offloading facility—was completed by the Corps from 2012 to 2014. The project has been designed as three open-backed islands with a connecting dike that serves as a wave barrier. The islands will be filled over the next twenty to thirty years by the Corps using clean dredge material from maintenance of the Green Bay Harbor.

The 2.5-mile long wave barrier along the remnant Cat Island shoals will protect and restore approximately 1,225 acres of shallow water and wetland habitat. The wave barrier provides the base for filling the three islands with beneficially reused fine sands dredged from the outer navigation channel.

By blocking wave energy, the 272-acre islands and wave barrier are recreating island habitat and reestablishing aquatic plant beds in the lower bay. Restoring the islands will lead to recovery of much of the important lower bay habitat that benefits sport and commercial fisheries, colonial nesting water birds, shorebirds, waterfowl, marsh nesting birds, amphibians, turtles, invertebrates and furbearing mammals. The wave barrier will provide long term protection to the barrier islands and restored wetlands from future storm and ice damage.

While the total project was originally estimated at $35 million, the final cost estimate is just under $17 million with Brown County providing 35%—or about $6 million—as match for the construction phases completed by the Corps. The project is a partnership between the Port of Green Bay, Brown County, the Corps, the EPA, the USFWS, the Wisconsin Departments of Transportation (DOT) and Natural Resources (DNR), the Lower Fox River/Green Bay Natural Resources Trustee Council, University of Wisconsin (UW) Sea Grant, University of Wisconsin-Green Bay and fourteen Port terminal operators. Funding has been provided from GLRI grants, a DOT Harbor Assistance Program grant, a DNR Damages Assessment grant and funds collected by the Port of Green Bay.

Oversight for the project and future management decisions are provided by the Cat Island Advisory Committee (CIAC) which was established by the DNR as part of its Water Quality Permit for the project. The permit establishes the CIAC as a five-member committee with one representative each from the DNR, the Port of Green Bay, the Corps, the USFWS and a citizen member. In addition, advisory members from UW-Green Bay, UW Sea Grant and other organizations provide input to the committee on a variety of issues dealing with management of the islands.

Impacts of the Cat Island Chain restoration have already been seen in improved water quality, re-vegetation of near shore areas and an increase in waterfowl species. The project is also seen as a model for beneficial reuse of dredge material. We expect to see impacts well into the future.

In 2015, Mark A. Walter was the Business Development Manager at the Brown County Port and Resource Recovery Department.

Wisconsin Lake Superior Scenic Byway

Mary Nowakowski

The story behind the founding of the Wisconsin Lake Superior Scenic Byway (WLSB) has as many twists, turns, hills and valleys as the 72-mile route that follows the shoreline of the Bayfield Peninsula. It is a compelling story that unfolded over 27 years when the dream of establishing a scenic byway predated both the National Scenic Byway and the State of Wisconsin's Scenic Byway programs.

The chronicle starts in 1986 when Bayfield Mayor Larry MacDonald and a group of local citizens envisioned a special designation for Wisconsin State Highway 13 along the Bayfield Peninsula. The informal group discussed how the highway could be promoted to showcase the unusual combination of geologic, historic, cultural and recreational features on the route.

The Apostle Islands National Lakeshore was established in 1970 and anchors the scenic route. The Apostle Islands archipelago includes 22 islands located just off of the Bayfield Peninsula. The Gaylord Nelson Wilderness Area was added in 2004. Sandstone cliffs—carved out by the wave action of Lake Superior—are a prominent geological feature along the Byway.

The riches of natural resources along the route are almost embarrassing. The Chequamegon-Nicolet National Forest, Frog Bay Tribal National Park, Bark Bay Slough, Houghton Falls, Lost Creek Bog, Apostle Island National Lakeshore Caves at Meyers Beach, Nourse Sugarbush and Port Wing Boreal Forest Natural Areas, Moquah Barrens Wildlife Management Area, and the Whittlesey Creek National Wildlife Refuge are all accessed from the Byway.

Historic and cultural sites are plentiful. There are ten historic sites, three historic districts and seven shipwrecks on the National Register of Historic Places. Within the boundaries of Apostle Islands National Lakeshore is the largest single collection of lighthouses in the country—seven of which are listed on the National Register.

The Red Cliff Band of Lake Superior Chippewa Reservation is also located along the Byway. The Tribe migrated from the eastern United States in the mid-1600s and followed the south shore of Lake Superior to a prophesized place where food grows on water—the plentiful crop of wild rice that is still harvested in the Kakagon Sloughs. Small towns linked by the route reflect the rich cultural heritage of immigrant lumberjacks, fishermen and brownstone quarry workers who came to the area in the late 1800s.

With this depth of resources, the establishment of a scenic byway should have been easy. But the process ebbed and flowed for years as different groups picked up the process only to have it lose momentum. In the meantime, the National Scenic Byway program was established in 1995 and provided a clear framework for the designation process. The State of Wisconsin program mirrored the national guidelines and was established by the Department of Transportation in 1999.

In 2011, a new committee was formed with guidance from University of Wisconsin-Extension Community Resource Development Agent Tim Kane. A group of community leaders and interested citizens met regularly to hammer out the details necessary to submit a formal application to the State of Wisconsin.

Phase 1 of the process required a mile-by-mile inventory of the present condition of scenic resources and assessment of complementary resources. This process allowed the committee to scrutinize the route using a standard set of guidelines and establish a baseline of current conditions as the starting point for writing the Corridor Management Plan (CMP).

The CMP addresses the goals, protection, promotion strategies, action schedule and responsible entities by which the WLSB is managed. The committee completed a very detailed CMP with five major goals, multiple objectives under each goal and specific activities that support each objective. Each objective and activity lists a lead entity, potential partners and deadlines for completion. The CMP serves as a clear road map for managing the Byway.

The state program requires that resolutions supporting the Byway be signed by every local government through which the route passes. But the WLSB took this one step further and established an Intergovernmental Council to help oversee the Byway. Each of the eleven communities—plus

Bayfield County and the Red Cliff Tribal Council—has a designated representative. The Council meets monthly to implement the CMP, talk about common issues and work to ensure that local ordinances do not compromise the long term goals of the Byway.

The WLSB was officially dedicated on April 18, 2013—27 years after the initial efforts began. Since then, the Council has assembled an impressive array of accomplishments. The Wisconsin Coastal Management Program (WCMP) awarded the Byway a grant to produce a printed map identifying recreational, cultural, historical and geological places of interest.

The map will be a complementary resource to the Lake Superior Water Trail Map that was funded by WCMP and produced by the Northwest Regional Planning Commission. The WLSB's website—www.lakesuperior byway.org—averages almost 2,000 visits per month and contains a wealth of information about the route. A 2015 WCMP grant will provide funding to construct ten interpretive kiosks along the route.

The WLSB combines promotion, protection and preservation along one of Wisconsin's most beautiful highways. The Byway invites travelers to experience Lake Superior's majesty—in all of its variety—along the state's northern-most border.

In 2015, Mary Nowakowski was the Chair of the Wisconsin Lake Superior Scenic Byway Intergovernmental Council.

THE NATIONAL MARINE
SANCTUARY SYSTEM

Ellen Brody and John H. Broihahn

For the past 40 years, national marine sanctuaries have protected special places in America's ocean and Great Lakes waters—from the site of a single Civil War shipwreck to a vast expanse of ocean surrounding remote coral reefs. The National Oceanic and Atmospheric Administration's (NOAA), Office of National Marine Sanctuaries serves as the trustee for this system of fourteen marine protected areas encompassing more than 170,000 square miles of ocean and Great Lakes waters.

Within these protected waters, whales feed and migrate, coral reefs flourish and shipwrecks reveal secrets of our maritime history. Through public engagement, research, management and education programs, national marine sanctuaries protect and interpret these special places.

The first and only designated national marine sanctuary in the Great Lakes is the Thunder Bay National Marine Sanctuary (NMS) off the coast of Alpena, Michigan in Lake Huron. Jointly managed by NOAA and the State of Michigan, the sanctuary was designated in 2000 to protect and conserve a nationally significant collection of shipwrecks. The sanctuary—which recently expanded to 4,300 square miles—now protects and interprets nearly 100 known shipwrecks. Thunder Bay NMS has played a significant role in the region's economy by promoting tourism and recreation in northeast Michigan.

In response to ongoing and widespread interest from the public in the value of sanctuaries to protect treasured places and enhance local economies, NOAA has launched a new, locally-driven sanctuary nomination process. For the first time in two decades, NOAA invites communities across the nation to nominate places in marine and Great Lakes waters for consideration as national marine sanctuaries.

The nomination process will result in an inventory of areas NOAA will consider for national marine sanctuary designation, taking into account input and support from local, regional and national interests and organizations. Consideration will also be based on a proposed area's national significance and the feasibility of managing it. The nomination process will not result in the automatic designation of any new national marine sanctuaries—designation occurs as a separate process that is highly participatory and often takes years to complete.

In December 2014, Governor Scott Walker submitted the State of Wisconsin's sanctuary nomination to NOAA. The nomination—which is focused on protecting and interpreting a nationally significant collection of shipwrecks—proposes an 875-square-mile area encompassing Lake Michigan waters adjacent to Port Washington, Sheboygan, Manitowoc and Two Rivers. The nomination package includes over 100 letters of support from a variety of businesses, community organizations, agencies, elected officials and units of local government.

The proposed sanctuary contains an extraordinary collection of shipwrecks as demonstrated by the listing of fifteen wrecks on the National Register of Historic Places overseen by the Wisconsin Historical Society and State Review Board. Archival and archaeological research indicates that the proposed sanctuary includes 122 reported vessel losses. Currently, 34 of the shipwrecks are known.

Fourteen of the known shipwrecks are intact with a high degree of hull integrity. Three vessels—the *Tennie and Laura*, the *Gallinipper* and the *Silver Lake*—possess standing masts, a rarity in the Great Lakes. The proposed sanctuary includes Wisconsin's two oldest shipwrecks discovered to date—the *Gallinipper* (1833) and the *Home* (1843)—both of which remain largely intact. The *Rouse Simmons*, often referred to as the Christmas Tree ship, is also in the proposed sanctuary.

In the spirit of regional cooperation, Two Rivers, Manitowoc, Sheboygan and Port Washington support a regional partnership to obtain a national marine sanctuary. Each community has developed a local stakeholder group to provide information and insights on the nomination process, and they have formed a joint Community Working Group that includes key representatives from each of the cities and counties. Their support and enthusiasm is indicated by resolutions passed by each community and county.

The nomination highlights several goals of the proposed sanctuary:

- Preserve and expand on the nearly 60-year investment the citizens of Wisconsin have made in the identification, interpretation and preservation of shipwrecks and other maritime resources.

- Build and expand on state and local tourism initiatives and enhance job opportunities.

- Create a heightened appreciation of Great Lakes' maritime heritage resources.

- Increase both physical and virtual access to the proposed sanctuary's maritime heritage resources and promote their recreational use.

- Promote a regional approach in establishing a Wisconsin national marine sanctuary with the cities of Port Washington, Sheboygan, Manitowoc and Two Rivers.

- Partner with other NOAA programs in the Great Lakes region—including the Thunder Bay National Marine Sanctuary, the Wisconsin Coastal Management Program and the University of Wisconsin Sea Grant Institute—to sustainably manage Wisconsin's maritime heritage resources and stewardship of the Great Lakes.

- Enhance educational programming and public outreach through partnerships with local, state and regional agencies and organizations to create innovative maritime heritage and Great Lakes educational programs, including science, technology, engineering and math (STEM) programs.

In February 2015, NOAA accepted Wisconsin's nomination into the inventory of places that will be considered for national marine sanctuary designation. As of August 2015, NOAA has not made a decision about initiating the sanctuary designation process in Wisconsin. However, NOAA applauds Wisconsin for advancing its proposal to protect and preserve its maritime resources.

In 2015, Ellen Brody was the Great Lakes Regional Coordinator at the NOAA Office of National Marine Sanctuaries. John H. Broihahn was the State Archeologist at the Wisconsin Historical Society.

NEW HOPE FOR ISLANDS
AT DEATH'S DOOR

Tim Sweet

Plum Island is located in the middle of the Porte des Morts—Death's Door—Passage where Green Bay and Lake Michigan meet off the northern tip of Wisconsin's Door Peninsula.

The island encompasses only 325-acres, but it has a very rich maritime history. Dating back to 1848, its importance as a shipping crossroads became apparent when Congress then set aside $3,500 for the construction of a lighthouse along Plum Island's southeastern shore. Unfortunately, it was built in the wrong location—after just ten years the station was abandoned and a new light was built on nearby Pilot Island to help guide ships through Death's Door.

Prompted by an increasing number of wrecks in the area, a Duluth-style life-saving station was constructed on Plum Island's northeastern shore in 1896. On the opposite side of the island, a front and rear range light and a steam-powered fog signal were added to mark the shipping channel between the bay and the lake. Keeper Martin Knudsen first lit the new Plum Island lights in May 1897.

Manned by members of the US Life-Saving Service—which was later absorbed by the US Coast Guard—the Plum Island station housed men charged with the role of protecting mariners and commerce in these waters. The range lights were cared for by members of the US Lighthouse Service until the late 1930s when the US Coast Guard took over responsibility of those facilities as well.

In 1969, the range lights were automated. Four years later, budget cuts led to only seasonal staffing of the Plum Island station. Finally, in the early 1990s a decision was made to permanently close the station on Plum Island.

For many years the historic maritime structures on Plum Island received very little attention and were not maintained. The future of the island seemed to be in limbo. The Bureau of Land Management became the government real estate agent of sorts in 1999 when it tried to find a new steward for the property. Once the Coast Guard completed a mandated clean up of lead paint and contaminated soil, both Plum and Pilot Islands were transferred to the jurisdiction of the US Fish and Wildlife Service (USFWS) in 2007. These two islands—along with nearby Hog Island—now form the Green Bay National Wildlife Refuge.

The islands were acquired to protect migratory bird and endangered species habitat. However, the USFWS also formed a partnership with the nonprofit Friends of Plum and Pilot Islands (FOPPI). FOPPI's mission is to support the goals of the preservation, restoration and maintenance of the maritime structures and other historic resources on Plum and Pilot Islands while providing opportunities for quality wildlife-dependent recreation on Plum Island.

Over the past seven years, FOPPI has helped the USFWS put a new roof on the Pilot Island lighthouse, repainted the Plum Island boathouse, restored the front porch of the historic life-saving station, replaced rotten boards on the Plum Island pier, cleared and established trails, erected trail signs and built an informational kiosk. The organization has also received grants to fund a building stabilization plan, a dock and breakwall engineering study, and a long-term planning study.

The USFWS announced at the FOPPI 2015 Winter Board Meeting the hiring of a full-time employee who will oversee seven Lake Michigan islands under its jurisdiction. In April, the FOPPI Board met with the USFWS to further discuss plans for the buildings on Plum and Pilot Islands that are listed on the National Register of Historic Places. These plans will stabilize the buildings and protect them from further deterioration. The USFWS has obtained funding to send an eight to ten member Action Team to the islands in the summer of 2015 to stabilize the buildings with the greatest needs.

In addition, Plum Island was open to day-use by the public in 2015 from Memorial Day weekend through Labor Day. Kayakers access the island by landing at the designated area next to the pier by the boathouse. The dock and breakwall were closed due to safety issues and must be repaired before they are opened for public use. Larger boats may moor offshore and use a dinghy, or the like, to land on the Island at the kayak entry point.

Many special events and workdays were offered during the spring and summer of 2015 for those who visit Plum Island or become actively involved in making a difference there.

For more details, visit the Friends of Plum and Pilot Islands website at www.plumandpilot.org or its Facebook page www.facebook.com/plumandpilot. More information on the Green Bay National Wildlife Refuge may be found at www.fws.gov/refuge/green_bay.

In 2015, Tim Sweet was the President of Friends of Plum and Pilot Islands.

THREE BRIDGES PARK

Corey Zetts

Many knew the Menomonee Valley by the smell that greeted them as they drove into Milwaukee—the combination of the Valley's yeast, tanning and foundry industries. But the reputation of the Valley has changed. The Valley is now nationally known as a model of revitalization with thousands of jobs and millions of visitors to entertainment destinations, and as a place where more than 22,000 people this year will enjoy nature on a secluded slice of land along the river.

These visitors include thousands of children from neighborhood schools who will study environmental restoration. They sample macro-invertebrates from the Menomonee River—indicators of water quality—watch for birds, check for snakes, listen for bats. These are ways the community is learning about restoration in their city's backyard—and helping develop an understanding of what works in urban land restoration in the process.

Located just outside downtown Milwaukee and within sight of the Miller Park Stadium is Three Bridges Park. Opened in July 2013, this 24-acre parcel is nestled along a one-mile stretch of the Menomonee River. As straightforward as its name is, the history of these 24 acres is complex.

This land was historically a wild rice marsh and a gathering place of Native Americans for the annual harvest. In the late 1800s, the marsh was filled and the land developed by the Milwaukee Road as a 140-acre railroad manufacturing complex. After the company went bankrupt, the large tract of abandoned factory and rail yards became a detriment to both the industrial Valley and residential neighborhoods on the bluffs above.

The land sat vacant for 30 years with the unstable bluffs eroding, collapsing and sending contaminated sediment into the Menomonee River. Kids grew up in the surrounding neighborhoods without knowing there was a river below because the Menomonee was separated from the surrounding city by railroad lines and steep bluffs.

Years of planning and dozens of partner organizations have brought a vision of a restored Valley to life. The development of Three Bridges Park was part of a comprehensive effort to improve job accessibility, science education, environmental and public health, and neighborhood vitality. Projects included transforming a vacant railyard into Three Bridges Park, turning a vacant bar into an environmental community center and reconnecting communities that had been separated for more than a generation by expanding the Hank Aaron State Trail.

With the support of the Wisconsin Coastal Management Program, conceptual designs were developed to create public access to the river, restore the riverbank and develop a public park. After a decade-long planning effort, Three Bridges Park opened in 2013.

The park includes two miles of accessible biking and walking trails that are part of the Hank Aaron State Trail. Twenty-four acres of native landscape for wildlife habitat provide a peaceful respite in the heart of the city that offers access to the Menomonee River for fishing and canoeing.

Three bike/pedestrian bridges provide access from surrounding neighborhoods to the park as well as to Valley jobs. A re-created glacial landscape of kames, eskers and drumlins—an adaptive reuse of material from a nearby highway reconstruction—are used to teach about ice age formations. Community gardens provide space for neighbors to grow food. And bluff-side locales offer panoramic views of Milwaukee.

The opening ceremony built upon the community's enthusiasm for the park and what it symbolized for a generation of Milwaukeeans who grew up knowing the Menomonee Valley as a dividing line. More than 1,000 people formed processions from each of the park's three bridge entrances—symbolically uniting north and south side neighborhoods that had been divided for decades—meeting in the middle to walk down to the Menomonee River together.

Three Bridges Park established an outdoor classroom for the Urban Ecology Center, an environmental community center that provides kids attending neighborhood schools with hands-on science education along with community and family nature-based programs. The Wisconsin Coastal Management Program also supported efforts to engage the community in the development of Three Bridges Park through experiential educational programming, citizen science and participatory land stewardship.

Urban Ecology Center programs engage the community in studying the impacts of restoring what had long been a degraded natural resource—tracking changes in the migratroy bird species seen on site, winter hibernations of snakes, bat physiology and more. Residents come to plant native plants in the park, weed invasive species and learn about changes that are happening through the restoration process. This community engagement is creating a sense of ownership of and pride in Three Bridges Park.

Today, the park offers a place for people to come together in what was once widely thought of as the dividing line in our community. Three Bridges Park itself is bridging nature and the city, allowing neighbors to cross over the industrial Valley and access a place of respite in the heart of Milwaukee. The park's programming is bridging the past and the future, educating about the rich history of this land and connecting people to its restoration through ongoing volunteer activities.

In 2015, Corey Zetts was the Executive Director of Menomonee Valley Partners, Inc.

2016

Foreword

Governor Scott Walker

Dear Friends of the Great Lakes,

Welcome to the fifteenth year of *Wisconsin Great Lakes Chronicle*. Since 2002, the *Chronicle* has given voice to community leaders and coastal managers on issues of importance to Wisconsin's Lake Superior and Lake Michigan coasts. We are pleased this year to highlight two coastal initiatives that will strengthen our state's economy and protect cultural resources.

On June 15, 2016, the Conference of Great Lakes Governors and Premiers Task Force released the first-ever regional strategy to jumpstart the Great Lakes-St. Lawrence maritime transportation system. The objectives are to double maritime trade, shrink the environmental footprint of the region's transportation network, and support the region's industrial core.

Wisconsin is a bit ahead of and in synch with this effort. In December 2014, the Wisconsin Commercial Ports Development Initiative (WCDPI) produced deliverables that will support freight and economic development at Wisconsin ports, such as a port infrastructure inventory, a Wisconsin marine commodity market analysis, an analysis of port planning and the Wisconsin Harbor Assistance Program, and the development of a Wisconsin commercial ports master plan with strategic initiatives. In addition, the WCDPI gathered data to be used as baselines for future metrics and identified port infrastructure needs and associated costs.

Funding for the WCDPI has been provided by the Wisconsin Coastal Management Program (WCMP) and the Wisconsin Economic Development Corporation (WEDC). Led by the University of Wisconsin-Madison National Center for Freight & Infrastructure Research & Education (CFIRE), project leadership included state staff from WCMP, WEDC, the Wisconsin Department of Transportation (DOT), and the Wisconsin Department of Natural Resources (DNR).

For the past 40 years, national marine sanctuaries have protected special places in America's oceans and Great Lakes waters, from the site of a single Civil War shipwreck to a vast expanse of ocean surrounding remote coral reefs. Wisconsin's recent nomination to the National Oceanic and Atmospheric Administration (NOAA) focuses on protecting, interpreting, researching, and enhancing access to a nationally significant collection of shipwrecks.

The proposed 875-square-mile sanctuary encompasses Lake Michigan waters adjacent to Mequon, Port Washington, Sheboygan, Manitowoc, and Two Rivers. All five communities and Ozaukee, Sheboygan, and Manitowoc Counties continue to be committed and engaged in this effort.

On October 5, 2015, President Obama announced NOAA's approval to have Wisconsin's Lake Michigan and Maryland's Mallows Bay nominations begin the process toward possible designation. NOAA, the Wisconsin Historical Society and WCMP are now working with local and state partners on drafting the Environmental Impact Statement (EIS) and management plans. When the EIS and management plans are completed, they will be made available for public comment.

It is an honor to achieve this stage of approval as there are only thirteen national marine sanctuaries and one national marine monument in the federal system. If approved, Wisconsin's Lake Michigan coastal communities can look forward to significant economic and quality of life benefits in the areas of tourism, small business development—such as new dive shops and boat excursions, enhanced recreation and educational opportunities—and of course the preservation and recognition of Wisconsin's historical maritime cultural resources.

We invite you to reflect on the following 2016 *Chronicle* articles that highlight restoration, revitalization, and economic development in Wisconsin's coastal communities. Finally, please visit and enjoy Wisconsin's coastal resources.

Scott Walker was elected Wisconsin's 45th Governor in 2010.

Transform Milwaukee Creates a Vision for an Industrial Corridor

Wyman Winston

Located northwest of downtown Milwaukee, the 30th Street Industrial Corridor was a manufacturing hub a century ago. At the time, development happened quickly with natural drainage ways and wetlands filled in and no provision made for water flowage systems or open green spaces used today in contemporary construction. Nonetheless, this industrial strip was the mainstay for the central city attracting employers, workers and housing.

During the past three decades, the Corridor has experienced a significant economic decline with industries leaving the area contributing to a large inventory of abandoned properties and foreclosures. As a result, the area has experienced significant challenges such as declining property values, high crime and widespread unemployment.

Despite these setbacks, the Corridor is poised for redevelopment due to its under-utilized industrial space, established transportation system and access to local workers. A key drawback to this urban district, however, is its poor environmental infrastructure.

Something needed to be done to build upon Milwaukee's proud economic tradition—not only in the 30th Street Corridor, but in other core industrial areas of the city. Understanding that Wisconsin's economic vitality is dependent upon a vibrant Milwaukee, a bold new initiative was required to grow businesses and restore the city as an energetic place in which to live and work.

On April 30, 2012, Governor Scott Walker and the Wisconsin Housing and Economic Development Authority (WHEDA) announced Transform Milwaukee, one of the most aggressive and comprehensive efforts in Wisconsin history to energize the state's largest city. Transform Milwaukee is a public-private partnership focused on restoring economic prosperity to the industrial, residential and transportation areas connecting the 30th Street Industrial Corridor, the Menomonee Valley, the Port of Milwaukee and the Milwaukee Aerotropolis located south of General Mitchell Airport.

Transform Milwaukee supports the Corridor through a sustainable solution to stormwater runoff that will reduce future flooding events. The Corridor is comprised of 7,000 acres within the Lake Michigan Basin— 3,000 acres drain north to Lincoln Creek and 4,000 acres drain south to the Menomonee River. Before development changed the landscape of the Corridor, the area was a complex network of wetlands and streams. Due to industrial-era engineering, rainwater was instead confined and routed to an inefficient system of storm sewers. Consequently, major storm events generate basement backups and flooding.

The Federal Emergency Management Agency (FEMA) has declared three flooding disasters in Milwaukee in the past decade. The most recent flooding event occurred in 2010 when a line of powerful thunderstorms struck the city. Vast flooding shut down streets and freeways and tens of thousands of residents were left without power.

The *Milwaukee Journal Sentinel* reported on the unprecedented nature of the event: "The rain fell so fast and furious—more than 7 inches in a couple of hours." The storm caused sewer overflows to area streams and Lake Michigan. It was reported that more than 1,000 properties experienced basement backups, 35 locations suffered severe flooding and private sector damage was estimated at $28.5 million throughout the city.

The Corridor was especially impacted and this industrial backbone needed significant re-imagining to prevent future losses. To that end, WHEDA and the Milwaukee Metropolitan Sewage District (MMSD) collaborated to create a vision for a Greenway Corridor. Other Transform Milwaukee partners include the Milwaukee Department of City Development, the Department of Public Works and the 30th Street Industrial Corridor Corporation.

In 2014, a comprehensive study to support a Greenway Corridor concept was completed. The concept features a continuous green pathway of reclaimed urban land running from north to south to help restore the natural drainage system lost during the original development of the area. The design will address not only flooding and basement backup issues, but also complement redevelopment activity for the Transform Milwaukee initiative.

The Greenway Corridor solution includes a series of three storm water basins that will collectively hold nearly 40 million gallons of water when the current system of pipes has reached capacity. In this densely developed urban stretch, the basins will strike a balance between the natural system of tributary streams and wetlands that used to occupy this area and the stormwater sewers.

Two basins are under construction and scheduled for completion in June 2018. The third and final basin is scheduled to be completed in 2022. When completed, the basins will provide a level of storm water flood protection ten times greater than the current infrastructure.

Since the basins are only active in extreme wet weather events, they will be built as green spaces that may be used for recreation, urban agriculture and environmental education. In addition, more than five acres of asphalt will be removed and replaced with wetland plantings, trees and permeable pavement. Green bio-swales are also being added by the City as part of street reconstruction efforts.

All of these measures will help to prevent flooding, basement back-ups and pollutants from entering waterways that flow into Lake Michigan. On April 27, 2016, construction crews started moving dirt to dig the all-important storage basins. Through collaborative planning by Transform Milwaukee partners, work has begun on a determined effort to reduce flooding challenges realized from over a century of industrial-based development in the Corridor.

In 2016, Wyman Winston was the Executive Director of the Wisconsin Housing and Economic Development Authority (WHEDA).

WISCONSIN POINT—URBAN WILDERNESS AND COASTAL ASSET

Mary Morgan

Wisconsin Point—with its twin, Minnesota Point—constitutes the longest freshwater sand bar in the world. The Point, located in Superior, is a 229-acre peninsula situated between Allouez Bay and Lake Superior. Unlike its counterpart on the Minnesota side, Wisconsin Point is protected by local ordinance from industrial, commercial or residential development. Unspoiled and pristine, the property features three miles of beautiful sand beach on the shores of the great and majestic Lake Superior. Allouez Bay has been identified as the largest freshwater marsh in the Great Lakes.

The Point has been designated as a Watchable Wildlife Area by the Wisconsin Department of Natural Resources and an Important Bird Area by the National Audubon Society. An abundance of birds can be found at the Point as it is a major flyway for migratory birds, and the waters of Allouez Bay draw plenty of waterfowl.

The Port of Superior entry is located at the end of the Point where a historic lighthouse rests. The lighthouse went into commission in October 1912. The lighthouse is listed in both the National and State Registers of Historic Places.

Home of a Chippewa burial site, the Point was once a primary Chippewa settlement. Chief Osaugie migrated from Michigan to Wisconsin Point in the early 1800s and became the native community's leader. Non-native claims to the land drove a contentious period ending in 1924 with a judicial ruling that Agate Land Company had clear title to most of the land. During the course of the court battles, the company was compelled to relocate the remains of the Chippewa cemetery to the Nemadji River Cemetery in Superior. The former Chippewa cemetery on the Point is identified with a sign and stone monument.

The leadership of the Fond du Lac Band of Lake Superior Chippewa is currently in negotiations with the federal government to obtain approximately eighteen acres of surplus federal land adjacent to the break-wall serving the Port. This portion of the Point includes two buildings—a maintenance garage and a dock that were part of the former lighthouse station.

In 2011, the Wisconsin Coastal Management Program and Wisconsin Department of Natural Resources funded a planning process resulting in the first-ever comprehensive master plan for Wisconsin Point and the surrounding area. Stakeholders and the general public provided significant input to the planning process and property owners of the Point and surrounding area led the planning process.

The *Wisconsin Point Area Management Plan* divides the Point into zones that have specific recommendations to meet prioritized goals. For example, certain areas have been identified for habitat restoration. Other areas serve recreational use and still others preserve cultural assets. This plan assists local leaders and researchers in securing funding for the most important initiatives on the Point by zone. The plan can be accessed at the City of Superior website at www.ci.superior.wi.us.

Quite a number of grand adventures take place on Wisconsin Point. Each spring, the City of Superior celebrates International Migratory Bird Day in May with an early morning birding hike led by a local birder. The Wisconsin Society of Ornithology (WSO) hosts a three-day field trip known as Jaegerfest every September. WSO notes Jaegerfest as "one of the highlights of the birding year."

For the last four years, the St. Louis River Alliance—with help from federal, state and local partners—has worked to lure the federally-endangered piping plover back to Wisconsin Point. The Alliance has led an effort to provide the proper habitat for the plover to comfortably mate on Lake Superior shoreline owned by Douglas County. Unsuccessful to date, the Alliance has made a valiant effort to return the bird to the Lake Superior shore and will continue to do so.

In 2015, a multi-agency project began to re-establish wild rice in Allouez Bay. Led by Douglas County, the project consists of reseeding Allouez Bay with a goal of 25 acres of wild rice habitat restoration by 2017. The Lake Superior Research Institute, Wisconsin Department of Natural Resources, City of Superior and Lake Superior National Estuarine Research Reserve have all played a key role in returning Allouez Bay to its pre-settlement habitat.

In 2016, the City of Superior in partnership with the Wisconsin Coastal Management Program will lead an effort to further restore habitat along the peninsula proper. Twenty parking turn-outs will be consolidated to four larger ones, each featuring a boardwalk to the beach. The turnouts and informal paths will be re-vegetated with native species to form contiguous habitat. The project will also include nearshore habitat restoration along Allouez Bay. The piping plover project, the wild rice project and the dune restoration project will assist in the de-listing of the St. Louis River as an Area of Concern.

Wisconsin Point serves as a recreational area for duck hunting, fishing, swimming, picnicking, birding, agate hunting and hiking. The Chippewa burial ground, Port of Superior and historic Lighthouse are destinations for locals and tourists. The magic of the Point, however, continues to be its coastal wildness and proximity to the greatest of the Great Lakes.

Mary Morgan retired in spring 2016 as Director of Parks and Recreation for the City of Superior.

Back to the Root

Mayor John Dickert

Racine's history is inextricably tied to the Root River. They even share a name, as *racine* is French for root. The river was responsible for the health of the city's early manufacturing economy, and 170 years later the city is once again turning to the river—this time as a source of recreation and retail.

For many years, industrial cities like Racine used their rivers as the primary form of transportation for commerce. In Racine, farm machines, wagon wheels, traveling trunks and other goods the nation depended on were floated down the river to distribute far and wide. Manufacturing use created urban landscapes that hid rivers behind warehouses and industrial buildings. Nonetheless, this arrangement provided the economic foundation for Racine.

Economic and technological evolution changed transportation over time. And in keeping with changing methods of transport and production, manufacturing along the Root River gave way to marinas, residences and retail. These new uses helped further the life of the riverfront. Nonetheless, the area struggled.

In 2006, the Root River Council began as a conversation among various community members concerned about the river. With the assistance of its first Wisconsin Coastal Management Program (WCMP) grant in 2008, the conversation grew into community workshops and a year's worth of community input eventually compiled into Back to the Root: An Urban River Revitalization Plan. The main goals of the plan were fourfold: create a sense of place, stimulate economic growth, improve water quality and allow public access and interaction.

Upon creating a community-focused plan, conversation turned to action. Imagine solving a very large puzzle. The best approach is to consider the puzzle as a collection of small sections. The more of these smaller sections you start putting together, the clearer the full picture becomes. Similarly, with a project as large as the Root River revitalization—covering five different redevelopment sites stretching over 300 acres—it has to be broken down into manageable pieces. The WCMP has been a major player and valuable partner in this journey to bring the full picture of the Root River redevelopment into view and residents back to the water.

In 2012, WCMP funded the RootWorks Comprehensive Plan. Vandewalle and Associates was hired as planning consultant and community meetings and stakeholder interviews were conducted. The plan developed site-specific standards for redevelopment and established 47 projects to achieve the renewal of this urban river. The City adopted the plan, changed zoning ordinances to reflect its vision and worked with the Racine County Economic Development Corporation to implement the plan.

The collaboration has paid off and the project management team meets twice a month with city, county and state officials, and non-profit and the private sector to implement RootWorks. While collaboration and partnerships help get it all done, they also serve as ways to reveal the picture on top of the puzzle box as the vision becomes clearer for residents. Developers beyond the scope of the project want to become part of this city with a sense of future. They want to be there, and they want to be there sooner rather than later.

Another segment of the puzzle was located across the river from the largest redevelopment site, a site clearly underused and underappreciated. In 2012, WMCP assisted the City with funding the West Bluff Overlook design for a bike path and outdoor classroom. The SC Johnson Company—one of the largest sponsors to date—donated a large portion of land to help with the bike path phase. The land donation was matched by Wisconsin's Knowles-Nelson Stewardship Fund which helps fund land acquisition and recreational development statewide. Funds are also leveraged from the Fund for Lake Michigan.

A 2013 WCMP grant funded plans and design recommendations for completing a dedicated riverfront path in downtown Racine to decrease stream-bank erosion and strengthen the connections between the riverfront path and commercial, retail and recreational hubs. In addition, the largest redevelopment site in the RootWorks plan is Machinery Row, a 17-acre development that includes the Riverfront Promenade stretching around a lazy arch in the river. The promenade will be part of a two-mile river-loop pathway allowing residents the first opportunity in the history of the city access to this area of the Root River. As a partner in the redevelopment, the City controls river access and continues discussions with WCMP to complete design work.

The project has brought together a wide range of public, private and corporate organizations that leverages the contributions of all—creative, monetary, muscular or intellectual. Partners include SC Johnson Company, Wisconsin Coastal Management Program, National Oceanic and Atmospheric Administration, Wisconsin Department of Natural Resources, River Alliance of Wisconsin, Business Improvement District Downtown Racine, Wild Ones, Watershed Initiative Network Root-Pike, University of Wisconsin-Parkside, Olympia Brown Unitarian Church, Racine Community Foundation and the City of Racine.

There is a clear vision, a working plan and realistic standards adopted by the city and an extensive network of partners. The RootWorks Plan has inspired developers to approach the city. With five waterfront development opportunities available, Racine is becoming a destination city for developers and tourists alike.

In 2016, John Dickert was Mayor of the City of Racine.

Wisconsin Invests in Shipbuilding Industry

Sheri Walz

Connected to the world by water, Wisconsin shipyards have a three-century history of building and maintaining commercial, military and recreational vessels for diverse global markets. Wisconsin marine manufacturing is a $6 billion industry that employs over 3,200 people statewide, the majority in northern Wisconsin and rural communities.

Recognizing the importance of waterborne transportation, the Wisconsin Legislature created the Department of Transportation (WisDOT) Harbor Assistance Program (HAP) in 1979. The program provides grants to harbor communities on the Great Lakes and Mississippi River to maintain and improve waterborne commerce.

Almost twenty percent of WisDOT's HAP awards have gone to projects benefiting the shipbuilding industry. Since 1982, WisDOT has awarded $25.6 million in HAP grants for fifteen dockwall and dredging projects at five Wisconsin shipbuilding facilities on the Great Lakes and Mississippi River. Over a 25-year project life, these projects are expected to generate over $730 million in economic benefits and create or preserve over 1,000 jobs.

Bay Shipbuilding. In 2014 and 2015, Bay Shipbuilding in Sturgeon Bay received two HAP grants totaling $5 million for dockwall rehabilitation and installation of an additional berth for construction and winter repair. Bay Shipbuilding has a history that dates back to 1918 specializing in articulated tug-barge units, dredging equipment, double hull commercial vessels and a wide range of offshore support vessels.

The company also repairs vessels ranging from tugs and barges to thousand-foot long bulk tankers—the company repaired and repowered 14 vessels of the Great Lakes fleet in the winter of 2016. Repair work includes removing hazardous materials and retrofitting vessels to be more energy efficient. Bay Shipbuilding reports that recent updates to the *M/V*

John G. Munson will reduce fuel usage 37 percent and cut carbon dioxide and carbon dioxide emissions.

Burger Boat Company. Manitowoc and Burger Boat Company received HAP grants between 1982 and 2013 totaling $6.8 million for five projects including dredging, dockwall construction and rehabilitation, launch well construction, utility upgrades and deep well relocation. Burger Boat believes these grants have helped make the company more competitive on new yacht and commercial vessel construction projects as well as for service and repair work on the existing fleet.

Burger Boats was founded in 1863, and at 153 years old is the oldest yacht builder in America. Burger Boats designs, constructs, maintains, refits and repairs aluminum and steel custom yachts. About 350 employees launch an average of three yachts a year and have four to six projects under construction at various stages of completion. They have also built commercial vessels such as research ships and tour boats.

Cruisers Yachts. From 2005 to 2013, Cruisers Yachts of Oconto benefited from three dredging and dockwall repair HAP grants totaling $3.6 million. The company's history dates back to 1904 and it has been located in Oconto since 1953. Cruisers employs over 450 employees in four plants that manufacture midsize to luxury pleasure yachts. The HAP-funded dredging maintains a navigable waterway for Cruisers to launch newly constructed vessels on the Oconto River to Lake Michigan and beyond. It also allows Cruisers to launch larger vessels, such as a new 59-foot flagship vessel in 2015.

Fraser Shipyards. Fraser Shipyards in Superior is in the midst of completing the third phase of a dockwall rehabilitation project that started in 2009 for which it received two HAP grants totaling $4.7 million. This 126-year-old company repairs and builds vessels and is the last major independent shipyard on the American side of the Great Lakes. The HAP funding represents almost half of a $10 million update that is allowing the company to modernize and add additional dock footage.

During the winter layup season, Fraser converts vessels to modern and efficient fuel sources—as an example, from steam engines that need to be refueled every ten days to modern fuels that can go about 30 days without refueling. Maintenance performed by Fraser can help lakers last for over 100 years in the fresh waters of the Great Lakes.

In 2015, seven vessels wintered at the shipyard for repairs, removal of asbestos, installation of pollution control technology to meet federal emissions standards and repowering. According to Fraser Shipyards, the winter of 2016 included its biggest job since the 1980s, a six-month, $20 million repowering of the Str. *Herbert C. Jackson*. Fraser is one of only four shipyards on the Great Lakes equipped to handle the job requiring seventy workers on two shifts.

Marinette Marine Corporation. In Marinette, three HAP grants totaling $5.3 million in 1982, 1999 and 2015 funded dredging, dockwall rehabilitation and construction at Marinette Marine Corporation. Marinette Marine was founded in 1942 to meet demand for naval construction and has designed and built more than 1,500 vessels. In 2016, the company was awarded $564 million to build its eleventh littoral combat ship for the US Navy, and is expected to continue construction of the ships for five years or more. The ships will detect and clear mines and engage in surface and anti-submarine warfare.

Wisconsin shipyards are at the forefront of supporting the nation's economy and security. The Harbor Assistance Program stands ready to assist shipbuilders and their employees fulfill the needs of America's maritime transportation system.

In 2016, Sheri Walz was the Harbors and Waterways Program Manager at the Wisconsin Department of Transportation.

Coastal States Organization and its Wisconsin Perspective

Mike Friis

Congress created the Coastal Zone Management Act in 1972 to support state initiatives that manage resources along the nation's oceanic and Great Lakes coasts. Among the ten oldest of the 34 federally-approved programs, the Wisconsin Coastal Management Program (WCMP) resides in the Department of Administration (DOA) where it has for 38 years partnered with local governments and organization to manage economic development, environmental protection and coastal hazards projects along the shores of Lakes Michigan and Superior.

As WCMP Manager, I have worked with countless dedicated and creative Wisconsinites over the past eighteen years. In addition, I have served on numerous regional and national associations who share a common vision of protecting America's coastal resources. One organization that has provided the greatest variety of rewarding challenges is the Coastal States Organization (CSO) where I have represented Wisconsin for over a decade and presently serve as Chair of this national association.

CSO works with the Great Lakes and salty coast states and territories to maintain a collective leadership role in the development and implementation of coastal and ocean policies at a national level. CSO advocates for support for state-based coastal programs as well as responsiveness of federal agency programs to issues and policies of state concern. Since states—and not the federal government—control most of the coastline for the public's benefit, the work is important.

CSO members and staff are looked to as resources by coastal stakeholders, other nonprofits and federal agencies such as the US Army Corps of Engineers, Federal Emergency Management Agency (FEMA), Environmental Protection Agency (EPA) and National Oceanic and Atmospheric Administration (NOAA). To underscore the importance of our nation's coasts, CSO routinely briefs Congress and federal agencies on the coastal economy, the benefit of coastal resources to our nation's quality of life, and the strategic economic advantage of diverse coastal businesses and recreation to tourism and sustainable economic development. I participate in these national briefings and in that way give the Wisconsin program visibility and provide a Wisconsin and Great Lakes perspective on critical issues.

CSO serves as an important network for state coastal and ocean managers. Work groups of members supported by CSO staff focus on coastal water quality, port and harbor issues, coastal hazards, coastal zone management, ocean policy and island affairs.

During my term as CSO Chair, we have addressed many policy issues and challenges. One of our successes was supporting a measure that would return more port fees—monies paid into a federal account known as the Harbor Maintenance Trust Fund—back to smaller ports like the ones that line Wisconsin's coasts. We also worked hard to ensure federal policies make it easier to use sand that is dredged from ports and ship lanes to be used in places that benefit the public and create resilient shorelines, such as at eroded beaches or barrier islands that have washed away.

We have also forged a partnership with the Association of State Flood Plain Managers (ASFPM) to help communities lower their flood insurance costs by taking environmentally sound actions like restoring seaside vegetation. This has been especially gratifying since ASFPM is a large and respected national organization based in Madison.

Together with ASFPM staff and other organizations, I represent CSO on the Digital Coast Partnership. This work complements my role managing the Wisconsin Land Information Program. The Digital Coast initiative was developed to meet the unique needs of the coastal management community to provide land information data, tools and training needed to intelligently manage coastal resources. The Digital Coast Partnership is achieving its goal of providing these resources in a relevant, useful manner.

As CSO Chair, I have worked to enable states to learn from each other by sharing successes and challenges so we are not all reinventing the wheel in our approach to managing increasingly threatened coasts. This is particularly important for vulnerable island states and territories including Hawaii, Guam, Northern Marianas Islands, Puerto Rico and the Virgin Islands that otherwise lack daily working relationships with contiguous jurisdictions.

Finally, CSO is working closely with NOAA to break down problems caused by federal agencies that do not coordinate enough, a problem known as *stove piping* (in Wisconsin—America's Dairyland—we think of it as *silos*). Many great NOAA programs provide science, data and other services that substantially help state coastal programs. To facilitate these programs better working together, I represent CSO on a NOAA-convened roundtable focused on intra-agency collaboration.

Through this roundtable, CSO works with the National Sea Grant, National Marine Sanctuaries Program, National Estuarine Research Reserve System and other NOAA programs that positively contribute to the coasts. To this end, I appreciate that NOAA recently reorganized to create the Office for Coastal Management. CSO will work to assist this office provide better service to states and their coasts.

In September 2016, Wisconsin will host the annual CSO meeting in Milwaukee. This will be my last meeting as Chair and I am excited to share and feature the good work of Wisconsin's many coastal partners to a national audience. It has been fun, rewarding and challenging, and I am so proud to have been the Chair of CSO.

In 2016, Mike Friis was Manager of the Wisconsin Coastal Management Program and Chair of the Coastal States Organization.

New Water Protects Our Most Valuable Resource

Bill Hafs

NEW Water—the brand of the Green Bay Metropolitan Sewerage District (GBMSD)—serves over 230,000 residents within a 285 square mile area and treats over 38 million gallons of wastewater each day. NEW Water is on a journey of transforming itself into a Utility of the Future—an initiative of the National Association of Clean Water Agencies—that recovers and manages valuable resources, develops partnerships to encourage economic development, and provides leadership to deliver the maximum environmental benefit at the lowest cost to the community.

NEW Water is located at the mouth of the Fox River, the furthest point downstream of the Fox/Wolf Watershed. The Lower Fox River Basin (LFR) and Green Bay are impaired by excessive phosphorus and sediment loading. A Total Maximum Daily Load Watershed Management plan for the LFR and Lower Green Bay was developed in June 2010. The plan identified phosphorus and sediment loading by sub watersheds and established restoration goals. In addition, the plan notes that NEW Water contributes about three percent of total phosphorus loading to Green Bay estimated at 1,266,657 pounds per year.

As early as 2012, NEW Water began a systematic planning process to consider Adaptive Management as an option for meeting its future Wisconsin Pollution Discharge Elimination System (WPDES) permit requirements. The Adaptive Management approach is an opportunity to work with municipalities and agriculture to get the lowest cost per pound for phosphorus reduction and potential economic benefit for agriculture with practices like nutrient management.

When its existing WPDES permit expires in 2019, NEW Water will be required to further reduce the levels of total phosphorus it discharges in the LFR and Green Bay. To meet the new water quality standards, NEW Water would need to build additional treatment to remove approximately

9,332 pounds of phosphorus per year at an estimated cost of more than $220 million.

Understanding that adopting an Adaptive Management strategy would require an analysis of cost factors, agency and landowner cooperation and scientific evidence, NEW Water in 2013 began a five-year pilot project in Silver Creek. Silver Creek is a small stream located one mile west of the Austin Straubel airport and flows from Outagamie County into Brown County through the Oneida Reservation. Silver Creek is a tributary of Duck Creek which empties into Green Bay. The watershed is representative of northeast Wisconsin in regards to soils, slopes and land use.

From the beginning of the pilot project, it was understood that partnerships would be critical to successfully achieve water quality standards in Silver Creek. Further, conservation best management installation would be needed.

The Oneida Tribe was involved in the planning efforts from the beginning and helped lead the process. Other partners include Outagamie County Land and Water Conservation Department, Tilth Agronomic Services, Ag-Ventures Agronomic Services, The Nature Conservancy, the US Fish and Wildlife Service, Ducks Unlimited, Brown County Land and Water Conservation Department, USDA Natural Resources Conservation Service, US Geological Service, University of Wisconsin-Green Bay (UWGB) and CH2MHILL. This partnership team has met regularly to coordinate and develop watershed management strategies.

In 2014 and 2015, water quality monitoring was conducted at five stream locations to establish a baseline, and soil samples were collected at 2.5 acre grids. Conservation planning was done on all fields to determine conservation practices needed. The conservation planning was conducted by a team including conservationists, a private agronomist, Oneida Tribal staff and CH2MHILL.

Modeling of the field runoff by UWGB and aquatic biological assessment was conducted by the Oneida Tribe's Aquatic Biologist. Inventory, modeling, assessment and monitoring were done to establish knowledge of current conditions. Water quality monitoring will continue throughout the pilot project, and soil sampling, modeling and aquatic biological assessment will be conducted at the end to assess impacts of conservation practices installed. Work thus far has produced several findings and observations:

- 77% of all water quality samples are higher than state criteria. 26% of soil tests were higher than 50 ppm phosphorous. High phosphorous soil locations were used to help prioritize conservation practice recommendations.

- Four to seven opportunities are available for structural conservation best management practices and operational practices on each field.

- Simple conservation plans with maps are needed for successful implementation, conservation planning can have positive impacts on farm profitability.

- Owners of over 90% of cropland have applied for the Environmental Quality Incentives Program (EQIP) cost share in 2016 from the Natural Resources Conservation Service.

- Fluctuating weather will likely require flexibility and more time for implementation to show results.

- Economic resources—staffing, state and local jurisdictional capacity, monitoring, financial—needed to attain water quality from non-point sources on a larger scale adaptive management project are not yet in place.

Water quality monitoring will continue in 2016 and 2017 concurrent with the majority of conservation practice implementation. Conservation practices such as nutrient management, cover crops, rotational grazing, grassed waterways, buffer strips and wetland restorations will be installed. Water quality improvements, aquatic restoration and the future of NEW Water's path will depend upon the installation, operation and sustainability of conservation practices by landowners and technical support by the partnership team.

In 2016, Bill Hafs was the Director of Environmental Programs of NEW Water.

Wisconsin Wetlands of International Importance

Katie Beilfuss

Wisconsin is home to a rich diversity of wetlands. Our coastal wetlands are unmatched for their importance to water quality, lake health and biodiversity. While many of us in Wisconsin have recognized this fact for years, recently our coastal wetlands have been drawing international attention.

Wisconsin Wetlands Association has long worked to change the public perception of wetlands from wastelands to treasures and highlight the unique natural benefits wetlands provide that make our state a better place to live. Our Wetland Gems® list of 100 high quality wetlands got us thinking—Might some of Wisconsin's gems also be globally important? We set out on a mission to bring wider recognition to Wisconsin's most important wetlands.

It turns out there is a well-established mechanism for recognizing internationally important wetlands. Since 1971, the Ramsar Convention on Wetlands has recognized *Wetlands of International Importance* as part of its work as a cooperative, non-regulatory means of wetland protection. More than 165 countries—including the United States—are members of the Ramsar Convention.

To date, more than 2,200 sites comprising 530 million acres have been designated *Wetlands of International Importance*, including the Okavango Delta in Botswana, the Everglades in Florida, and the Pantanal in Brazil. All sites must satisfy the same rigorous criteria to qualify as Wetlands of International Importance. The United States has designated 38 sites totaling nearly 4.6 million acres—far fewer than our neighbors to the south as Mexico has designated 142 sites. We can do better, and Wisconsin is a great place to start.

In 2009, a committee with statewide knowledge of Wisconsin's wetlands came together to look over the Wetland Gems® list to identify those that would satisfy the rigorous criteria established by the Ramsar Convention. Starting at the top of the final priority list, Wisconsin Wetlands

Association began approaching each site's landowners by offering assistance in completing the nomination process. Seven years later, three coastal sites have been designated *Wetlands of International Importance*: the Kakagon/Bad River Sloughs on Lake Superior, the Door Peninsula Coastal Wetlands, and the Chiwaukee Illinois Beach Lake Plain in Southeast Wisconsin along the Illinois border.

At the mouths of the Kakagon and Bad Rivers along Lake Superior in Ashland County lie some of the most extensive and highest quality coastal wetlands in the Great Lakes. Owned and cared for by the Bad River Band of Lake Superior Chippewa Tribe, this is the only tribally-owned Ramsar site in the US These rivers and other streams that flow into the sloughs cut through a clay plain deposited during the last glaciation. The associated wetland complex comprises more than 16,000 acres of wetland habitats that support many species of rare plants and animals. This vast wetland complex is an important spawning and nursery area for many fish species as well as critical stopover habitat for migratory birds. These wetlands also have cultural significance—the site supports the largest natural wild rice bed in the Great Lakes basin and members of the Bad River Band have harvested wild rice here for centuries.

The Door Peninsula Coastal Wetlands complex comprises lands and waters featuring high quality regionally- and globally-significant wetland communities, including Great Lakes ridge and swale, interdunal wetland, northern wet-mesic forest, northern sedge meadow, calcareous fen and boreal rich fen. These wetlands support colonial nesting waterbirds, wetland-dependent breeding and neo-tropical migratory birds, Great Lakes migratory fish, and numerous resident wetland-associated mammals and amphibians. Of particular note are three federally endangered species: the Hine's emerald dragonfly, dwarf lake iris and dune thistle. Researchers believe that 30–40% of the world's Hine's emerald dragonfly population is found in these wetlands.

Covering approximately fifteen miles of coastline along Lake Michigan across the Wisconsin-Illinois border, the Chiwaukee Illinois Beach Lake Plain contains the highest quality coastal dune and swale ecosystem in the region. The 3,716-acre Lake Plain supports six globally rare wetland plant communities. In addition, the site supports two federally-protected wetland-dependent species: the eastern prairie fringed orchid and the federally-endangered piping plover. The area serves as important breeding habitat for many wetland dependent bird species and provides critical migratory stopover habitat for at least 310 migratory bird species. It provides significant tourism opportunities for local communities, engages community members in volunteer conservation stewardship, and provides high quality examples of coastal wetland communities for education and scientific research.

Not only does designation as a *Wetland of International Importance* recognize and celebrate decades of effective conservation work, it also provides a unique opportunity for communities to realize economic benefits. Communities recognize that many tourists are drawn to their area because of the natural resource opportunities present in and near them. These communities have embraced the designation and promote their area's status as a *Wetland of International Importance* as an effective marketing tool.

California now is the only state in the nation with more designated *Wetlands of International Importance* than Wisconsin: they have six, and we now have five—Horicon Marsh and Upper Mississippi River Floodplain Wetlands in addition to the three coastal wetlands. Wisconsin Wetlands Association, working in collaboration with our partners, will continue helping communities achieve the benefits associated with this prestigious designation.

In 2016, Katie Beilfuss was Outreach Programs Director at the Wisconsin Wetlands Association.

2017

Foreword

Governor Scott Walker

Dear Friends of the Great Lakes,

With federal, regional and local partners, the Wisconsin Coastal Management Program (WCMP) supports community planning, port and economic development, public access, water quality, hazard mitigation and other projects along our Lake Michigan and Lake Superior coasts. The demonstrated success of these partnerships has produced 39 years of significant benefits for our state, the Great Lakes region and the nation.

In summer 2016, WCMP was a member of a state agency team that responded to historic flooding in the Lake Superior basin. WCMP connected with local partners to assess needs and find resources to address damage in the lakeshore area. WCMP assistance included funding to Iron County to develop a plan for rebuilding Saxon Harbor, a safe harbor that was destroyed by last year's storms.

Additionally, the program has secured funding for key remote sensing data (LiDAR), a critical disaster planning tool. WCMP continues work with affected communities to develop plans to mitigate potential future flooding events.

The City of Superior received nearly $1.5 million of WCMP funding for ecological restoration and public access improvements at Wisconsin Point. This project began with a small WCMP grant to develop a management plan. The restoration of Wisconsin Point will both preserve land that has long held great cultural importance to Native American communities, and support the local economy by providing access to residents and visitors for recreation.

Two Rivers used WCMP funding to support projects on the city's waterfront. The projects will improve and maintain infrastructure, enhance and expand boating access, and plan for the redevelopment of a former manufacturing property. WCMP support will position the city to strategically redevelop coastal resources in a manner consistent with its local vision.

Recently funded by NOAA, a project designed for "Improving Economic Security in Coastal Wisconsin" will be a collaborative effort led by WCMP with the University of Wisconsin Sea Grant Institute, the UW Madison Civil and Environmental Engineering Department and the Southeast Wisconsin Regional Planning Commission. This project proposes to reduce damages caused by coastal hazards, such as erosion, coastal storms and fluctuating water levels. Guidance will be developed regarding protecting bluff, beach and harbor ecosystems as well as the coastal economy. Four coastal counties, 22 municipalities and various state and local organizations will participate in the effort by exploring future opportunities through scenario development and improved risk communication.

Wisconsin is blessed to have Lake Michigan and Lake Superior as our gateway to the world. Stewardship and strong partnerships will ensure we can preserve and protect Wisconsin's coastal resources for the benefit of the entire nation.

Scott Walker was elected Wisconsin's 45th Governor in 2010.

Saxon Harbor Recovery and Redevelopment

Jason Laumann

July 11 and 12, 2016 brought multiple rounds of intense thunderstorms to northwestern Wisconsin. Historic rainfall caused destructive flash flooding resulting in three fatalities and millions of dollars in damage to roads, bridges and infrastructure. The storms intensified as they moved eastward across the region and reached a crescendo over northern Iron County where upwards of fourteen inches of rainfall turned normally tranquil Lake Superior tributaries into raging torrents.

The full fury of the storm struck Saxon Harbor at 7:45 p.m., first with downburst high winds, and then with torrential rainfall. The engorged waters of Oronto Creek washed away a campground and marina, destroyed dozens of boats, swept away vehicles and RV's and turned the nearshore waters of Lake Superior into a debris-laden, turbid slurry.

As the skies cleared and the floodwaters began to recede, it became clear that Saxon Harbor had been erased from the landscape like a sandcastle in the tide. Tragically, the storm also claimed the life of Mitch Koski—firefighter and former mayor of Montreal, Wisconsin—who had been responding to a call for help from Saxon Harbor when his vehicle was swept away in Oronto Creek floodwaters.

This historic storm changed not only the local landscape, but the way we in the north perceive our vulnerability and risk to natural disasters. It exposed weaknesses in our infrastructure and raised debate about whether these types of storms are going to become more frequent, disruptive and deadly.

The loss of Saxon Harbor also stunned this rural northern county of less than 6,000. The harbor is critically important to Iron County's tourism-based economy and also serves as an important safe harbor for boaters along the south shore.

In the wake of the disaster, recovery efforts began quickly.

In order to qualify for federal disaster assistance, total damage needed to exceed $8 million. The Federal Emergency Management Agency (FEMA) determined the final loss estimates for the region totaled $26.2 million, while losses for Iron County totaled $14.6 million with over $7.2 million at the Saxon Harbor Marina and Campground alone.

A Presidential Disaster Declaration issued in August 2016 included the seven counties most significantly impacted by the flood. The declaration paved the way for federal aid for recovery and rebuilding. State agencies provided additional support with clean-up and expedited permitting for recovery projects and technical support. The Wisconsin Coastal Management Program (WCMP) provided a $24,450 planning grant to aid in long-term reconstruction planning.

The rapid-response recovery planning process began in September 2016 with an online survey used to gauge public perceptions and values associated with Saxon Harbor. The survey was designed by a planning team consisting of representatives from the Iron County Forestry and Parks Department—which managed Saxon Harbor operations and the campground, the Iron County Planning and Zoning Department and the Northwest Regional Planning Commission (NWRPC). The purpose of the survey was to inform the reconstruction design process to improve the harbor and campground during the rebuild and over the longer term. Survey response greatly exceeded expectations with nearly 1,200 completed surveys received.

Survey results were synthesized by NWRPC and distributed to the public and the Iron County Asset-Based Community Development (ABCD) Steering Committee. The Board-appointed ABCD Committee is charged with developing a long-range asset-based strategic plan for Iron County. Survey indicators were used by the committee to formulate a series of reconstruction and post-rebuild strategies to improve Saxon Harbor. A new section was added to the ABCD planning document which included the recommendations and specific directives for Saxon Harbor, along with a timeline for implementation. The desired future land use map also identified areas for future recreation expansion including the areas east of the harbor where the new campground will be constructed.

In April 2017, the Iron County Board approved hiring Foth Infrastructure & Environment, LLC as the engineering consultant for harbor reconstruction. Board approval was also granted to relocate the campground from its previous footprint adjacent to the marina to a 3.8-acre site on the east side of the harbor. State laws prohibiting the construction of a campground in a floodplain without an adequate flood warning system prevented the relocation within the original footprint. Due to the discovery of an active eagle nesting site at the proposed campground location, a new site was selected near the confluence of Oronto and Parker Creeks out to County Trunk Highway A. This site will potentially allow for the creation of new and expanded camping opportunities, new interpretive facilities, possible future trail development and connectivity with the North Country Trail and even possible future retail. Many of these new opportunities are the direct result of public sentiments expressed in the redevelopment survey.

The engineering consultant has mostly completed surveying and data collection. Due to the presence of an active eagle nesting site, the proposed campground will be relocated near the confluence of Oronto and Parker Creeks out to County Trunk Highway A. Engineering is expected to occur during the early to late spring of 2018 with construction in summer and fall of 2018. Iron County has set a target date of May 2019 for reopening the marina and campground.

In the meantime, a single small craft launch will remain open, along with the pavilion, parking lot and access to the beach.

Thanks to local, county, state and federal partners, Saxon Harbor will again be a hub for economic, recreation and maritime activity in Iron County.

In 2017, Jason Laumann was the Deputy Director of the Northwest Regional Planning Commission.

MILWAUKEE'S HARBOR DISTRICT

Lilith Fowler

It's hard to pinpoint the exact moment when a tide begins to turn. In the case of Milwaukee's Harbor District, it might have been in 2010 when the University of Wisconsin-Milwaukee decided to locate its brand new School of Freshwater Sciences across the street from an eight-story high pile of coal. Back when cars on East Greenfield Avenue were routinely covered in a layer of fine black dust, it was surely not as obvious a choice as it seems now that the pile is permanently gone. But the investment in the new building gave credibility to people in Milwaukee who had been looking at improving the area for years.

The harbor had once been a vast marsh—home to a thriving ecosystem of fish, mammals, birds and native communities. In the nineteenth century, the deep river and protected harbor attracted European settlers in droves and put Milwaukee on the map. A bustling economy replaced the ecosystem. Meandering waterways were dredged and straightened, and marshland was filled in to make way for silos, lumberyards, tanneries, foundries and an iron mill to process and ship goods around the world.

By the end of the twentieth century, a visitor to the area would have found that the busy foundries and tanneries had closed leaving behind toxins in the soil and river sediments. Channelized rivers were like a desert separating Lake Michigan from upstream habitat. The Inner Harbor of 2010 had neither a vibrant ecology nor a healthy economy.

As we launched a revitalization effort, our question was: How do we rebuild both?

In 2014, a number of partners came together to create Harbor District, Inc. (HDI), a new nonprofit dedicated to creating a model working waterfront for the twenty-first century. The organization brings together a variety of stakeholders including property owners, businesses, city and state government, and civic leaders. HDI's operating assumption is that we can "have it all." By finding creative solutions, we can build a waterfront that is simultaneously a productive home to businesses, a place for people to visit and recreate, and a healthy—though altered—ecosystem.

Our first step was to bring all stakeholders together to develop a shared vision and a plan to achieve these goals. We gathered ideas from neighborhood fourth graders, multinational corporations and many people in between. We made sure the fish have a voice at the table, too. Gradually, we have been able to build consensus around key elements of a vision for the future.

First, people want access to the waterfront. Broadly, they share the belief that a business which does not require exclusive access to the waterfront should not have it. Second, they want a healthy environment in the form of both attractive rivers and greenspace and the protections to keep them that way. Third, they like the mixed-use character that the area has always had—port and job-creating uses should be able to blend in with other uses.

As the planning process winds to a conclusion, we come to the really fun part: The creative problem-solving that will let us "have it all." One of our first pilot projects is Habitat Hotels. The steel dockwalls and dredged bottom of the Inner Harbor, essential for shipping, will never be high-quality fish habitat. Therefore, we need a retrofit that offers fish a spot to rest and feed on their way through. The Habitat Hotels are designed to be cheap and easy to build, install and maintain. Metal baskets with stones or planting media are mounted on a long pole. The pole is welded to the dockwall above the waterline, but the baskets sit well below the surface where they can provide a home to aquatic plants and macroinvertebrates. The project is especially exciting because we are building partnerships with local high schools to build the hotels and grow the aquatic plants for them.

We are also exploring the possibility of a trash collecting water wheel for the Inner Harbor. Pioneered in Baltimore, this contraption has booms that trap floating trash and funnel it to a conveyor belt—driven by a water wheel—that lifts the trash out of the water and conveys it to a dumpster. We have found a location for it—now we just need a name worthy of its role as the partner to Milwaukee's trash skimmer boat, the *Lynyrd Skymmr*.

Business recruitment will be an important piece of our next phase as we seek companies that share our vision for a vibrant district within a "water-centric city." Milwaukee's Menomonee Valley redevelopment showed us that a district with good sites and a high-quality brand can successfully attract new jobs to former brownfields.

In addition to these projects, we will consider how to create safe public access for fishing and biking at the Port's facilities, whether we can perforate dockwalls to create a sort of post-modern wetland, and—perhaps most important of all—how to put a basketball court on a barge, or build a playground from shipping containers. In short, how to make a "working waterfront" that works for everyone.

In 2017, Lilith Fowler was the Executive Director of Harbor District, Inc.

Two Rivers: Turning Our Face Back to the Water

Greg Buckley

Our city's origins were on the water.

Native Americans plied the East and West Twin Rivers in canoes from upstream tributaries to their confluence at Lake Michigan where they ventured to the rich fishing grounds offshore. French Canadians from the St. Lawrence came in the 1830s, also drawn by the lake fishery. Fish tugs still make port in Two Rivers.

Early woodworking industries used the waterways to bring logs to the mills and ship products to market. By the mid-1800s, mills lined the riverbanks and the harbor was choked with logs. Industrial uses came to dominate the waterfront and remained there long after water transport ceased to be a requirement. Two Rivers, like many manufacturing towns, turned its back to the water.

The Hamilton Manufacturing complex was the dominant feature of the waterfront and economy from 1880 until corporate parent Thermo Fisher Scientific announced its closure in 2012. By then, the Hamilton facility extended over three city blocks and formed a wall between the city's downtown and harbor. Thermo Fisher has since cleared the entire Hamilton site revealing water views hidden for over a century.

City leaders believe the Hamilton property is the centerpiece of a downtown waterfront where Two Rivers can make an economic pivot to the future where we can truly "turn our face back to the water." Through a series of waterfront plans—each supported by the Wisconsin Coastal Management Program (WCMP)—Two Rivers has made great progress over the past fifteen years to capitalize on its water resources.

Improving Infrastructure. In the early 2000s, the City secured Federal earmarks for rebuilding the north and south harbor breakwaters on Lake Michigan. Other investments in storm water infrastructure, water treatment and green infrastructure are improving water quality at Lake Michigan.

The deteriorating 17th Street Lift Bridge was replaced to preserve a vital link between downtown and the beach, not only for cars but for a growing bicycle and pedestrian trail system. A $3.5 million local investment leveraged $10.5 million in Federal and State infrastructure funding and new bridge was dedicated in 2013.

Deterioration of the 1930s-era Harbor Park seawall had city officials worried about a catastrophic failure of the structure. The City undertook a $3.5 million seawall replacement, park and docking improvements project using $400,000 of local funds and grant monies from the Wisconsin Department of Transportation Harbor Assistance Program, the Department of Natural Resources (DNR) Recreational Boating Fund and Stewardship Fund, the WCMP and the Department of Administration's Community Development Block Grant program. The project was dedicated in September 2016 with Lt. Governor Rebecca Kleefisch cutting the ribbon.

Long a popular sport fishing port, Two Rivers has invested in its launch ramp and fish cleaning station. DNR's Urban Rivers Grant Program and Recreational Boating Program assisted with construction of a new fish cleaning station in 2015. Fish wastes once flushed into the sewer are now processed into fish-based fertilizer at a plant in Algoma. Parking lot and storm water improvements are planned for 2017.

The 2013 Harbor Master Plan makes clear the need for changes to the harbor entrance to mitigate storm surge and alleviate shoaling in the outer channel. In 2015, the City and US Army Corps of Engineers partnered in a wave attenuation study of the outer harbor. The City is now pursuing funds to complete design and construction of the preferred alternative from that study—a dogleg addition to the south pier.

Promoting Water Assets. The City Council funded street and parking improvements and a paved beach walk to facilitate access along the Lake Michigan beach. The City has also partnered with organizers of major events including Kites Over Lake Michigan and the Coolest Coast EVP® beach volleyball tournament.

Two Rivers Rotary took the lead in raising $125,000 for a permanent event venue—Rotary Beach Pavilion was dedicated in 2015. The River Trails Project—a joint venture with the Village of Mishicot and Bay-Lake Regional Planning Commission—promotes kayaking and canoeing along the East and West Twin Rivers.

Celebrating Our Water Heritage. Rogers Street Fishing Village and Museum commemorates the area's commercial fishing industry, early French Canadian settlers and history of the US Lifesaving Service and Coast Guard at Two Rivers. WCMP partnered with Rogers Street and the City to fund a boardwalk project and a replacement Fresnel lens for the historic South Pier Lighthouse.

Two Rivers is an active partner in the proposed Wisconsin Lake Michigan National Marine Sanctuary that will extend south to Mequon. The waters off Two Rivers and Rawley Point contain some of the most historic shipwrecks on the Great Lakes, including the "Christmas Tree Ship" *Rouse Simmons* and steamer *Vernon.*

A tribute to the Native Americans of the Great Lakes and the birch bark canoe will rise on the shore of Lake Michigan in 2018, the work of Manitowoc native artist R.T. "Skip" Wallen. Bronze figures comprising the sculpture will stand eleven feet in height.

Looking to the Future, community leaders believe carefully planning for, investing in and promoting the City's water assets can be a basis for long-term, sustainable economic development. We appreciate the support the Wisconsin Coastal Management Program and other partners in State and Federal government have provided for these efforts.

Two Rivers . . . we're turning our face back to the water.

In 2017, Greg Buckley was the Two Rivers City Manager.

WISCONSIN HARBOR TOWNS ASSOCIATION

Kathy Tank

In 2000, a group of people sat down to talk about the feasibility of creating a Wisconsin initiative based on the model of Cruise Michigan, a joint economic development and tourism effort between the State of Michigan and a selection of Michigan-based Great Lakes cruise ship companies. The group included representatives from the Wisconsin Coastal Management Program, the Wisconsin Commercial Ports Association, the Wisconsin Department of Tourism, and individuals from lakeside communities including tourism directors, mayors, parks directors and marina operators.

Many meetings and much time were invested on this topic. Ultimately— after listening to cruise ship operators, polling all of the Wisconsin Great Lakes communities on their willingness, infrastructure and capacity for large ships, and studying economic considerations—the conclusion was reached that this model would not be sustainable for Wisconsin.

However, something more valuable than a cruise ship initiative came out of those initial meetings, something that has proved very sustainable. This initial group created strong, solid partnerships that extended between agencies, organizations, the public sector and private sector. This group concluded that collaboration between our Great Lakes communities would be valuable to promote Wisconsin's tourism industry, advance the Wisconsin Coastal Management Program's goal of encouraging people to enjoy and protect the Great Lakes, support Sea Grant's educational initiatives, and more.

So even as the idea of a "Cruise Wisconsin" was set aside, the focus changed and the partnership continued moving forward. The group started focusing on what this collaboration would look like. Who should be included? What kind of organizational structure should it have? How can it be made financially sustainable? What would be its mission? And most challenging—how can we make it work?

The group realized that the only way this potential organization could be effective would be if it had participation from each community along Lake Michigan, Green Bay and Lake Superior. Or to put it another way, from each Harbor Town community, big or small.

The challenges were geographic with partners stretching from Kenosha to Superior. Just handling the logistics of meetings seemed overwhelming. There were also fiscal challenges, with communities ranging in size from Milwaukee to Bayfield and related abilities to contribute. And the biggest challenge was selling the value to each individual Harbor Town, because without all of them, the collaboration would not work.

A working group consisting of then-Bayfield Mayor Larry MacDonald, Department of Tourism representatives Kit Sorenson and Ruth Goetz, and Mike Friis from Wisconsin Coastal Management became invaluable. They believed strongly in this initiative and lobbied all of the partners until we got buy in.

It was decided that each community—regardless of size—would pay the same membership dues and have the same representation. After trying several different meeting formats, it was agreed to have several in-person meetings a year on the Lake Michigan side, with conference call-in available. Meetings were planned to coincide with statewide tourism meetings. And annual meetings were scheduled all over the Harbor Towns area.

In 2000, the Wisconsin Harbor Towns Association (WHTA) was officially born and moving forward. The first—and still primary—project was to create a Wisconsin Harbor Towns Association guide featuring all of the communities and their offerings. It was designed to be valuable to boaters and land-based leisure travelers. It would also serve as an access guide to Lake Michigan and Lake Superior.

Wisconsin's Coastal Management was and remains the primary partner for this project. WHTA finished the sixth printing of the guide in spring 2017, and has plans to distribute 98,700 copies over the next couple of years. Grants from the Wisconsin Department of Tourism helped to market the first two editions of the guide. Website development and e-newsletter creation followed.

Since that time, WHTA—with the support of Wisconsin Coastal Management—has been strengthened through other partnerships and joint projects. It was the birthplace of the Wisconsin Marine Association and the Clean Marina Program. It has worked with *Discover Wisconsin* on three Harbor Town-based television programs—one focusing on Lake Superior, one on Lake Michigan and one on Wisconsin Great Lakes beaches.

UW Sea Grant is working with Harbor Towns on several Wisconsin coastal access programs that it is developing. The Wisconsin Department of Natural Resources, the Bay-Lakes Regional Planning Commission, the Wisconsin Historical Society, Boat US and Discovery World have all provided content for the guides.

And, most exciting, Harbor Towns has worked very closely with NOAA's National Marine Sanctuary program, the Wisconsin Historical Society, the Wisconsin Coastal Management Program, and other State of Wisconsin agencies in creating a regional based concept of a National Marine Sanctuary in Lake Michigan from south of Port Washington to Two Rivers. The purpose of this sanctuary is to protect and educate about the cultural and maritime resources of the many shipwrecks in this stretch of Lake Michigan. The regional partnerships that will be required to manage the sanctuary will be based on the existing partnership created through the Wisconsin Harbor Towns Association.

Thanks to the vision, perseverance and commitment of its members and partners, the Wisconsin Harbor Towns Association is truly a success story.

In 2017, Kathy Tank was the Executive Director of the Port Washington Tourism Council and Past President of the Wisconsin Harbor Towns Association.

Follow the Drop:
A Watershed Odyssey

Bill Moren and David Libert

From the inception of the Port Washington Historical Society's Port Exploreum Museum, opportunities for inspirational discovery have been at the core of its mission.

The Lake Michigan Learning Lab is a project of the Port Exploreum in Port Washington that provides an innovative, interactive set of learning experiences for middle and high school students—particularly grades six to nine—in southeastern Wisconsin. Tuesdays are reserved for classroom visits.

The Lake Michigan Learning Lab offers students an opportunity to study Lake Michigan ecology and maritime heritage as a scientist would—making predictions, gathering data, analyzing results, drawing conclusions and identifying relationships.

The Port Exploreum has selected the theme of "Follow the Drop: A Watershed Odyssey" as a focus for student learning based on input from local stakeholders. A watershed focus provides an opportunity for students to study an array of issues associated with both the natural and human factors affecting water quality for our region and the future health of Lake Michigan.

Through this program, students have the opportunity to build understanding and expertise on the causes, effects and possible solutions for issues such as flooding, erosion and water pollution using a set of six thematic exhibits at the Port Exploreum and eighteen pre- and post-visit lessons. These resources are provided to teachers and students in the form of a Teacher Lesson Guidebook—a collection of existing and new resources—and a Student Science Notebook that serves as a resource for data collection, reflection and analysis.

One of the thematic exhibits is the Virtual Watershed Table, an interactive 55-inch touchscreen table that students think of as a giant iPad. When a student touches the surface, the attract screen divides into four different two-dimensional settings—urban, suburban, industrial and agricultural.

When the screen image is touched, the student is presented with a challenge. In the case of the industrial setting, that challenge is "You are an elected official deciding how to use limited funds and tax incentives to help industry, but your choices will also affect the health of your waters. Your goal is to recommend projects that are good for your citizens and that don't harm the water for fishing, swimming and drinking."

A touch on the screen then opens to a series of three questions with multiple-choice answers. When an answer is chosen, the industrial image changes to reflect that answer, and a table appears displaying nine categories of potential watershed impacts. After answering the questions, students are able to learn if they made "good, OK or poor" choices in regard to the waterways being swimmable, fishable and drinkable. The next exhibits cover soil infiltration, stormwater runoff and the results of green infrastructure. First the students make predictions and then observe infiltration rates through four different soil types.

Then using two rain garden models, they develop an understanding of how human manipulation of soil composition within green infrastructure can prevent adverse water events.

Two exhibits, Fish Daze and the Lake Michigan Table, are unique to the Port Exploreum and not found in any other museum. Fish Daze is an interactive game where two contestants compete against one another and the clock to identify and grab virtual images of sport fish, invasive species and pollutants and place them in the correct container. It is a fast moving, fun leaning experience.

For many students and visitors, the Lake Michigan Table is the most compelling exhibit. This is an eight-foot, three-dimensional table in the shape of Lake Michigan. Live feeds from NOAA of current wind direction and speed, cloud cover, wave height, surface temperature and, in winter, ice cover are projected from above onto the table's surface. When the table is touched, its image changes to five geographic zones. When the zone's selection wheel is touched, information on lake conditions, history, water depths, areas of interests, locations of shipwrecks and the real time location of vessels with the AIS software is displayed. When the image of the vessel is touched, its name and course are displayed.

The final activity in the student's visit is a scavenger hunt. Students develop an awareness of the ecology and maritime history of Lake Michigan and Port Washington by interacting with maritime level exhibits noting important facts and answering related questions on the interactive Lake Michigan Ecology touchscreen.

This quiz contains eleven multiple choice questions from the nine pre-visit lessons. When the correct answer is selected, a screen containing additional written and visual information appears.

The Watershed Odyssey program has been designed to entertain and engage students. The program facilitates student understanding of science concepts and creates a macro level awareness of watershed issues and connections to local organizations where they can learn more and take action to preserve our freshwater so it is a resource for future generations.

Additionally, special weekend events are planned at the Lake Michigan Learning Lab for the general public as they, too, have a keen interest in a healthy watershed and Lake Michigan.

The Lake Michigan Learning Lab is preparing future community leaders to understand, appreciate and protect our valuable Great Lakes resources.

In 2017, Bill Moren was a Board Director of the Port Washington Historical Society. David Libert was Managing Director of Southeastern Wisconsin Watersheds Trust, Inc.

J. Philip Keillor Fellowship

Adam Bechle

Many Wisconsin homes on Lake Michigan and Lake Superior are threatened by shoreline erosion and bluff failures, hazards that have been exacerbated in recent years by above-average lake levels. While stopping erosion may seem like the straightforward solution to protect property, the physical processes behind this hazard are only one aspect of this challenging issue. Economics, public trust, community relationships and personal emotions are just some of the many factors that must be considered when managing coastal hazard risks.

For over 30 years, Wisconsin communities and residents looking for guidance in dealing with the complexities of coastal hazards turned to Phil Keillor, Wisconsin Sea Grant's first Coastal Engineering Specialist. To celebrate Phil's legacy, the Wisconsin Coastal Management Program (WCMP) and the University of Wisconsin (UW) Sea Grant Institute partnered to fund the J. Philip Keillor Wisconsin Coastal Management/Sea Grant Fellowship in 2016. This fellowship provides funding for a recent graduate to work with WCMP and UW Sea Grant on linking science and policy to tackle coastal hazard challenges that face Wisconsin.

I am honored to be the first recipient of this fellowship. As a recent graduate in Civil and Environmental Engineering from the University of Wisconsin-Madison, my background has been focused primarily on the physics of coastal hazards. The fellowship has been a great opportunity to learn how to use this knowledge to inform decisions about the management of coastal lands both by communities and citizens. Under the mentorship of WCMP and UW Sea Grant staff, I have learned first-hand the importance of communication, coordination, engagement and collaboration in developing effective solutions to coastal hazards.

My main project in the fellowship was to revise the UW Sea Grant Coastal Processes Manual, a resource for local officials and property owners that demonstrates methods to estimate their risk to hazards like erosion and flooding. The manual was originally written by Phil Keillor in 1987 and last revised in 1998—however, advances in coastal science and changing environmental conditions in the last two decades require many updates to be made.

Though I initially focused on technical details, a NOAA training on risk communication helped me step back from my lens as an engineer and tailor the revisions to the needs of the intended audience—from local planning staff looking for clear explanations of quantitative risk analysis techniques to property owners with pressing coastal issues but limited background knowledge on the subject.

I solicited feedback from known manual users which led to improvements in the document's organization and the inclusion of a site assessment guide that complements the manual's calculation-based methods. I also reached out to content experts to gain their insights on each chapter before jumping back into the revisions. By focusing on effective risk communication practices in addition to sound technical information, the revised Coastal Processes Manual will continue to be a valuable resource for Wisconsin's communities and residents.

Many of the connections that assisted me with the manual were made through the Wisconsin Coastal Hazards Work Group. This WCMP-led group coordinates statewide entities that deal with coastal hazard issues, including UW Sea Grant, the Wisconsin Department of Natural Resources, Wisconsin Emergency Management, the Association of State Floodplain Managers and the University of Wisconsin. My first work group meeting was a whirlwind of projects and new faces. As a sign of the networking opportunities provided by the fellowship, I have since worked with nearly everyone on the work group and at our most recent meeting was involved in over half of the agenda items.

I also engaged with the public and local officials through UW Sea Grant's Lake Michigan Coastal Bluffs Integrated Assessment. The aim of this project is to create a list of possible adaptation, policy and outreach actions in response to bluff erosion using an approach that integrates scientific knowledge with policy and stakeholder perspectives. During community conversations, we learned that while property owners wanted to implement reliable practices to protect their homes, they were also worried about unintended consequences that their actions may have on neighbors.

Participants expressed a great deal of interest in partnering with neighbors to find win-win solutions that would address these concerns. Public officials echoed this sentiment and were interested in improving dialog and cooperation between jurisdictions. This experience opened my eyes to key opportunities for collaborative projects to improve Wisconsin's resilience to coastal hazards.

Encouraged by this positive energy towards collaboration, I led a grant writing effort to support a new framework for Wisconsin coastal communities to work together on coastal hazard issues. Working with WCMP, UW Sea Grant, and UW-Madison Civil and Environmental Engineering, we envisioned establishing a network where communities would work with technical experts to jointly identify vulnerabilities to coastal hazards, prioritize opportunities to cooperatively address these issues, and plan the implementation of these practices together. We were awarded a NOAA Coastal Resilience Grant to do this work and are excited to move this initiative forward.

These are just some of my most noteworthy experiences in a valuable year of professional growth as the Keillor Fellow. My mentors and the projects I became involved with pushed me to develop new skills in risk communication, coordination, engagement and collaboration. I am certain that I will leave the fellowship more prepared to help address the many types of challenges that face Wisconsin's coasts.

In 2017, Adam Bechle was a Postdoctoral Associate with the Wisconsin Coastal Management Program and University of Wisconsin Sea Grant Institute.

Kids on the Coast: The Rivers2Lake Education Program

Deanna Erickson

In September 2015, I had 600 pounds of freshly harvested wild rice seed in the back of my car and 30 fifth graders standing in front of me, all anxious to crawl into a fleet of canoes. Lindsay Braman's students from Lake Superior Elementary School in Superior already knew how to paddle the boats. In fact, they had been canoeing on the St. Louis River every year since second grade with the Rivers2Lake Education Program.

Our task was straightforward: load the wild rice into the canoes, paddle out onto Allouez Bay in the St. Louis River and spread the seed into shallow water. The work was part of a multi-state, multi-agency, and tribal effort to bring back wild rice, or *manoomin*, to a river being restored from decades of pollution. After three years studying Lake Superior and the St. Louis River—the largest estuary in the Great Lakes—the students were knowledgeable and worked hard even as the wind picked up. They knew they were contributing to the future of their community.

Rivers2Lake is the foundational education program at the Lake Superior National Estuarine Research Reserve. Based on Barkers Island in Superior and the surrounding St. Louis River Estuary, the Reserve works in partnership to improve the understanding of Lake Superior's coast and estuaries. A partnership between the University of Wisconsin-Extension and the National Oceanic and Atmospheric Administration (NOAA), we address issues affecting the watershed through the integration of research, education, outreach and stewardship.

Each year, a dozen pre-kindergarten to twelfth grade educators from the Lake Superior watershed enroll in the program. They spend four days traversing the St. Louis River from headwaters to estuary to Lake Superior, learning from resource managers, scientists and fellow educators along the way. They listen closely to staff from the Fond du Lac Band of Lake Superior Chippewa who share their wild rice and sturgeon restoration efforts. They tour the Western Lake Superior Sanitary District which cleans municipal water, paddle the Pokegama River, participate in Reserve research projects and monitor water quality.

In 2016, the National Park Service and the Bad River Watershed Association became key partners as well and provide perspectives from the south shore of the Lake. The Wisconsin Department of Natural Resources also now connects enrolled teachers and students with restoration projects along the coast.

After the Institute, teachers head back to their classrooms. But the program isn't complete. Rivers2Lake staff provide year-round mentoring and support to teachers as well as funding for classroom resources and transportation to field experiences. The students in their classrooms participate all year, too, and staff work hard to help them meet Wisconsin's educational standards while learning from the Lake and the rivers near their schools. All of this is in pursuit of the program's goal of integrating the Lake Superior watershed into education as a foundation for engaging place-based learning, Great Lakes literacy, stewardship and watershed restoration.

Since 2012, 64 teachers and 2,023 students have participated in the program. On average, each teacher participates in 80 hours of professional development and each student receives about eighteen hours of outdoor and inquiry-based instruction annually. Rivers2Lake has contributed over $70,000 directly to the schools and teachers with whom we work. From 2013 to 2015, the Wisconsin Coastal Management Program provided key funding to the Rivers2Lake program, complementing funds from NOAA's Great Lakes Bay Watershed Education Training Program (B-WET).

And what have teachers and students done with all of their experiences? At South Shore School in Port Wing, teachers are beginning work with several agencies to collect data on watershed health and fish communities. They are reporting their findings to state and national databases and working toward integrating the watershed throughout the school, across grades and subjects.

Students in Bayfield recently learned how to operate an underwater Remotely Operated Vehicle (ROV) to look for invasive species. They are also collecting dragonfly larvae from Lake Superior estuaries to be analyzed for mercury with the support of the National Parks Service.

Rivers2Lake teachers at Superior Middle School began taking students outdoors weekly to make scientific observations and recently won a grant to build an accessible trail behind their school. Students at Northern Lights Elementary have been monitoring the heavily impacted Faxon Creek for two years, sharing their findings with the research community and the City of Superior.

Rivers2Lake students and teachers have studied vernal pools, paddled rivers, removed invasive species, monitored crayfish populations, analyzed sediment data, presented to their families, and collaborated with scientists all the way from the Fond du Lac Ojibwe School to Ashland. They also reseeded wild rice which came up in the summer of 2016 in Allouez Bay, a hopeful new beginning for this keystone species.

These and many other projects are worth watching for in the future. Learn more about Rivers2Lake by visiting our website at www.rivers2lake .org or learn about the Reserve and our new public learning center at www .lakesuperiorreserve.org.

In 2017, Deanna Erickson was the Education Coordinator at Lake Superior National Estuarine Research Reserve.

2018

Foreword

Governor Scott Walker

Dear Friends of the Great Lakes,

Welcome to the 17th year of *Wisconsin Great Lakes Chronicle* and the fortieth year of the Wisconsin Coastal Management Program. This anniversary year is an appropriate time to recognize and celebrate the many people dedicated to the stewardship of Wisconsin Great Lakes.

Lake Michigan and Lake Superior are among the most precious of Wisconsin's natural resources. These vast inland seas have for centuries provided, clean water, transportation and economic development for Wisconsin residents.

Wisconsin Great Lakes Chronicle has over the years told the stories of many who have gone beyond the call to ensure the health and prosperity of Wisconsin coasts. For example, in 2015 we learned about the restoration of the Cat Islands in Green Bay. This important project led by Brown County and the US Army Corps of Engineers used dredge material to restore a chain of islands damaged by waves in the 1970s. The result is a new line of islands that provide wave protection for the bay and habitat for waterfowl, fisheries and other wildlife.

The 2017 *Chronicle* described work to recover Saxon Harbor on the shores of Lake Superior. This important harbor of refuge was damaged in severe storms and flooding that swept northern Wisconsin in 2016. Through the leadership of Iron County and other local officials, work is underway to restore Saxon Harbor as an economic, recreational and marine resource for the area.

In 2013, the *Chronicle* highlighted the work of several communities dedicated to providing clean beaches for residents and visitors. Projects in Racine, Milwaukee and Door County were acknowledged for implementing best practices to improve and maintain the beaches health. The article noted that clean beaches attract visitors to coastal counties and have a positive impact on the state's economy.

Wisconsin's ports were featured in a 2011 *Chronicle* article that underscored the importance of this infrastructure to Wisconsin coastal communities. Ports across our Lake Superior and Lake Michigan coasts support billions of dollars of economic activity and thousands of jobs for Wisconsin families. Local officials and port-related industries are working together to ensure these economic assets continue to serve as Wisconsin's gateways to world markets.

It is my privilege to thank the thousands of women and men who are devoting their time and talents to Wisconsin Great Lakes ensuring they will continue to be a destination and economic driver for generations to come.

Scott Walker was elected Wisconsin's 45th Governor in 2010.

Ashland Ore Dock:
Redeveloping an Icon

Sara Hudson

The Ashland Ore Dock—originally the Soo Line Ore Dock named for the railroad company that constructed it—defined Ashland's lakefront for nearly a century. The original 1916 dock structure was 900-feet long, 60-feet wide and 80-feet high with four lanes of railroad track lining its high platform. At the time of its construction, Ashland was a bustling town of 16,000 people and the main port on the southern shores of Lake Superior. While other Ashland docks were built of wood, the Soo Line Ore Dock was unique because of its modern construction including concrete and steel.

A 900-foot addition in 1925 extended the structure to 1,800 feet, the longest ore dock on the shores of Ashland. Over 10,000 virgin timber pilings created the base to support the largest concrete structure of its time. Each side of the dock was lined with 150 ore chutes—or giant funnels—into which rail cars dumped iron ore to waiting ore ships below. Hundreds of ore boats bound for Milwaukee, Cleveland and Detroit loaded with iron ore from Michigan's Upper Peninsula carried their bulk cargoes from the Ashland dock.

The dock's design was revolutionary for its day. Among its most significant and iconic features were 72 diamonds that lined the inside of the 1925 section's base. These hexagonal-shaped openings are found every three feet, and are ten feet wide and 40-feet long. They were constructed for wave attenuation and to help support the load of the dock.

Ultimately, the dock served as an economic asset for the community for less than 50 years. In 1965, the last freighter filled with iron ore pulled away from the dock and since then this immense structure stood vacant and started to become one with nature. Action became necessary to prevent the dock from becoming a hazard and return the site as a community asset.

In 2013, demolition of the superstructure's concrete cathedral-like arches commenced and the Ashland Ore Dock Charitable Trust was created. The Trust was established with money gifted to the City from

Canadian National Railroad to restore, develop, maintain and ensure the dock remained open for public use.

When the first 800 feet of the Dock was opened to the public in 2015, 600 people showed up to celebrate, share stories and experience being out on the Ore dock. At this same time, numerous public meetings and design workshops were held by City of Ashland staff, community members and SmithGroupJJR, the City's consultant. These meetings informed the Ashland Ore Dock Concept Design Report, an inspiring document that put into words and pictures the community's bold vision for a three-phase redevelopment project: Diamond Access, Gateway Access, and Upland Redevelopment.

The Ashland Ore Dock Redevelopment project will implement the community's vision of turning the Historical Soo Line Ore Dock and adjacent post-industrial land on Lake Superior's southern shoreline into a multi-functional, simple and yet authentic destination amenity that all community members and visitors can access. This project will advance a community whose economy was predominantly manufacturing built on the natural resources of area, to one that leverages the natural resources as a different kind of economic development tool: tourism and nature-based outdoor recreation.

The Ashland Ore Dock Redevelopment Project is a catalyst to create new opportunities for jobs and attract investment and new people to the area. This project is a legacy link—a bridge between the history of place and those seeking to live and visit the area. It builds on the City's parks system as a resource that few other communities have—a system of green along the waterfront that is non-privatized and can be used by all regardless of age or economics.

With the help of the Wisconsin Coastal Management Program (WCMP), Ashland has been successful in turning its post-industrialized waterfront into recreational opportunities. In 2017, the WCMP assisted in making the vision of the Ashland Ore Dock Redevelopment a reality by granting the City funds for the final engineering and construction documents needed for the Diamond Access and Gateway Access projects. WCMP grant monies also helped acquire additional funding for construction of the Diamond Access project.

Upon completion, this park will be a lakefront jewel—a destination that links the community's heritage with current community goals by promoting tourism and catalyzing economic development of formerly industrial properties. It will also offer universal public access for fishing and viewing on a historic piece of maritime infrastructure that extends over 1,800 feet into Lake Superior and gives additional access to approximately five miles of Lake Superior shoreline—an amenity and resource that is a one of a kind opportunity.

The Ashland Ore Dock has been a city icon for over 100 years. Generations of Ashlanders have ties to the dock—relatives worked on them, people fished in the diamonds and teenagers jumped off the end into the frigid waters of the lake. It is part of the City's history—a piece of infrastructure that represents the heritage of a community that should be experienced and told to others. Ashland is the Oredockers.

In 2018, Sara Hudson was Director of the City of Ashland Parks and Recreation Department.

Dunes Lake—A Forgotten Paradise

Mike Grimm and Greg Coulthurst

In 1917, Hjalmar Holland, an early Door County historian, wrote *"It is little known and seldom visited ... a beautiful place ... this obscure little paradise"* about an area that was and still comprises a large unbroken tract of forest, open wetlands and undeveloped wilderness lakes. It is a Great Lakes coastal landscape of small discrete habitats—like dolostone outcrops, springs and marl fens—within a larger forest of cedar swamps and upland conifer hardwood stands.

Dunes Lake is the natural feature that dominates the area with its inlet and outlet streams, numerous springs, and extensive emergent marshes and fringing fens. Approximately five miles northeast of Sturgeon Bay, the lake cannot be seen from any road. Public access is from Haberli Road and requires a canoe or a kayak for a one-mile paddle down Geisel Creek.

Conservation interest in Dunes Lake and its surrounding wild land began in the late 1980s when a group of field biologists from the University of Wisconsin-Green Bay published a report of their biological inventory of the lake and the surrounding forest and wetlands. They considered the site to represent an outstanding example of Door County's native vegetation and biota and recommended its preservation for the benefit of rare species such as the American black duck, American white pelican, Black-crowned night heron, Caspian tern, Great egret and King rail.

In the early 2000s, staff from the Door County Soil and Water Conservation Department (SWCD) and The Nature Conservancy (TNC) noticed an accumulating number of troubling signs of ecological stress in the waters of Dunes Lake and the waters flowing to and out of the lake. There appeared to be an increase in filamentous algae attached to the cobble of the stream bed. Dark unconsolidated organic muck had accumulated in the lake to the point where canoes got stuck. There was a marked decrease in the native mussels at the outlet of the lake and duckweed nearly covered the entire surface area of the inlet stream. In addition, the stand of cattails around the perimeter of the central basin of the lake had increased rapidly over a few years. All were indicators of an increased rate of eutrophication.

In 2008, the Door County SWCD and numerous other partners started a five-year study of the Dunes Lake Watershed that resulted in the identification of the major nutrient sources that were impacting the dunes and the connecting water bodies. This study resulted in a long term plan titled *Water Quality Evaluation and Planning for the Dunes Lake Watershed, Door County, Wisconsin 2008–2012.*

The SWCD proceeded to reduce the sources of nutrients that were causing the accelerated rate of eutrophication. The SWCD secured cost share grants to address nonpoint sources of pollution on watershed farmland, and provided numerous educational efforts with residents of a sanitary district in the watershed. The SWCD also coordinated a study for a passive treatment system which could be added to the existing sanitary treatment system to proactively address future phosphorus discharge limitations.

By 2016 grant funding was secured to conduct a hydraulic dredging pilot project to start addressing legacy phosphorus accumulated in the lake. This project removed approximately 10,000 cubic yards of phosphorus rich sediment over a two-acre area on the northeast end of the inner lake. In 2017, the SWCD in partnership with the Town of Sevastopol installed a public parking area on property owned by the Town to increase public accessibility and secure designated parking for the lake. These strategic efforts enabled the partnership to fine tune estimates for future and complete restoration needs for Dunes Lake through larger and more competitive funding sources.

The partnership is now actively submitting grant applications to complete hydraulic dredging on approximately eighteen acres within Dunes Lake inner basin, continue invasive cattails treatments within the wetland complex and reestablish connectivity for migrating northern pike, suckers and other native Lake Michigan fish species.

The project has over time taken on a variety of partners who have made short- and long-term contributions over the various phases of this extensive and encompassing restoration initiative. Key technical and financial partners at the local level include The Nature Conservancy, the Door County Soil and Water Conservation Department, Doorland Preserve landowners, the Sevastopol Town Board and the Glidden Drive Association.

State and regional partners include the Wisconsin Coastal Management Program, Ducks Unlimited, the Wisconsin Department of Natural Resources, the Wisconsin Geological and Natural History Survey, UW-Oshkosh, the Fund for Lake Michigan, Partners for Fish and Wildlife, the Great Lakes Protection Fund and the Raibrook Foundation. Federal support has been provided by the National Oceanic and Atmospheric Administration and the US Fish and Wildlife Service.

The truest measure of the project's importance has been citizen involvement. Numerous local individuals have volunteered their time and expertise to the important project. Without their support, the Dunes Lake area might well have remained forgotten and lost its claim to being an unspoiled paradise.

In 2018, Mike Grimm was a Conservation Ecologist with The Nature Conservancy and Greg Coulthurst was a Conservationist with the Door County Soil and Water Conservation Department.

MANAGING COASTAL RESOURCES: A SMALL CITY'S PATH TO SUCCESS

Tom Mlada

As Mayor of the City of Port Washington the past six years, I was privileged to join fellow elected officials, City staff, community leaders and stakeholders in crafting plans and policies for effective management of our precious coastal resources and assets. Truly, Wisconsin's coastal communities are special places and we must take necessary actions to both showcase and safeguard them.

In our coastal community, tourism continues to increase in importance to our economy by powering a resurgence of economic activity within our lakefront business district and inspiring substantial investment. For instance, over the past six years our City invested more than $10 million in our lakefront to enhance recreational opportunities, community walkability, bikability and public access and connectivity.

Today, we offer four miles of unimpeded public lakefront access and two additional miles of public beach. With the 2013 opening of the national award-winning Coal Dock Park—a 17-acre remediated and reclaimed former coal storage area on the lake requiring a nearly $3 million investment, our City boasts nearly 40 percent of total parkland along the lake. These lakefront parks serve to provide a buffer to development and function as key stormwater management tools.

In order to invest in this way, our City must be good fiscal stewards and identify opportunities for revenue growth. For us, that meant strategic lakefront development to generate resources needed to re-invest back into important asset protection efforts. With all our lakefront development, we have worked diligently to ensure maximum setback, stormwater management, planting of erosion-controlling native vegetation and protection of wildlife habitat.

In providing such extraordinary waterfront access to our residents and visitors, we also embraced the responsibility of doing all we can as a community to help them enjoy it safely. Thankfully, we have been success-ful in our commitment to a safe waterfront experience.

Working with Great Lakes Surf Rescue Project, we initiated preventative education that provided every student in the Port Washington-Saukville School District with a specially-designed "Water Watcher" card with valu-able water safety information courtesy of our local YMCA. We collaborated with the Department of Natural Resources and local Scouting groups to construct life jacket loaner stations for our beaches and marina, and the Port Washington Yacht Club installed life rings and signage on our harbor walk and beaches.

The investment of multiple state and local funding partners has en-abled us to enhance the safety of and accessibility to our breakwater. And our City partnered with Professor Chin Wu of the University of Wisconsin-Madison, the Wisconsin Coastal Management Program and University of Wisconsin Sea Grant to deploy ground-breaking rip current identification technology that people can access via mobile devices. Our collective waterfront safety efforts were celebrated with a keynote speech invitation in April 2017 to the Great Lakes Water Safety Consortium Con-ference in Sheboygan.

Many of our impactful partnerships began with local volunteers. Our Environmental Planning Committee (EPC) led our city-wide rain barrel initiative and advocated for the City Forestry Department to expand an-nual tree planting (an outstanding stormwater management tool!) to more than 500 using a City-owned nursery for supply.

These successes and others resulted from EPC collaboration with Green Tier Legacy Communities, Lake Michigan Stakeholders, 1000 Friends of Wisconsin, Ozaukee Washington Land Trust and NOAA. Similarly, our City's Active Community Environments (ACEs) Team championed walk-ability, bikability and connectivity initiatives focused along our waterfront. Thanks to these partnerships and our generous volunteers, the impact of these efforts on our City budget was zero dollars.

Breakwater and harbor infrastructure safeguard our people and prop-erty, yet securing funding for their sustainable upkeep has proved difficult. Nonetheless, we succeeded in mitigating local taxpayer impact by secur-ing over $4 million in state and federal funding for breakwater repair and reconstruction while investing only $500,000 of our own. This is a significant local commitment, but we repaired and improved over 60 percent of the breakwater protecting our harbor and marina.

Lastly, our coastal community is beginning to experience climate change impact that accelerates our need for resilience planning. Bluff integrity poses a serious dilemma creating concern about public safety, loss of parkland and related infrastructure, public access to the beach, and impact to tourism. Moreover, with more dramatic swings in water levels comes a more dramatic pace of beachfront erosion and infrastructure degradation.

Our City is looking to take these challenges head-on through policy-based initiatives. For example, we continue to embrace our standing as Wisconsin's first "Clean Marina" and recently partnered with UW Sea Grant on a Green Infrastructure Code Audit. We collaborated with Clean Wisconsin to institute a city-wide ban on coal-tar based sealants and continue our work with NOAA, the State Historical Society and numerous local and regional stakeholders to advance our National Marine Sanctuary nomination to final designation for local protection of our most precious lakebed treasures.

As Mayor, I was proud of Port Washington's leadership on environmental stewardship and am confident our City is all the better for it today. The work continues and thankfully so too the partnerships and the people necessary to showcase and safeguard our special places, vital resources and unique assets.

In 2018, Tom Mlada was the Director of Development for the Ozaukee Washington Land Trust and former Mayor of Port Washington.

GREAT LAKES ACCESSIBILITY FOR ALL

Mike Friis

To truly appreciate something, it is important to have exposure to and experiences with it. This is true with music, art, schoolwork and life experiences.

Wisconsin's Great Lakes resources are no exception. They are a source of recreation, commerce and spiritual renewal. The tributaries, rocky shorelines, sandy beaches and high bluffs of Lake Michigan, Green Bay and Lake Superior are our gateway to their waters. Access to and creating opportunities for appreciation of these places is an important mission of the Wisconsin Coastal Management Program (WCMP).

But while many people may think nothing of taking a walk along the shore, getting into a watercraft, wading into the water or fishing from shore, for others it is not so simple. By their nature, some of these special public spaces are remote or difficult to access for persons who lack physical or financial means. According to a 2012 US Census Bureau report, nearly 20 percent of the country's population had a disability. This group does not include the growing number of aging Americans with unreported yet very real physical limitations. Their loss of access to these public treasures and developing an appreciation for our Great Lakes coastal resources is a loss for us all.

Providing coastal access for our physically disabled and older neighbors and visitors is a responsibility WCMP takes seriously. Through grants and with firm support from the Governor's Wisconsin Coastal Management Council, the WCMP supports innovative ways to encourage the enjoyments of our coastal areas by those who may not have thought it possible before.

Accessibility is achieved through partnerships with local governments and nonprofits. Many groups use the WCMP's funding assistance to develop ideas, plans and construction of trails, fishing piers and boat launch sites that can be utilized by people with different physical abilities. In addition, many accessible coastal sites are in population centers where these amenities can be enjoyed and enrich the lives of as many of our fellow Wisconsinites and visitors as possible, regardless of income.

Examples of those innovative projects include the Mobi-Mat at the City of Racine's North Beach. The Mobi-Mat is a roll-out beach access path that provides a safe, stable surface for individuals of all abilities including those with walkers, wheelchairs, parents with strollers and emergency response vehicles.

Families may now bring small children to the water where the next stewards of the natural wonders of the Great Lakes will develop a personal interest, fondness and sense of place. Older residents not otherwise able to traverse the beach are now able to reach the waves at North Beach where the sounds and feeling of the water at their feet can enrich their lives and revive memories that can be shared with loved ones.

At the ribbon cutting for the North Beach mat installation, Dr. Julie Kinzelman of the City of Racine Public Health Department relayed the story of an elderly lifelong Racine resident in a wheelchair who had an emotional first experience ever at his hometown beach because of new-found accessibility. This man's story was poignant and affirming of the effort to bring people of all abilities to the beach.

Another condition that can result in a lack of opportunity and exposure to outdoor recreational experiences is obsolete structures in extensively built environments. In Milwaukee, the WCMP has partnered with the City, County, the Milwaukee Metropolitan Sewerage District and numerous nonprofits to provide accessibility to coastal assets in old industrial areas including those along the Menomonee River.

The Menomonee River in the heart of Milwaukee was a forgotten place just below the bluffs of working class neighborhoods where access was blocked by railroads, highways and high sheet pile walls along factory property lines. The River provided no public entry points to the thousands of residents who lived within walking distance to it.

Through the WCMP's support of several projects along the Menomonee River, public access has been opened, sheet pile walls have been replaced by natural riverbanks with paths to the river's edge, and canoe launches and fishing piers have been built. Today the River is visited by anglers, families and even classes of children sampling the river's macroinvertebrates through Urban Ecology Center programs.

"It's shocking today to see the photos of the channelized, inaccessible waterway just 20 years ago," says Corey Zetts, Executive Director of the Menomonee Valley Partners. "Today, along this same stretch of the Menomonee, you can see fish, herons and a diverse cross section of the Milwaukee community walking, fishing or just taking in the view. Through the WCMP's investments, 30,000 people enjoyed the public space along the river last year. There are now vibrant stretches of riverfront which were unavailable to previous generations."

These partnerships and investments from the WCMP are providing thousands of people with new connections to the Great Lakes, its shores and tributaries through trails, boat launches and fishing piers. These amenities enhance quality of life for all people and allow for personal experiences with our Great Lakes resources that create and foster a stewardship ethic that will preserve them.

In 2018, Mike Friis was the Director of the Wisconsin Coastal Management Program.

GREAT LAKES COASTAL RESILIENCY STUDY

Alex Hoxsie and David Bucaro

From Hurricane Katrina in 2005 to Hurricanes Harvey, Irma and Maria in 2017, major storm events in recent years have exposed the vulnerability of many of our coastal systems and underscored the need for more comprehensive coastal planning to improve resiliency.

In the aftermath of Superstorm Sandy which caused $65–70 billion of damage in 2012, funding was appropriated to the US Army Corps of Engineers to conduct a comprehensive study to identify and address the vulnerability of coastal populations, infrastructure and resources at risk throughout the North Atlantic coastal region. This study was designed to help federal, state, and local governments identify areas of high flood risk and implement management strategies to reduce that risk. Similar efforts are proposed for the South Atlantic coast in the wake of the 2017 hurricanes. These recent natural disasters will likely prove to be the costliest storms on record in America.

While the planning strategies that come out of these disasters are incredibly valuable, they are also sadly reactive. If similar planning tools for prioritizing investment in coastal resiliency had existed prior to Katrina, Sandy, Harvey, Irma and Maria, the loss of human life and cost of damage may have been drastically reduced. Rather than repeating history and waiting for a similarly destructive event to impact the Great Lakes coast, there is an opportunity for proactive development of a resilience-based coastal planning strategy to save money, lives and property in the future.

Severe storms on Lake Superior in 2016 and record lake levels on Lake Ontario in 2017 resulted in two declared federal disasters. While these declarations included incentives for hazard mitigation, it perpetuates the pattern of waiting for disaster to strike before taking action and reminds us that the Great Lakes coast is not immune to natural catastrophes.

Scoping the Great Lakes Coastal Resiliency Study (GLCRS) began in 2016 as a regional initiative of the eight Great Lakes States working in collaboration with the US Army Corps of Engineers, National Oceanic and Atmospheric Administration, US Geological Survey, Federal Emergency Management Agency, and US Environmental Protection Agency. Coastal resiliency is the ability of coastal areas to withstand, recover from and adapt to disturbances and underlying stress while maintaining economic, environmental, social and cultural values.

The GLCRS will investigate opportunities to improve resilience within both built and natural coastal environments and result in a plan that identifies vulnerable areas and recommends measures to increase resilience. Without such a plan, we expect increased risk of coastal damage in the future and management strategies that continue to address this problem through a piecemeal approach that is both inefficient and limited in effectiveness.

The study area encompasses over 5,200 miles of shoreline along the five Great Lakes and their connecting channels where approximately 4.2 million people live within two miles of the coasts. Study highlights will include community impacts such as shore protection, public utility infrastructures, major population centers and expansive real estate development throughout the basin. Economic factors will include the Great Lakes' $17 billion maritime economy, the $14 billion fishing economy, 60 commercial harbors, recreational boating, and cold-rolled steel production—an industry particularly critical for the automotive sector. Finally, environmental issues such as littoral sediment transport processes, coastal habitats and biodiversity will be studied.

The GLCRS will result in the development of a risk-based vulnerability assessment to create an interagency investment strategy for coastal resilience projects. The study will first look at a range of potential future conditions that take into account climate variability, shoreline development, watershed loadings from agricultural and urban land uses, invasive species, storm damage and other stressors to map coastal vulnerability over the project area.

Second, an array of structural, non-structural, natural, nature-based, institutional and regulatory measures will be evaluated for their ability to improve coastal resilience. Based on the results of a risk-based vulnerability assessment, combinations of these measures will be recommended to address the needs of the Great Lakes coasts.

The study is expected to take 36 months to complete and is spread out over four calendar years. Currently, the US Army Corps of Engineers has requested funding in 2018 to finish developing a detailed scope of work that will serve as a blueprint and roadmap for the rest of the study phases.

In Phase I, the study team will identify problems and inventory existing conditions. This effort will focus on gathering existing coastal data related to resiliency and identifying any gaps. Phase II will be comprised of filling these data gaps. Once the data gaps are filled, the team will run a risk-based vulnerability assessment to determine which coastal areas are most in need of resilience planning. Finally, Phase III will wrap up the study with a reach-specific evaluation of vulnerabilities and a coastal resiliency plan for the Great Lakes.

The final report—developed collaboratively by a diverse group of federal, state and local partners—will serve as a unifying plan for coastal management. As we move forward into an uncertain future, this study will encourage a partnership approach to coastal resilience planning, increase the return on investment for coastal projects, and continue to protect the people, infrastructure and resources that define the Great Lakes coasts.

In 2018, Alex Hoxsie was a Planner and David Bucaro was an Outreach Manager with the US Army Corps of Engineers, Chicago District.

Visualizing Wisconsin's Coasts with Story Maps

Joe Dwyer

Every Wisconsinite that makes visiting the Great Lakes part of their routine travel itinerary is bound to have their favorite spot (or spots!). It might be strolling through one of the north shore's quiet lakeside parks, or exploring downtown Green Bay on the newly refurbished CityDeck boardwalk, or even a spot in the middle of Lake Michigan where the fishing simply can't be beat, or anywhere in between. Every Wisconsinite has their reason for loving their personal Great Lake spot, and deservedly so. But, how do we get those first-time visitors or out-of-state tourists find their spot?

In the past, this was done with the use of brochure-like guides or gazetteers. These paper guides included maps that expertly laid out images of the coastline and symbolized the access points, parks and attractions adjacent to the Great Lakes. These were invaluable in their time as "on-hand" resources for both the new and veteran traveler. However, with the increasing intersection of technology in our daily lives, visitors are looking to trade the paper for the phone. That's where my Fellowship project comes in.

I landed in Madison, Wisconsin as a NOAA Coastal Management Fellow with the Wisconsin Coastal Management Program and University of Wisconsin-Sea Grant. My two-year Fellowship project goal is stated simply "to promote vibrant coastal communities by linking a comprehensive inventory of public access sites with geospatial technologies to encourage natural heritage tourism." As I began my Fellowship in August 2016, I viewed this overall goal as having two distinct pieces, the first of which was to create a comprehensive public access inventory.

Many of these sites have already been documented over the years in various forms. Organizations such as Wisconsin Regional Planning Commissions have even been digitizing their regional sites for years. My role was to collect and aggregate these separate sources, identify any potential gaps in the data, and organize a detailed list of amenities available at each site.

The final dataset includes 430 coastal sites stretching from the mouth of the St. Louis River to Saxon Harbor, including the Apostle Islands, and from the Menominee River to the tip of Door County and down more than 200 miles of uninterrupted shoreline to the Illinois border. The dataset has been uploaded into an online interactive map viewer (available at bit. ly/2I7WaEo) on desktop or mobile devices to explore every one of these sites and what they offer.

Visitors can now use this resource to find new sites in their favorite areas or discover completely new areas they weren't aware of before. However, this is only the *what is there* aspect of my project. The next step is to encourage folks on the *why you should go there*.

This part of my Fellowship is also heavily dependent on innovative and easy to use online apps, but critically, these tools are designed to be engaging as well as informative. One of the tools I have used most often are ArcGIS Story Maps. As the name suggests, these applications are a way for maps to tell a story. Rather than a static, paper map, the digital format allows for the creator to add text, photos and videos to create context and the ability to "walk" the user through their story. However, as exemplified by these story maps, the best way to learn is by using them.

Coastal visitors are encouraged to explore story maps created for some of our partner organizations. For instance, users can travel the coast to learn the history of Wisconsin's lighthouses using the Lighthouses of the Great Lakes Story Map created for the Wisconsin Harbor Towns Association. Another story map, developed with the Wisconsin Historical Society, creates an immerse experience to explore the dozens of shipwrecks located off of the mid-Lake Michigan coastal communities of Port Washington, Sheboygan, Manitowoc and Two Rivers. Specifically, the Story Map allows individuals to find out more about the ship and follow along as it traveled its final voyage. Additionally, we have added information about the maritime heritage of these communities and modern day "things-to-do" during a visit.

That last piece is a critical one because it is not the intention of these apps to replace a visit to these resources, but rather encourage it. It is hoped that these tools will spur people to think, "Wow, I didn't know I could do that!" or "I can dive a shipwreck?"

Getting people to these places is step one—step two is to get them to fall in love and cherish the resource. Luckily, in Wisconsin this is not difficult because the abundant, varied resources of the Great Lakes do that all on their own. With that love comes a passion to protect these resources. Those that value the Great Lakes and its resources will advocate for them, work to defend them and ensure that future generations are able to enjoy them. This is how we create champions and stewards for our natural environment and here in Wisconsin, all you have to do is get them there.

In 2018, Joe Dwyer was Coastal Management Fellow with the Wisconsin Coastal Management Program and University of Wisconsin Sea Grant Institute.

Improving Coastal Resilience Through Digital Coast

Jake Thickman

The NOAA Digital Coast program is an online collection of data, tools and training for coastal communities and professionals. In addition to housing technical resources, the program coordinates the Digital Coast Partnership, a collection of non-governmental organizations that work to address coastal issues across the country.

As a Digital Coast Fellow, I have worked on a two-year project in collaboration with two partner organizations—the Association of State Floodplain Managers (ASFPM) and the Coastal States Organization (CSO)—based at the ASFPM offices in Madison, Wisconsin. My fellowship project is focused on improving coastal community resilience to flood hazards through an analysis of current federal and state environmental policies and programs, ultimately seeking to help establish a more holistic approach to coastal flood risk management.

A number of policy guidance documents have been produced by organizations representing coastal management professionals—including from ASFPM and CSO—in an effort to update coastal management policies and practices in light of changing threats to productive ecosystems. To this point, however, no framework exists for implementing the progressive policies put forth.

The goal of my project is to fill this gap in knowledge through a review and synthesis of federal and state policies that may potentially influence coastal flood risk, identifying successful policies at the state and federal level, and detailing future policy strategies to support the comprehensive nature of effective coastal flood risk management. Ultimately, I am exploring ways that Digital Coast resources can be used in flood risk management efforts.

My project began with an overview of the coastal management policy objectives and strategies put forth by ASFPM and CSO in order to determine common goals between the organizations and identify specific policy objectives for the project. Five main objectives were ultimately identified: increase state management capacity, promote alternatives to structural flood risk mitigation, incorporate long-term forecasts into mitigation efforts, achieve a balance between disaster recovery and risk mitigation spending, and broaden the scope of coastal flood risk management efforts.

Based on these objectives, I conducted a review of federal and state coastal management policies and practices and compiled all relevant policy documents into a digital library for future reference. As part of this analysis, my work identified the responsibilities, roles and connections between environmental policies and programs, and created links to the previously identified policy objectives. Federal coastal flood risk management policies were reviewed in their entirety, while state analyses consisted of case studies on Wisconsin, New York, Florida and Washington. These states were selected to represent the Great Lakes, East, Gulf and West coasts.

A wide variety of federal and state programs were examined in order to capture the full scope of coastal flood risk issues and management. At the federal level over 30 programs were examined across agencies such as the Federal Emergency Management Agency, the National Oceanic and Atmospheric Administration, the US Army Corps of Engineers (USACE) and the US Department of Housing and Urban Development.

State analyses were equally comprehensive and covered topics including state coastal management programs, shoreline zoning, wetlands regulations, floodplain regulations, building codes, erosion management programs and state climate adaptation initiatives. The goal in taking such a broad approach was to emphasize the connections between environmental management policies and programs. If these connections are not recognized, management efforts can often exist in silos within separate agencies or levels of government, reducing the overall effectiveness of environmental activities including coastal flood risk management.

While preparing state case studies, several Wisconsin Coastal Management Program initiatives stood out in terms of addressing coastal flood risk. In particular, the facilitation of the Wisconsin Coastal Management Council and the Coastal Natural Hazards Work Group coordinate activities involved in coastal issues at multiple levels of government.

During this process I also sought out mechanisms to increase collaboration between state and federal agencies in coastal flood risk management efforts using the USACE Silver Jackets team as a model. Silver Jackets team leaders were contacted in Wisconsin, New York, Florida and Washington. Efforts were made to examine the coastal element of these teams and how Silver Jackets program resources might be leveraged by coastal states and communities in the future in conjunction with the use of Digital Coast tools where possible.

The final piece of my fellowship project consists of research on moving towards a holistic framework of coastal flood risk management, and investigating the advisability, viability and specific steps needed to implement the five identified coastal management policy recommendations from ASFPM and CSO. Based on the analysis of successful coastal flood risk management policies and programs at the federal and state levels, the report outlines strategies and actions that may be utilized to improve existing flood risk management frameworks or develop new management initiatives as hazards in coastal areas continue to evolve.

Upon completion of my fellowship position all policy documents, summary reports and guidance documents collected and produced throughout the project will be made available through ASFPM's Flood Science Center webpage. We look forward to providing policy leaders with additional tools to provide for the safety of residents and visitors on our coasts.

In 2018, Jake Thickman was a Digital Coast Fellow at the Association of State Floodplain Managers and Coastal States Organization.

INDEX OF AUTHORS